12-WEEK WORKBOOK STUDY TO A PROVEN PATH TO SEXUAL INTEGRITY; HELP WITH PORN, LUST, MASTURBATION OR SEX ADDICTION FROM A BIBLICAL PERSPECTIVE

A study providing straightforward help with issues of lust, pornography, masturbation or other forms of sexual addiction from a Biblical perspective

The battle for sexual integrity is fierce. You must be constantly on guard. This study provides you with the tools necessary to be victorious.

The name for Proven Men Ministries, Ltd. was derived from our acronym PROVEN MEN™ and stands for men who are stamped "proven" by the Lord because they are striving to be:

Passionate for God,
Repentant in spirit,
Open and honest,
Victorious in living,
Eternal in perspective, and
Networking with other ***PROVEN Men.***

Those who have used this study and experienced lasting victory over addiction to pornography or related sexual issues have two things in common: They have developed the attitude that:

(1) pornography—or other sexual sin—is no longer an option, and

(2) they are willing to do whatever it takes—God's way this time.

You're invited to become connected with us and join our team. Plan to use this twelve-week study to gain the necessary tools to stand firm yourself, while at the same time encouraging and being encouraged by other PROVEN MEN.

Published and printed in the U.S.A. by Proven Men Ministries, Ltd., Lynchburg, Virginia.

Second Edition

ISBN: 978-1-940011-12-7

Details in stories or anecdotes have been changed to protect the identities of the persons involved.

Interior Design: 1106 Design

Cover Design: Prototype

Hesch, Joel

12-Week Workbook Study to a Proven Path to Sexual Integrity; Help with porn, lust, masturbation or sex addiction from a Biblical perspective / Joel Hesch.

1. Sex—Religious aspects—Christianity. 2. Temptation. 3. Christian men—Religious life. 4. Sexual Health Recovery.

12-WEEK WORKBOOK STUDY TO A PROVEN PATH TO SEXUAL INTEGRITY; HELP WITH PORN, LUST, MASTURBATION OR SEX ADDICTION FROM A BIBLICAL PERSPECTIVE

A study providing straightforward help with issues of lust, pornography, masturbation or other forms of sexual addiction from a Biblical perspective.

TABLE OF CONTENTS

TESTIMONY

"The 12-week study is intensive. So I thank God who has helped me stay faithful to this phenomenal, anointed study. The study led me to making a goal of reading the Bible and praying with the attitude of getting to 'know' God. This has been an essential part of my sobriety. I was ashamed, at first, to think that I didn't know God, or that I even had to pray for God to give me a desire to be pure and holy in His presence. But God helped me to be humble, and humility allows me to see that God's purpose is for men to be close to Christ, and to meet personally with the Lord through the Bible and prayer."

Passionate for God,
Repentant in spirit,
Open and honest,
Victorious in living,
Eternal in perspective, and
Networking with other ***PROVEN Men.***

Introduction: Daily Heartwork

Most men struggle with sexual impurity—pornography, masturbation, lust, or fantasy—and many are trapped in bondage to it. Breaking free requires more than self-will. You need God's strength. Fortunately, He provides a path to lasting freedom. These materials not only teach you how to be on guard, but to trust in and rely upon God's power to live out sexual integrity. You'll learn how to embrace and apply the following six essential components of a ***PROVEN*** life:

Passionate for God. By taking the focus off yourself (including your rights and circumstances) and putting it onto the Lord, you'll discover the perfection and goodness of God, who deserves to be praised. Your newfound passion for the Lord replaces the lust for selfish desires and practices. During times of intimate worship, you'll experience God's very nature and receive His healing in all areas of your life.

Repentant in Spirit. Until seeing your conduct as wrong because it separates you from closeness to God, you won't truly want to change. Repentance is not self-manufactured, and it means more than merely having feelings of guilt or shame. Rather, it's a gift from God, granted to those who humbly seek Him with all of their hearts. True repentance includes both confessing sins and submitting to God, which leads to a changed life.

Open and Honest in communication with God and others. One inward reason people turn to false forms of intimacy (i.e., pornography, masturbation, or fantasy) is that it seems safer or easier than the work required in real, *open and honest* relationships. But your heart and soul inwardly long for true intimacy. Fortunately, God will enable you to fully trust. He will also teach you how to be open and to permit feelings to surface so you can engage in fulfilling and real relationships, instead of escaping into the false forms of intimacy that have ensnared you.

Victorious living in God's strength. You cannot overcome temptation or defeat lust in your own strength. Yet, by daily guarding your heart and turning to Christ, you'll lead a victorious life. Each moment you yield to the Lord and rely upon His power, your actions become pure and holy as He is pure and holy. He won't lead you into, but through temptation while in charge of your life!

Eternal in your perspective. Dwelling on the temporary (your present circumstances) leads to acting according to immediate thoughts and desires. Taking on an eternal perspective, however, brings hope and perseverance during temptations and trials. By looking to God's promises and allowing Him to be your guide, you'll live out integrity in all circumstances. You'll no longer be worn out from chasing temporary pleasures or defeated from the constant battle of trying to control life.

Networking with other PROVEN MEN. Christ always sent His disciples out two-by-two. Victory over an addictive behavior is not won alone. Other ***PROVEN MEN*** become great sources of encouragement and act as iron sharpening iron (Proverbs 27:17). Become part of the team.

Each of these six "letters" is vital for breaking and remaining free. This study helps you put them into place. If undertaken with humility and purposefulness, it will position you to have the Lord renew your mind, transform your heart, spark your soul, and change your desires. The work is challenging. It requires commitment, perseverance, and a willingness to do "whatever it takes" to meet with the Lord and receive His healing. Therefore, make a permanent and irrevocable decision to seek the Lord with all of your heart, mind, and body.

In the past, you have probably tried using your own strength. This is self-reformation, and it doesn't work. Now it's time to turn to and rely upon God. The study is sometimes referred to as *"Heartwork"* because it is designed to position you to meet with the Lord daily and be changed by Him. A person's sinful conduct changes only when his heart toward God changes. You'll be shown how to stop striving in your own power and how to give up control to the Lord. To be set free, you must really want to turn from sin and live out a ***PROVEN*** life of holiness in dependence upon the Lord. This is the beginning of a fulfilling relationship with the one True God who loves you and the start of lasting freedom from the bondage of sin.

We highly recommend that this study be used by a small support group or two men working through it at the same time. Although each man works independently through the study every day, the two should gather on a weekly basis to share their struggles and victories while discussing what they are learning. *Networking* is a vital component to getting the most out of the study.

You should note that *networking* with other men means more than surface relationships, which is the same style of relating that has led you to false forms of intimacy. That's why you must avoid the temptation to go without true accountability. Otherwise, you'll simply move on to the next book or program and continue relying on your own strength. There is something powerful about regularly confessing sins and sharing your trials that helps free you from guilt, shame, and other traps that keep you from meeting with the Lord and experiencing His healing. In other words, there are two important parts of guarding your heart. The first is turning to the Lord in devotion and dependence, and the second is linking up with other men with whom you are being vulnerable, open, and honest about your feelings, challenges, and direction in life. Also, keep this eternal perspective: Healing is a lifelong process. Undoing years of habits and backward thinking (following the ways of the world instead of the Lord) won't just happen overnight and it shouldn't end in twelve weeks. It takes time and effort to implement into your life the characteristics associated with being stamped Proven. Don't treat the study as a twelve-week program or expect a quick fix. Those who want the easy way out or a list of things to avoid will not persevere or stand up under the trials of life that surely will follow. Instead, consider the study as a blueprint for daily guarding your heart. Before a builder starts construction, he carefully examines the blueprint, and during the building process he keeps referring to the plans. You should return to this study and continue doing other Bible-based studies for the rest of your life.

Won't you join with us by purposing to become God's friend and be transformed by Him each day? Leading a Proven life is all about humbly seeking and relying upon the Lord and developing the spiritual disciplines leading to newness of life. When you strive for sexual integrity, God will give you His power and strength to live out your commitment to purity, love, and devotion.

Make a donation. After you begin this journey and start experiencing breakthroughs and victory, please consider making a tax deductible donation to support our mission of restoring families one man at a time by helping people embrace a proven way of life that produces lasting victory from strongholds of pornography and sexual addiction. It is our vision to reach one million men and families by helping those who want help through our 12-week study combined with accountability. As a non-profit organization, we are relying upon the generous donations from supporters like you. So, if this study is a blessing to you, then become a blessing to others and make a donation through our website: www.ProvenMen.org.

TESTIMONY

"First and foremost, Proven Men has allowed me to witness and embrace that God is 100% consistent in His character 100% of the time. My all consuming, blinding, persistent self-worship and pride inhibit me from recognizing that I am indeed selfish and prideful.

"No matter how much I hope, I cannot change God, justifying my sin. I have never really prayed nor have I ever really been content. God does not merely take away my temptation for above all else He wants me to seek Him in a relationship talking to Him openly not at Him. My cross to bear, among other things I will recognize and pick up later in my relationship with God, is, indeed, to pursue a 'proven' life. Not even a hint of sexual impurity is admissible; therefore, every thought must be recognized for what it is, if it is sin, and released to God. This practice overflows from impurity to issues of anger, laziness, greed, discontentment, all of which I realized control me.

"I have gained the desire to be a needy dependent, content servant of God. Though it will be difficult I want to remain in pursuit of open and honest relationships with other proven men as well as my wife."

Passionate for God,
Repentant in spirit,
Open and honest,
Victorious in living,
Eternal in perspective, and
Networking with other ***PROVEN Men.***

Orientation to Daily Heartwork Study

1. This study is based upon a five-day format with some light weekend work, so begin on a Monday. Schedule a specific time each day to do the study. Most find that the first thing in the morning is best, even though it means getting up early. It sets a good tone for the rest of the day and prepares you to battle temptations. In addition, it can be hard to find blocks of time later in the day. However, if you simply cannot do it in the morning, be diligent in protecting whatever time you set. It may mean that you must cut out television, Internet, or other entertainment or recreation.

2. The study is very intense because it addresses an intense problem. Plan on devoting forty-five minutes each day. The time it takes to cover everything varies greatly from person to person. Even if you spend forty-five minutes a day, you may find that you cannot complete all of the daily items. This is especially true if you are meditating upon verses and searching your heart. If you have time, you can review some of those items on the weekend. If not, that's okay. Don't beat yourself up. First, guilt and shame are already nooses around your neck that make throwing in the towel or escaping into fantasy appealing. Second, meeting with God is what changes you, not finishing all the work in this study. Therefore, guard against merely checking off homework instead of openly meeting with the Lord. The key point to remember is that you should seek quality and quantity of time meeting with the Lord. Again, don't be consumed with whether you finish the material. If you open your heart to meeting with the Lord each day for the time set, even completing one half of the material each day is excellent.

3. It's best to use the study in a small group or with another man. Healing will be thwarted if you use these materials just like reading another book or following the latest self-help program. In fact, one of the roots that keep you in bondage to sexually immoral practices is a lack of real intimacy with the Lord and other men. A Proven life depends upon developing close relationships and putting into practice what you are learning. Don't try to go it alone. It's crucial to seek out an accountability partner before starting the study. You should talk to him once a week, sharing your temptations, failures, and victories. Give him permission to ask you what your mind dwelt upon and how you struggled. Regardless of the level of his compulsion, ask him to do the study with you. He'll be glad he did.

4. Share daily with someone (your wife if you're married, or a male friend if you're single) the exciting things you are learning. Sharing spiritual truths wisely opens your heart to the healing power of God, and it strengthens and encourages others. The Bible says, "Confess your sins to each other and pray for each other so that you may be healed" (James 5:16).

5. Seek a broken spirit (soft heart). Feeling guilty is not the same as being repentant (Hebrews 12:16–17; 2 Corinthians 7:10). God only changes a willing heart that seeks after Him. Therefore, purpose to meet with the Lord to get to know Him. Yield your entire life to God, asking Him to conform your will to His. Commit to doing "whatever it takes" to be free from bondage to sin and enter into a new relationship with God. Accept that healing is a lifelong process, but one in which you'll experience victories along the way. Be committed to staying the course even as setbacks occur. Dedicate the next year to seeking the Lord and doing this study and the suggested studies in Appendix M at the end of this study.

WEEK ONE

TESTIMONY

"Proven Men Ministries has been a blessing to my life. I was born again at an early age and grew up in a Godly, Christian home. I lived for Christ closely until I was around 15 or 16, and then drifted away from God. Over the next 15 years of my life I continued to spiral downward and allow myself to sink deeper and deeper into sin. Over the 35 years of my life I had grown like an onion, yes an onion. I had put on so many different layers and had pretended to be so many different people that I truly did not know who I really was. The Holy Spirit began to wake me up at night bringing different areas of my life that needed correcting to my attention. As you can imagine this was truly a hard place in my life. Then came my hardest one . . . the one that I hid way down deep in my heart . . . the one that was 'my secret.' It, of course, was sexual sin. Praise God now for peeling that layer off. It seemed like the website of Proven Men just popped off the page to me. I went to the website and the devil instantly said to my mind, 'Ahh, this is just another bunch of people that's going to tell you all you have to do is pray and read and 'poof' you will be all better.' I, however, continued to do more reading, I then obtained the book *Proven Men Study.* The next morning I began to read it. Oh man, guess what, this person was just like me, I was so amazed that there actually was someone out there just like I was. [I then started realizing] really deep down I was a prideful, hateful, angry, full of lust and a greedy person, that I had always hated in other people. Wow, imagine finding out that you was the person that you actually always despised the most, a hypocrite. But 8 weeks ago, after doing the purity study, I learned the most important thing in my life: God does really love me, He really does want me to be different. For all the times I had pushed him away, when I came to Him, He was right there to draw me closer to Him."

Passionate for God,
Repentant in spirit,
Open and honest,
Victorious in living,
Eternal in perspective, and
Networking with other ***PROVEN Men.***

MEMORY VERSE

Matthew 22:36-39: "'Teacher, which is the greatest commandment in the law?' Jesus replied, 'Love the Lord your God with all of your heart and with all of your soul and with all of your mind.' This is the first and greatest commandment. And the second is like it: 'Love your neighbor as yourself.'"

Begin this morning by memorizing the weekly memory verse. Read through it several times. Over the next twelve weeks you'll be asked to memorize twelve short passages of Scripture, which are listed in Appendix R. At the end of this Proven Men study, you should be familiar with and even able to recite each one. Here's a helpful suggestion: Write the verses on 3x5 cards and take them with you wherever you go.

DAILY READING

As you go over the Daily Reading, be sure to mark up your page and jot down notes. You should not just gain knowledge, but engage in a time of reflection and plan out how to incorporate these things into your life.

Right now, read the article, *"Why Jesus?"* attached as Appendix E at the end of this study, then return here.

- Have you asked Jesus into your heart and made Him Lord of your life? These are the first steps in the process of guarding your heart. Record your commitment to Christ here—write down what you feel in your heart right now for the Lord.

____

____

____

____

- The next step is making a decision to turn over complete control of your life to Jesus. Record your decision below.

HEARTWORK

The *Heartwork* section is a time to engage your heart, not your mind. Begin right now with this simple prayer: "Lord I need you. Soften my heart. Reveal yourself to me."

As you start this journey of sexual healing, ask yourself, "Am I truly willing to make pursuing God's healing a priority above all else in my life over the next twelve weeks?" If so, consecrate this time of healing right now. When you make this commitment, you can expect plenty of distractions to arise. Your job might demand more time or energy, or your spouse, family, and friends may need more of your time. You may also find it difficult to get up forty-five minutes earlier each day or otherwise fit this *Heartwork* study into your daily routine. At times you're going to ask, "Can I really do this? Is there no end to this tunnel?"

You've entered into a spiritual battle, a time to turn to, not away from, God. You'll want and need His power. In the past, you relied on your own strength, and it didn't work. This time, rely on God. Be patient. No matter how hard it will seem, the Lord won't abandon you. Stay committed. You have God's promise to transform you: "The one who calls you is faithful, and he will do it" (1 Thessalonians 5:24).

PRAY

Spend five minutes in prayer. Prayer can be simply talking to God. Picture the Lord with you right now (He is with you). Tell Him of your fears and struggles. Ask Him to open your heart to His healing path and to give you His strength and power to wake up early each morning or otherwise set aside time each day to meet with Him and to carry out your commitment to sexual integrity.

If it's hard to pray for five minutes without your mind wandering, don't be discouraged. New relationships take time to form. Stick to it, and keep talking to God with a goal of meeting with Him. Set a timer if you need to, but do spend at least five minutes in prayer.

Here's a helpful suggestion: Write down a short prayer or list prayer items in the space below, such as the name of a person to pray for or a situation or need that is on your heart.

READ THE BIBLE

Always have a Bible handy while doing the daily study. You will be asked to read from it each day because the Bible is the living and active Word of God, capable of penetrating your soul, convicting you of sin, transforming your thoughts, and renewing your heart (Hebrews 4:12). In the pages of Scripture, you will meet with and experience the Lord. Right now, read and meditate on these verses: John 1:12–13; 3:16–21; and 1 John 3:1–3. Then, finish today's study.

MEMORY VERSE

Matthew 22:36–39: "'Teacher, which is the greatest commandment in the law?' Jesus replied, 'Love the Lord your God with all of your heart and with all of your soul and with all of your mind.' This is the first and greatest commandment. And the second is like it: 'Love your neighbor as yourself.'"

WEEK 1 DAY 2 (TUESDAY)

Ask God to open your eyes to what He considers impurity and sin and to give you His desire for absolute purity and holiness as you read *"The Nature of Sexual Immorality"* in Appendix I (turn there now). What insights did you discover, and how will they impact your life today? Write your thoughts below.

HEARTWORK

What grabs your attention from this passage of Scripture: "You have heard that it was said, 'Do not commit adultery.' But I tell you that anyone who looks at a woman lustfully has already committed adultery with her in his heart" (Matthew 5:27–28).

Stimulating your sexual drive by outside sources (i.e., other than unselfish intimacy with your spouse) is improper and fuels a lust that cannot be quenched. Setting expectations of how often you must have some form of sexual release is living for self-gratification, which only sets your heart on a continuous pursuit to satisfy a nature that will always want more. What changes will you make as a result of these truths? Will these changes include considering others more important than yourself? Will they include taking on an eternal perspective? Write out your commitments.

Meditate on each of the following verses and jot down any insights or commitment to turn from evil:

"Let those who love the Lord hate evil, for he guards the lives of his faithful ones and delivers them from the hand of the wicked" (Psalm 97:10).

"To fear the Lord is to hate evil; I hate pride and arrogance, evil behavior and perverse speech" (Proverbs 8:13).

"Love must be sincere. Hate what is evil; cling to what is good" (Romans 12:9).

PRAY

Spend five minutes talking to God right now. Use a watch or set a timer if you need to.

- Ask the Lord to cause you to see and hate the ugliness of pornography, lust, fantasy, and masturbation.
- Tell God how you will turn to and trust in Him.
- Confess your selfishness (wanting to be first), self-sufficiency (wanting to be in control), self-gratification (wanting to be served), greed (wanting more), and pride (wanting it on your terms).
- Ask the Lord to be the master and to make you a willing servant. (Include all of these things in your prayers every day this week.)
- Be sure to pray for other Proven Men that they too will hate sin. Write down their names as you pray. Be specific in your requests to God.

READ THE BIBLE

Read Psalm 119:1–16. Make this the song of your heart!

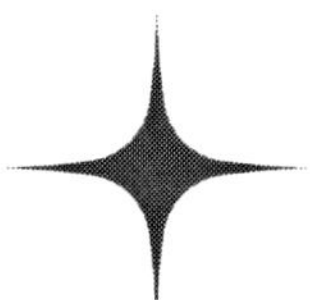

SPECIAL NOTE:

Occasionally, there will be a "Special Note" at the end of a day. Turn to this as time permits and only after prayer and Bible reading.

The letter R in PROVEN is for Repentant in Spirit. Do you see lust, fantasy, pornography, and masturbation as 100 percent wrong? If you don't see them as evil, or if you have not chosen to hate them, then you most likely are only playing a game at trying to stop. Therapy, religion, or even this study won't make you stop sexual immorality. Change must come from a *desire of the heart followed by reliance upon the Lord.* Impure things such as pornography and fantasy must be viewed as unhealthy and undesirable evils that are no longer welcome in your life. State your desire and determination to hate such sins by writing a short prayer to God expressing your deep Godly sorrow over your impure lust greed, pride, self-sufficiency, and refusal to turn over every area of your life to God.

___

___

___

___

MEMORY VERSE

Matthew 22:36–39: "'Teacher, which is the greatest commandment in the law?' Jesus replied, 'Love the Lord your God with all of your heart and with all of your soul and with all of your mind.' This is the first and greatest commandment. And the second is like it: 'Love your neighbor as yourself.'"

WEEK 1 DAY 3 (WEDNESDAY)

DAILY READING

Ask God to open your heart and reveal truth to you as you read the first two and one half pages of the article *"Freedom from Sexual Bondage"* in Appendix J. (Stop reading after the paragraph, "Make a Commitment Now.")

HEARTWORK

- What are the twin root issues that keep sexual sins alive?

____

____

____

- List ways in which you have been self-consumed, selfish, or proud.

____

____

____

- How do selfishness and pride hinder your relationship with God, and why is that important to know?

____

____

____

____

PRAY

Set a timer if you must, but pray for five minutes.

- Pray for the gift of repentance. Keep asking as if your life depends on it.
- Ask God to open your eyes to the sin of separation from Him. Spend time talking to God about the direction of your life and how you are now choosing Him over the world.
- Ask the Lord to strengthen your family and other Proven Men. (List them as you pray.)
- Openly discuss with God anything else He presses upon your heart. Keep talking to, listening for, and sharing with God.

READ THE BIBLE

Read and meditate on Luke 10:1–20. When you are finished reading, ask yourself these questions:

- Why were the men filled with joy when they returned?

____

____

____

- What was Jesus' response?

- Why do you think He responded this way?

- What lesson did Jesus want them to learn about finding lasting joy?

Reminder: On a daily basis, you should be sharing exciting truths you are learning from this study with your wife, if you're married, and with others. This is an important step in the transition from closed relationships to open and real relationships that bring about healing. It also builds trust and draws you closer to others.

MEMORY VERSE

Matthew 22:36-39: "'Teacher, which is the greatest commandment in the law?' Jesus replied, 'Love the Lord your God with all of your heart and with all of your soul and with all of your mind.' This is the first and greatest commandment. And the second is like it: 'Love your neighbor as yourself.'"

DAILY READING

Read the rest of the article *"Freedom from Sexual Bondage"* in Appendix J. Write down any insights you discover.

____

____

____

____

Describe in your own words the battlefield and the road to victory.

____

____

____

____

____

Even though setting boundaries does not stop sensual desires, boundaries are still important. You can't heap burning coals on your lap and not get burned (Proverbs 6:27–28). Write down how you will begin to avoid and remove the coals that have fueled illicit sensual desires.

Record anything else you have learned today and how you will begin living out a Proven life.

HEARTWORK

Have you made a total commitment to live for Christ and yield completely to Him so that He lives and acts through you? (Reread this sentence, meditating on what it means. Make that commitment now.)

It's time to put to death the selfishness and pride that have kept you in bondage. Start living in victory and freedom today through the power of God. It begins with yielding control to the Lord and choosing to follow His ways.

PRAY

Seek a Proven life.

- Ask God to light in you a fire and passion to seek Him with all your heart. Spend several minutes right now talking to God about your desire for purity and a real relationship with Him based upon your gratitude and love for Him.
- Repent of (turn from) the sins you once welcomed in your life.
- Talk openly to the Lord, sharing struggles, fears, hopes, and dreams.
- Ask Jesus Christ to give you His strength to fight temptations and a desire to live a life dependent upon Him so that you will live in victory.
- Ask God to give you an eternal perspective and to renew your mind and change your backward thinking about what really matters in life.
- Confess how you have refused to be vulnerable with other men, and tell God how you will begin networking with others (including men with whom you develop close relationships) allowing them to be a part of your life and of the healing process.
- Ask for God's seal to be stamped on you Proven. Right now, pray for other Proven Men, writing down their names as you pray. (You'll soon realize that five minutes is not enough time for prayer!)

____

____

____

____

READ THE BIBLE

Read and meditate on Psalm 119:17–48.

MEMORY VERSE

Matthew 22:36–39: "'Teacher, which is the greatest commandment in the law?' Jesus replied, 'Love the Lord your God with all of your heart and with all of your soul and with all of your mind.' This is the first and greatest commandment. And the second is like it: 'Love your neighbor as yourself.'"

DAILY READING

A little-known book in the Bible, Obadiah, contains an important point and warning: '"The pride of your heart has deceived you, you who live in the clefts of the rocks and make your home on the heights, you who say to yourself, 'Who can bring me down to the ground?' Though you soar like the eagle and make your nest among the stars, from there I will bring you down,' declares the Lord" (Obadiah 1:3–4).

Write out answers to these questions: What does pride do? What is the result?

____

____

____

____

Did you notice that pride leads us into seeing ourselves as being self-sustaining and independent from God? Have you seen yourself this way? It's time to embrace the truth and surrender to the Lord.

As you contemplate the effects of pride in your life, remember that pride deceives you into selfish thinking (and actions) in the area of sexual impurity, the very matter over which you want victory!

The Bible says in 2 Chronicles 26:16, "But after Uzziah became powerful, his pride led to his downfall. He was unfaithful to the Lord his God..."

We are unfaithful to God and others in many ways, including various ways of withholding, neglecting, or cheating. Jot down a few notes regarding how you have been selfish, proud, or unfaithful toward:

God

___

___

___

Your spouse (or future spouse)

___

___

___

Family members

___

___

___

Friends or others whom the Lord brings to mind

____

____

____

____

Do you see how selfishness and pride fueled these thoughts and actions? How will you respond? It's not enough to feel guilt or shame. You must want to die to selfishness and humbly turn to the Lord for renewal. Slowly read the following verses, noting how these things sometimes describe your heart and actions.

> "In his pride the wicked does not seek him; in all his thoughts there is no room for God" (Psalm 10:4).
>
> "But for those who are self-seeking and who reject the truth and follow evil, there will be wrath and anger" (Romans 2:8).
>
> "For where you have envy and selfish ambition, there you find disorder and every evil practice" (James 3:16).

Can you see how those who engage in sexually immoral practices are guided by this same selfish ambition? What will you do about it? Will you shrink back into fantasy to escape reality, or will you open up your heart and soul to the Lord and allow Him to grant you true repentance that leads to humility? *Your healing depends upon which master you choose to serve: Self or God.*

Be encouraged! Many who were once slaves to sexual sin have been set free by God. Today is the day for you to switch masters and wholeheartedly seek after the Lord, living to obey Him and enjoy His presence. Explain in your own words how the switch is made, and then make an everlasting commitment to being God's loyal and faithful friend, turning to and trusting in Him.

HEARTWORK

Pride and selfishness blind us to the truth about our relationship with God, which is designed to be one of dependency upon Him. Ask the Lord to show you how pride has blinded you to His truth.

Read through the list of feelings in Appendix F. Write down how you feel now, and how you have felt at various times during the week. (Practice being aware of your feelings.)

What plans do you have for tonight? Friday nights often bring heightened temptations. Plan ahead for engaging in Godly activities. Break the rituals you once followed and replace them with seeking after the Lord. Tonight, read Appendix A and select one or more of the relational exercises. Why not also write a love note to the Lord and spend a night in praise and worship?

____

____

____

____

PRAY

Be sure to spend at least five minutes in prayer, but don't ask for your own blessings, such as an easier time at work, a raise, or a new car. Instead, remove yourself from the focus of prayer. Pray for others. Ask God to heal someone you know who is sick, to save someone you know who has rejected God, and to have mercy on someone you know who is hurting. It's good to pray for your family as long as your request isn't something intended for your own benefit (e.g., asking God to make your wife a better cook or help your children behave so they are quiet around you). It's also appropriate to confess sin and ask God to work in your life to break your prideful heart. Right now, talk to God. Tell Him your struggles and how you need Him to overcome them for you.

READ THE BIBLE

Read Romans 6:17–23.

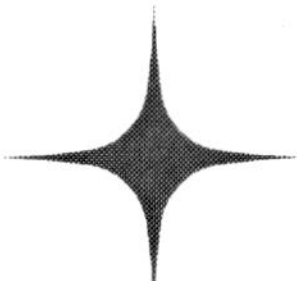

SPECIAL NOTE:

Are you beginning to see the big picture now? You were created to love and worship God (Matthew 4:10) and to have a personal relationship with Him (James 2:23; John 1:12; 1 John 3:1). Write down how this helps you see why a self-seeking heart keeps you from living out your purpose in life and leads instead to sinful practices.

___

___

___

You have learned that the proud don't seek God (or have room for Him) and that self-seekers reject truth. Explain how, when you are self-seeking, you reject God's truth about an intimate relationship with Him. Also, how does a self-seeking life inhibit vulnerability with a spouse and with others?

___

___

___

Married men: You've now made a list of ways in which you were selfish. It's time to bring your wife into the process. That includes having "the talk" with her this weekend. Today, mark your calendar and invite her to set aside 30 to 60 minutes this weekend for "couch time." You can tell her that you want to share what you are learning in the Study, where you are at, and where you are going, because you want to rebuild trust and foster openness and honesty. (The weekend portion of this Study has a more detailed outline for you to use, so plan to review it before you sit down with her.)

MEMORY VERSE

Matthew 22:36-39: "'Teacher, which is the greatest commandment in the law?' Jesus replied, 'Love the Lord your God with all of your heart and with all of your soul and with all of your mind.' This is the first and greatest commandment. And the second is like it: 'Love your neighbor as yourself.'"

Over the weekend, read *"My Purpose in Life"* in Appendix L. Spend time talking to God about your purpose in life. Reaffirm your commitment to meeting with the Lord daily.

If you have not already done so, read *"Joel's and Tim's Stories"* in Appendix Q. It will take some extra time to complete the weekend work, but it will lay a good foundation.

Married Men: Couch Time
Plan to have a regular "couch time" talks about what you are learning, how you are growing, and areas that remain tough for you. Here's a suggested outline for this weekend's talk.

Share with your wife your revelation of ways in which you have acted selfish. Look at the lists in the companion book at Chapter 7 for ideas, such as wanting to be waited upon, finding faults in others, being quick to justify your actions.

With respect to the specifics about sexual integrity lapses, such as porn or masturbation, don't make her pry it out of you. She needs to understand the true scope of your lust problem. So tell her how often you look at porn or masturbate. Give her the true scope of the problem, including the temptations and triggers. But don't give every detail of every woman you ever fantasized about. Before your meeting, you should read Appendix C to the companion book, "What do I tell my Wife or Fiancée?"

This talk will be painful for both of you, but necessary for the healing process. Secrets kill relationships because if you can't reveal the current you and tell her your true struggles and trials, you really don't have a true marriage and will never grow individually or collectively as a married couple.

WEEK TWO

TESTIMONY

"As I work through the first two weeks of the study, my eyes have been opened to just how selfish my life has been. Now I realize the only way to freedom is to love the Lord with all my heart, soul and mind. I strongly recommend this study."

Will you establish a regular practice of singing love songs to God and fixing the eyes of your heart upon His glory? Make a commitment now to seek the Lord with all of your heart.

Passionate for God,
Repentant in spirit,
Open and honest,
Victorious in living,
Eternal in perspective, and
Networking with other ***PROVEN Men.***

MEMORY VERSE

Philippians 4:8: "Finally, brothers, whatever is true, whatever is noble, whatever is right, whatever is pure, whatever is lovely, whatever is admirable—if anything is excellent or praiseworthy—think about such things."

WEEK 2 DAY 1 (MONDAY)

DAILY READING

Today you will focus upon how to put a few of the PROVEN letters into practice in your life.

The letter V in PROVEN is for Victorious in Living. All who seek the Lord will find Him, and those who walk according to God's Spirit will not stumble (2 Peter 1:5–10). Slowly read the following Scripture verse and state in your own words what God is trying to teach you: "Do nothing out of selfish ambition or vain conceit, but in humility consider others better than yourselves" (Philippians 2:3).

____

____

____

- How does considering others better (or more important) than yourself help you win the battle against selfish ambition?

____

____

____

- What practical things will you begin to do to put others first?

____

____

____

____

R is for Repentant in Spirit. God will change you from the inside out if you really want to be changed. Being changed, however, is not the same thing as simply asking God to remove temptations. Real change means a transformation of the heart. Tell God of your desire to be His friend and purpose to spend time with Him in order to become just like Him.

Below are two verses that explain why you remain trapped in sin. The first shows why "programs" don't work. The second shows why Internet blocks and other defensive postures alone don't work. Rather, you need to meet with God daily.

"Since you died with Christ to the basic principles of the world, why, as though you still belonged to it, do you submit to its rules: 'Do not handle! Do not taste! Do not touch!'? These are all destined to perish with use, because they are based on human commands and teachings. Such regulations indeed have an appearance of wisdom, with their self-imposed worship, their false humility and their harsh treatment of the body, but they lack any value in restraining sensual indulgence" (Colossians 2:20–23).

"When an evil spirit comes out of a man, it goes through arid places seeking rest and does not find it. Then it says, 'I will return to the house I left.' When it arrives, it finds the house unoccupied, swept clean and put in order. Then it goes and takes with it seven other spirits more wicked than itself, and they go in and live there. And the final condition of that man is worse than the first" (Matthew 12:43–45).

- State how these verses impacted you.

Meditate upon this portion of Scripture:

"My dear brothers, take note of this: Everyone should be quick to listen, slow to speak and slow to become angry, for man's anger does not bring about the righteous life that God desires. Therefore, get rid of all moral filth and the evil that is so prevalent and humbly accept the word planted in you, which can save you. Do not merely listen to the word, and so deceive yourselves. Do what it says" (James 1:19–22).

Those who are full of pride are often quick to speak (i.e., tell others their opinions), quick to judge (i.e., compare themselves to others), and quick to find fault (i.e., have a critical spirit). They also complain and tend to become frustrated or angered easily.

- Do you see this in your life? Explain.

- It's time to do business with your pride. Being humble is how you guard your heart. What does it mean to be or do something "humbly," and why is that important?

- Will you seek to be humble? Will you pursue repentance? *Right now, bow your head and ask God to make you a humble person and to humble you! (Then do not reject His refining work in you.) Write a short prayer to the Lord.*

Think through 1 Corinthians 8:1–2, which says, "We know that we all possess knowledge. Knowledge puffs up, but love builds up. The man who thinks he knows something does not yet know as he ought to know."

- State the principle found in this passage and think through how you will incorporate it into your life.

Lasting healing will not result from focusing entirely upon removing sexual temptations from your life, but requires the filling of your heart with God by:

- Reading His Word (the Bible).
- Hearing His voice through conversational prayer.
- Allowing Him to flow through you as you love and serve others.

The last letter in PROVEN is N, Networking with other Proven Men. God does not leave you alone to fight temptations. Proven Men are as iron that sharpens iron (Proverbs 27:17). Trust in God and stand alongside your fellow Proven Men. Then do what the word of God says (James 1:22). If you adopt all of the PROVEN letters into your life, you will lead a victorious life! Stay on the path.

HEARTWORK

Your daily study includes a *Daily Reading* that is designed to equip you in living out a Proven life. Highlight and take notes as you read, and let these spiritual truths penetrate your heart. It also includes a *Heartwork* section that takes you a step deeper and positions you to meet with and be changed by the Lord. Right now make a commitment to open your heart to God each day through the use of this study.

PRAY

Spend five minutes in prayer. Be sure to keep the focus off yourself and on God. To help you stay focused, jot down the name of a person you want God to bless or give strength to, and then pray for that person (being careful not to merely think about him). When you have finished, jot down the next person's name. After five minutes you'll have several names written down. You might find that meeting with God becomes easier because you're more focused, and you realize that there are many others you want to ask God to guide and protect. Here is a suggested outline:

- Pray for your family (list each family member).
- Pray for other Proven Men (list them).
- Pray for your church leaders.

READ THE BIBLE

Always have a Bible handy while doing the daily study. You will be asked to read from it each day because the Bible is the living and active Word of God, capable of penetrating your soul, convicting you of sin, transforming your thoughts, and renewing your heart (Hebrews 4:12). In the pages of Scripture, you meet with and experience the Lord.

Right now, read and meditate on Colossians 3:1–17. This is a key to a new Proven life.

____

____

____

MEMORY VERSE

Philippians 4:8: "Finally, brothers, whatever is true, whatever is noble, whatever is right, whatever is pure, whatever is lovely, whatever is admirable—if anything is excellent or praiseworthy—think about such things."

WEEK 2 DAY 2 (TUESDAY)

DAILY READING

Remember to highlight and take notes as you daily read through the study, and let these spiritual truths penetrate your heart.

Never forget that healing comes only from God.[1] In fact, the Lord says that apart from Him you can do nothing of eternal quality (John 15:5). It's prideful to think that you can bring about any achievement. In fact, you actually oppose God when you strive in your own strength to free yourself from bondage to sexual immorality. (See James 4:6: "God opposes the proud but gives grace to the humble.")

No one deserves to go to heaven, but rather our sins are forgiven and heaven is opened through faith in Christ, which is a gift of God (Ephesians 2:8–9). Still, people often seek to set aside their faith when it comes to living a holy life, somehow deceiving themselves into thinking that the ability to refrain from evil is found in their own strength.

When you face a crisis or problem, is your first reaction to take matters into your own hands? A lifestyle of self-effort and self-striving produces a self-centered and prideful heart, which is a barren field yielding mainly weeds of selfish practices, including pornography, fantasy, lust, or masturbation.

Where should you turn? The problem with all self-help techniques and efforts is that they are of human origin and will eventually crumble. You'll remain puffed up or deceived. Just as pornography or fantasy brings only momentary pleasure, self-effort only grants temporary relief. The weeds are never fully uprooted, and total freedom remains out of reach.

DAY 2

Regardless of the number of times you've failed before, don't remain in despair (self-pity). Although God alone heals, you're not exempt from responsibility. Your duty is to position yourself to receive God's gift of healing and then cooperate, purposefully walking in step with Him.

The Lord won't force Himself upon you. You must earnestly want God's healing, ask for it, and carry it out. *How? By making the pursuit of God—knowing and loving Him—your top priority!* (Read that line again.) As you embrace this, you'll finally accept and understand that you really are needy and utterly dependent on Him after all. A Godly form of humility will follow and break your prideful spirit. In fact, it's your pride that has kept you apart from God and refused His power to overcome evil.

Rejoice in this knowledge! God promises to raise up the humble. Seek the Lord diligently and dependently. Seek to be the opposite of proud. Begin your new life of seeking the Lord with this prayer:

Rescue me, Lord; I am a wretched sinner. I have been striving in my own strength, living to please myself. I have turned away from You and rejected Your love and grace. I am in great need. I call upon You. I turn to You and yield my entire life to You. This time, I submit myself in every area of my life.

A true prayer for God to change you is one that is always heard. Place your faith in Christ and ask Him to strengthen you. God always allows you a choice to rely on His power or to use your own. You can keep sinning even after He makes available a way of escape. By now you should have figured out that in the past, you only pretended you wanted to stop. You preferred to keep sinning if it meant you could remain in control.

Get into a practice of reviewing the Daily Readings, jotting down key points as well as new insights or commitments. Make your notes here. (It's never enough simply to hear truth; it must be adopted as your own.)

____

____

____

HEARTWORK

Are you finally willing to do whatever it takes? Then submit to God and receive His grace, strength, and healing. Keep asking the Lord to reveal Himself to you and to break your stubborn, prideful heart. Right now, take a moment to *kneel and plead with God to give you a longing to be an obedient child*—one who desires to sit at His feet and enjoy His company. Make the above prayer the cry of your heart as you kneel.

Did you meet with God just now? Push through obstacles and numbness. Only when you're living out your purpose in life—to seek God with all of your heart in a loving relationship and to treat others with respect and love—can you be ready to act upon the grace God gives to heal your wounds, transform your mind, and grant you a victorious life. This requires a real hunger for God and a sense of dependency. The Lord wants to give you these things, so ask. God richly rewards a repentant heart and will implant in you a desire for new open relationships. Ask the Lord for mercy and a growing desire to be with Him. Then stay the course. Make it a priority to do the daily *Heartwork*.

Consider the following questions and carefully think through your answers:

- Who does the healing of sexual impurity in my life?

- Do I really believe that healing is 100 percent by God, or do I still think God "helps" me do the work?

- Why does it matter whether I think I do the work with God's help or that God does the healing and I am the obedient servant?

- What does it mean to reject self-effort, and how do I do this?

You've learned a lot today. Now it's time to put what you've learned into action. Begin your new direction in life by developing personal goals. If you don't have clearly defined goals, how will you know if you achieve them?

Read the *"Sample Life Goals"* in Appendix B. Add to this list, writing your own specific goals in the column or on a separate sheet of paper. Your goals should be based on where you are right now and where you realistically see yourself going. Regularly update your goals and evaluate your progress.

PRAY

Spend at least five minutes in prayer. Keep asking God to place a burden in your heart for others. Keep the focus of your prayers on God. Your goal should be to develop a relationship with God. He is not a vending machine that gives you whatever you desire if you just say the right words.

- In your own words, ask God to change you, to humble you, and to give you a broken and contrite heart.
- Talk to God about what is on your heart.
- Tell God of your struggles and how you need Him to overcome for you.
- Pray for other Proven Men and for your family. List them as you do.

____

____

____

READ THE BIBLE

Purpose to accept and believe that the Bible is the Word of God. Today, read Hebrews 4:12, John 1:1–14, and 2 Timothy 3:16. Don't race. Ask God to reveal truth to you and to open your eyes and melt your heart as you read and meditate on Scripture. Next, meditate on the memory verse.

MEMORY VERSE

Philippians 4:8: "Finally, brothers, whatever is true, whatever is noble, whatever is right, whatever is pure, whatever is lovely, whatever is admirable—if anything is excellent or praiseworthy—think about such things."

Do you see the memory verse also means that you are to stop thinking about those things that are inconsistent with the fruit of the Spirit? (Galatians 5:22–23)

What kind of things do you tend to dwell on? Jot them down.

____

____

____

____

Think through how to dwell on things that are true, noble, right, pure, lovely, admirable, excellent, or praiseworthy. List some things you will begin focusing on instead of selfish ambition or fantasy.

____

____

____

____

____

Your thought life will be your biggest battleground. Therefore, keep this week's memory verse in mind and ready for use as you are taking captive all impure thoughts or fantasies and making them obedient to Christ (2 Corinthians 10:5). Make a plan now, and train your mind to think about things that are true, noble, right, pure, lovely, admirable, excellent, or praiseworthy. Then, when you are tempted to lust, fantasize, or masturbate, or when anger or greed enters your mind, you can stop and replace these thoughts with things you just learned. Remember, God's will for you is to be joyful always, praying continually, and giving thanks in all circumstances (1 Thessalonians 5:16–18). This can occur only when you train your thought life to dwell on these things throughout the day, not just when you are tempted.

DAILY READING

To yield fully to God, you must understand and appreciate His nature and character. For instance, if God were sometimes fallible, then you would be justified in occasionally acting according to your own best judgment. If God were not all-powerful, you should add your strength and effort to His. If God didn't have your best interest in mind, you might not want to follow His every command. However, if God is perfect and all-knowing, He will never be wrong. If He is all-powerful, your own efforts merely stand in the way. If God is absolutely good and unconditionally loves you, His commands and His ways will always be right for you.

What reason do you rely upon for not trusting God? Oswald Chambers once said, "The core of all sin is the belief that God is not good." It's true. If you refuse to see God as good, you'll never trust Him or turn over complete control of your life to Him. Instead, you'll constantly question His plan and think you know a better way.

To overcome your incorrect view of God or lack of faith that He is always good, you must get to know Him so you can see Him for who He really is—perfect (and perfectly good). Examining Him closely, you won't find any flaws. As you see the real nature of God, you'll be drawn to Him. That's why the daily *Heartwork* places such emphasis on spending copious amounts of time in praise and worship of the Lord.[2]

The more time you spend meeting with God (not just learning about Him), the more the eyes of your heart will be open to Him. As a result of being awakened to God, you will trust Him. You will stop striving in your own strength and gladly follow His path. Old familiar

Bible verses will take on totally new meaning. You will begin to embrace Proverbs 3:5–6, which states, "Trust in the Lord with all your heart and lean not on your own understanding; in all your ways acknowledge him, and he will make your paths straight." What a precious promise!

- What struck you, and why are you glad you read the Daily Reading?

____

____

____

____

____

____

____

____

____

HEARTWORK

Turn to God right now with an open heart. Tell Him of your desire to know Him and to see Him as good. Now read the *"Attributes of God"* in Appendix D. As you read, ask God to reveal to you that He is perfect and that He possesses each of these attributes completely. Ask God to instill in you the knowledge that He is good and can be trusted. Don't race through the list, but contemplate each attribute. Meditate on the Lord and ask the Holy Spirit to open wide your soul to God. Return here after reading Appendix D.

Make a decision whether you believe and trust that God is perfect in all of His attributes. If you have any doubts or struggles, tell God about it and ask Him to change your heart and mind. Admit that you cannot overcome these doubts or struggles by yourself. Ask God for His power and strength, then accept it and rely upon Christ.

Will you agree to do whatever it takes to be free from bondage to sin by receiving God's healing? Real healing is not just grace to end sexual sins. It's restoration from all sins such as anger, greed, boastfulness, pride, and self-centeredness. It's a replacement of selfishness for things pure and praiseworthy. Make a firm decision right now. Pause and talk to the Lord. Tell Him you're willing to do whatever it takes. If you're not willing to do whatever it takes, you're not really desiring sexual integrity. The result will be more charades of simply going through the motions. End it now. Take on a new motto: *Lord, I am willing to do whatever it takes!*

The third letter in PROVEN is O, which means Open and Honest. This involves open communications with others. Make sure that daily you're telling others (especially your wife, if you're married) new or exciting things you're learning. Don't hold it all in. Expressing feelings and discussing how the Lord is working in your life will not only cause you to grow, but it will also encourage others.

PRAY

Go to God in prayer right now and ask Him to make you:

- hungry for His holiness,
- a needy, dependent servant, and
- grateful and content.

Don't just give this lip service, but consider kneeling right now and earnestly asking God for these three things. Ask as if you will die if you don't receive them from God. It may be that you need to pour out your heart to God for many days before you see your heart changing in these areas. Be persistent. Show God you mean business and really want to live a Proven life.

Spend five or more minutes in prayer, meeting with God and praying for others. Pray for other Proven Men to make similar commitments. Your prayers act to support and strengthen one another as iron sharpens iron. Go through each element of the letters of a Proven life, asking God to impart each letter into their lives. (Jot down their names.)

____

____

____

____

READ THE BIBLE

Read Genesis 1. Purpose to get to truly know God.

MEMORY VERSE

Philippians 4:8: "Finally, brothers, whatever is true, whatever is noble, whatever is right, whatever is pure, whatever is lovely, whatever is admirable—if anything is excellent or praiseworthy—think about such things."

WEEK 2 DAY 4 (THURSDAY)

Ask God to prepare your heart to meet with Him. Review the first weekly memory verse from this study. Plan to write the memory verses on note cards so they're always handy to review. (Remember that all twelve weekly memory verses are listed in Appendix R.)

DAILY READING

Yesterday's study focused on the perfect nature of God. Today, in contrast, you will examine your imperfect, sinful nature. Do you admit that you are fallible? Do you believe that you are unable to control life? Right now, ask God to humble yourself in your own eyes.

It was pride that caused Satan, the most beautiful and powerful angel created by God, to demand to be in control and ask other angels to worship him. How puffed up he became as he focused on himself. Satan sought to become his own god. Therefore, he no longer had a place with God and was cast out of heaven. How fitting that Satan was sent to earth, where man idolizes his own body and seeks to control life, preferring to receive praise rather than give it to the only One who is truly deserving. No wonder Satan knows exactly how to tempt each of us!

God created people for His good pleasure. Is it so strange that the Creator wants those He created to worship Him and enjoy an intimate relationship with Him? However, in His vast love, God also gave us the freedom to choose not to be thankful. What about you? Are you thankful to God? It's only when you accept your true position as a created being that you gladly turn to the Lord and live out your purpose in life, fully experiencing God Himself.

The Lord doesn't want you to beat yourself up or to be discouraged over your sinful condition. No! He wants you to take on His perfect character and nature. God calls each of us to a deeper place where we can be transformed by Him. Consider the riches that the Lord offers. First, He has adopted you as a son. Yes, God's love is so great that while you were still a sinner, He chose to adopt you and to be your forever Father (Romans 5:8, Ephesians 1:5). Second, the Lord wants you to be His friend. He wants you to be just like Him and to experience divine intimacy.

Once you've received new life in Jesus Christ and accepted a new relationship with God, He implants wisdom and power. The Holy Spirit permanently indwells those who turn to Christ and guides their lives. He teaches of a new eternal hope and a place in heaven reserved for His followers. Do you long to dwell in heaven free from all evil and sin? How grand a thought and how real it will become! Begin living today in the power of God.

By keeping an eternal perspective, you'll retain God's vision and hope for your life. Remember that you're just passing through this world en route to your permanent heavenly dwelling. While on this journey, you're to enjoy the things of God while passing up the selfish pleasures Satan tempts you with.

Will you choose to please your eternal Father, or will you choose to please Satan, who wants you to be like himself—a prideful rebel? *Each time you turn to selfish thoughts, you enter the domain of the devil.* As God's enemy, Satan wants to steal your praise. If he cannot win your worship, he settles for your pride and self-sufficiency. When you seek to please yourself instead of God and when you don't see God as good, perfect, and worthy of praise, then Satan justifies his rebellion and scorns God. Did you know that Satan goes before God day and night accusing each of us, the people the Lord created (Revelation 12:10)? Therefore, as you keep on sinning and rejecting God, you please Satan; *yet Jesus stands in heaven defending you.* Accept that God loves you deeply and wants the best for you. Christ offers Himself freely to and for you. His ways are gentle and forgiving, not harsh and judging. The Lord laid down His life for you and wants to give you real and eternal life.

It will take effort, but determine to record the key points and note any insights God revealed to you from the Daily Readings. Write them down here.

HEARTWORK

It's time to make a decision: Do you believe that you are proud and sinful by nature but can put on the new nature of God by yielding to Him? If you have any doubts, tell God about them and ask Him to change your heart and mind.

Spend a moment contemplating these questions and record your answers:

- Do I believe God really wants me to be sexually pure and holy, and do I trust that He can heal me?

- Do I really want to be sexually pure and holy, and do I trust in God to heal me?

Read Ephesians 4:17–24. Read the passage again slowly.

- What truths had an impact on you? (There are at least seven key points to record—keep asking God to reveal His truths to you. Write down those that you see.)

- Describe areas in which you have lost "sensitivity" to sin. Also, list any sinful desires against which you have stopped an aggressive fight.

- Do you tend to sexualize things? For instance, when you see a man hug a woman, do you wonder if they have sex? When you see a woman, do you consider her body shape? Are you often on a hunt for more stimulation (e.g., surfing the Internet for greater thrills, flipping through TV or magazines for something sensual, positioning yourself to be in view when a woman bends over, or frequently turning your head to look around to make sure you don't miss something)? Describe how thoughts and actions like these are sometimes true of you.

____

____

____

____

____

____

- Do you tend to view women as sex objects or see them as existing to meet your needs? Describe your view of women.

____

____

____

____

____

____

- Explain how fantasies (such as wondering what it would be like to be with a certain woman, dreaming about being a hero, dwelling on how to acquire wealth or possessions) distract you from being hungry for God's holiness; from being a needy, dependent servant; and from having a grateful heart.

____

____

____

____

All fantasies, not just sensual ones, drive you away from true intimacy and lead you into the delusion that you can control life and don't need God or anyone else. Will you embrace this truth? Write a short prayer stating that you believe and trust in the Lord and want to be His close friend.

____

____

____

____

PRAY

The second letter in PROVEN is R, which means Repentant in Spirit.

Confess to God right now and repent of the ways you have been double-minded (e.g., you ask a friend over for lunch because you want to borrow his mower; you ask God to heal your mother's cancer, not only because you care for her, but also because you don't want your life disrupted by her moving in with you; you say you want freedom from pornography but look forward to the next swimsuit magazine; you want others to see you as holy, but you don't want to put the Lord first).

- Confess how you have chased after the things of the world and have focused on yourself instead of God.
- Confess how you have viewed others as sexual objects.
- Ask God to change your heart and attitude in these areas. Keep going to the Lord with a repentant heart and talk about your sins and struggles.
- Confess any sin the Lord brings to your mind. Ask for God's forgiveness and healing.
- Ask God to make you hungry for His holiness.
- Ask the Lord to give you eyes to see that you are needy and dependent upon Him.
- Ask God to give you a grateful spirit.
- Spend time praying for other Proven Men. (List their names.)

____

____

____

____

READ THE BIBLE

Although God gives willing men a new nature, you still have the responsibility to do what God commands. To get a better understanding of how you are to act as part of a team of Proven Men, read and meditate on Ephesians 4:25 through 5:7.

MEMORY VERSE

Philippians 4:8: "Finally, brothers, whatever is true, whatever is noble, whatever is right, whatever is pure, whatever is lovely, whatever is admirable—if anything is excellent or praiseworthy—think about such things."

DAILY READING

God is perfect, yet man has a sinful nature that is bent upon selfishness. The two don't mix. So how can man interact with God? First, the precious and redeeming blood of Christ covers you if you've turned to and trusted in the Lord, and thereby you obtain God's own righteousness. This opens the door, but your responsibilities don't end there. You must walk through the doorway and seek the Lord. You were created for a relationship with God, not merely to abstain from sin. You cannot be fully satisfied apart from an intimate relationship with God. To attempt to fill the void in their lives, people who are not walking in step with Christ turn to other things such as sex, drugs, alcohol, entertainment, or sports.

Do you want peace and fulfillment? Then set your heart toward God and away from yourself and the world. Passionately seek God and earnestly pursue a daily relationship with Him. Repent each time you turn away from God to chase after selfish gain. It's not that God opposes your desire for pleasure, but He knows that the selfish path you chose leads to destruction and emptiness.

Think about it another way: If a married man sneaks out of the house at night to go to a prostitute, won't that hurt the spirit of his wife as well as his own? The adulterer shows by his actions that he thinks intimacy and sexual fulfillment are found outside of his wife. The same is true about looking at pornography.

Your relationship with the Lord must begin with the realization that God is absolutely perfect and wants to give Himself fully to you. Yet, when you go your own way you're saying that what God offers isn't as good as what you can find on your own. When the Lord says, "Thirst after me and you will be totally fulfilled" (Matthew 5:6), you don't believe it. You reject intimacy with God, thinking you're happier if you can include side trips away from Him.

It's the sin of trying to live independently from God that makes chasing after sexual pleasures wrong. God purposely created both male and female to unite in sexual pleasure as husband and wife. Yet those who chase after the false allure of pornography or sexual exploits outside of this design have closed their eyes to the Lord and are seeking to create their own universe. That's the essence of why men remain trapped in bondage to sexual sin. They have pridefully turned away from God.

Dear friend, repent. Hate evil and cling to good. Kill the prideful spirit that keeps you from being a needy, dependent servant of God and from living out your purpose in life. True fulfillment will follow. Are you being open and honest in your relationships? Don't deceive yourself. God isn't fooled. He says that although many will pretend by using Christian slogans, they are not His children in their hearts (Matthew 7:21–23). God knows when you merely give Him lip service, and your heart is far from Him and bent upon chasing after idols. Each time you turn to pornography, fantasy, lust, masturbation, greed, envy, or jealousy, you have closed out God. This shows that you have turned inward and become self-centered.

Fortunately, God isn't interested in slamming the door on you. He loves you and wants you to run to Him. No matter how you've sinned or how long you've strayed away, He wants you—His precious son—back. This is the lesson Jesus was teaching in the parable of the prodigal son (Luke 15:11–24). After the wayward son had demanded his inheritance, he left his father to venture into a new life. He chased after every worldly pleasure until all his money was spent. Alone and in despair, the son finally returned home. The father didn't lecture or demand restitution. Instead, he ran and greeted the son with open arms.

What about the other son in that story? He was a rule follower but didn't have God's heart of mercy. He complained when God redeemed his brother. His pride and selfishness were even greater sins because he never repented.

The Lord is even more willing to forgive you and to run to meet with you. Purpose to develop a real relationship in which you openly communicate with God and actually experience Him. It's the way things are meant to be!

Take the time to meditate on each central idea in this Daily Reading. Identify and write down the key points, then meditate on how these things speak to you.

____

____

____

____

HEARTWORK

Make a decision whether you really want an intimate relationship with God more than the false intimacy[3] of fantasy and pornography. Watch out for double-mindedness. Love God for who He is and not for what He can do for you. If you have any doubts or struggles in trusting God, tell Him about them and ask the Lord to change your heart and mind. Be open and honest.

- Ask God to reveal to you how to have an intimate relationship with Him. List any commitments.

____

____

____

____

____

____

- Are you committed to meeting with God daily while doing this *Heartwork* as well as through prayer and Bible reading? (If not fully, honestly evaluate what might be holding you back.)

When doing the daily *Heartwork* (including reading the Bible), make sure you're not just learning information. Head knowledge won't change you but will only puff you up (1 Corinthians 8:1) and deceive you (James 1:22). Take to heart what you read and apply it in your life, always remembering that your goal is meeting with the Lord and experiencing Him. Read Colossians 2:20–23 (read it three times):

> "Since you died with Christ to the basic principles of this world, why, as though you still belonged to it, do you submit to its rules: 'Do not handle! Do not taste! Do not touch!'? These are all destined to perish with use, because they are based on human commands and teachings. Such regulations indeed have an appearance of wisdom, with their self-imposed worship, their false humility and their harsh treatment of the body, but they lack any value in restraining sensual indulgence."

- What are some ways that you either merely give an outward appearance of trying to change your impure behaviors or rely upon your own strength to fight temptations? (List them.)

____

____

____

____

• Do you see how rules, such as avoiding certain practices (e.g., do not look or touch), fail to stop the desire to do sinful acts? Does this reinforce why setting strict boundaries (e.g., what magazines to read, movies to watch, Internet sites to visit, stores to avoid) won't, by itself, set you free from lust or addiction to pornography? That's why following a "program" isn't the cure. Therefore, set your heart toward God and give up control of your life to Him. He wants to free you.

The fourth letter in PROVEN is V, which means Victorious in Living. Living by God's Spirit results in leading a victorious life. Once you're set free by the Lord, you don't need to carry labels, such as "recovering sex addict." Your life is no longer measured by the number of days free from certain sinful conduct. Proven Men are focused upon experiencing God daily and living out all six elements of a Proven life. When you put on Christ, you walk in His light. It's only when you turn your focus back on yourself or try to overcome in your own strength that you lose ground and fail.

Proven Men say, *I am free because it is no longer I who lives, but Christ who lives in me* (based upon Galatians 2:20). Therefore, we are no longer in bondage to sin. Sure, we all continue to battle temptations and have some setbacks, but we now purposefully give over to the new nature and are called children of God. You are God's adopted son. Now that's true freedom! It's time to become a needy, dependent servant. Won't you accept God's offer to live by His grace?

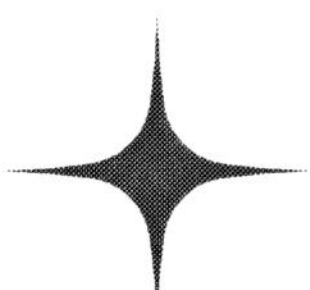

SPECIAL NOTE:

Has this Study been a blessing to you? If so, please make a generous tax deductible donation through our website so that we can restore more men's lives. www.ProvenMen.org.

PRAY

Be sure to keep the focus off yourself in prayer and on God. Meet with Him for the purpose of getting to know Him. Right now, spend five minutes talking with God in prayer. This time don't pray, "Lord, help me do xyz." Rather, tell God: "I yield to you; change me, transform my mind, and heal my soul." Talk openly to the Lord about each issue or struggle you face, giving Him control over everything. Practice this approach to relational prayer right now. Praise and thank God with all your heart. Open up to Him about things you're thankful for. Ask God to implant in you a desire to be grateful and content and to be hungry for His holiness. Pray earnestly for your family and others. (List them as you pray.)

____

____

____

____

____

READ THE BIBLE

Keep asking God to open your heart to Him while you read Proverbs 16.

MEMORY VERSE

Philippians 4:8: "Finally, brothers, whatever is true, whatever is noble, whatever is right, whatever is pure, whatever is lovely, whatever is admirable—if anything is excellent or praiseworthy—think about such things."

If you have not already, read the article *"My Purpose in Life"* in Appendix L and *"Joel's and Tim's Stories"* in Appendix Q. In addition, read the *"Relational Exercises"* again in Appendix A. Plan to use Saturdays and Sundays for putting into practice the things you are learning. Take time on weekends to pray, read the Bible, finish daily *Heartwork*, and reread portions that have had an impact on you.

Week 2 had a lot packed into it. Consider spending time this weekend in review. The Lord will renew your mind and transform your heart during the time you spend meeting with Him. Keep sharing with others the exciting things you are learning and new insights you are gaining.

This PROVEN Model is the prescription for healing from sexual impurity. Will you go to God and earnestly seek Him? He will custom-tailor treatment for the healing of your wounds. Talk to the Lord right now. Commit to stop striving in your own effort. Yield fully and completely to God. This time, yield all areas of your life to Him. Agree to live out your purpose in life together with and in reliance upon God. Refer to the PROVEN acronym on a daily basis as a way of keeping your life on track.

WEEK THREE

TESTIMONY

"I am now on the third day of the second week of your study. My family has seen positive changes in me. I truly want to change. What I am feeling now can kind of be described like solving a difficult Calculus problem. The answer is in the back of the book, and others have solved it before you, and you sit there for hours trying to figure it out—encouraged only by the fact that others have gone before you."

Passionate for God,
Repentant in spirit,
Open and honest,
Victorious in living,
Eternal in perspective, and
Networking with other ***PROVEN Men.***

MEMORY VERSE

Galatians 2:20: "I have been crucified with Christ and I no longer live, but Christ lives in me. The life I live in the body, I live by faith in the Son of God, who loved me and gave Himself for me."

Spend a moment asking the Lord to soften your heart and to show you how to yield your life totally to Him.

DAILY READING

Do you ever feel unworthy? Do you find yourself thinking that God's promises are for others and not yourself? It's pretty easy to slip into self-condemnation and self-pity. Perhaps you don't measure up to those around you, let alone to God's standards, but condemnation is not the way of the Lord. If you've become a Christian reborn through faith in Christ, God claims you as a son. Did you know that God the Father personally selected you to be a gift to Jesus?[4] Listen to the words Christ spoke: "All that the Father gives me will come to me" (John 6:37). Yes, God the Father gave you as a gift to Jesus. Picture a big bow on your chest and God smiling as he hands you to Christ as a gift. In response, Christ considers you precious, and He will never drive you away; instead, He will lead you into everlasting life (John 6:39). Even if you don't feel worthy, it's true. The fact that none of us truly deserves God's love makes the gift so special! A perfect God loved you perfectly while you were yet a sinner, and He freely gives of His very self to remove your stain and replace it with His robe of righteousness. Many movies have tried to capture the essence of this mystery with stories where an ordinary person wakes up one day to find out that he is a relative of a noble family and is in line to become king. The Lord's promises, however, are not fables or make-believe, but the real thing. You were living a selfish life, but God adopted you as a son and made you a permanent heir to the kingdom. In essence, you're a forever prince. Start believing it. Reject Satan's doubts and lies. The devil wants to take away your joy, and he even asks you to renounce your position. Listen to the voice of God gently calling you to turn to Him and wear the robe He has for you. To draw you to Himself, the Lord uses love, not shame, encouragement, not blame. As you draw near to God, you'll learn to accept His unconditional love and your position in heavenly places. Jesus proved His love on the cross and bought your freedom. Go to the Lord. Meet with Him and accept His noble training.

Jot down any notes, feelings, insights, or decisions.

HEARTWORK

The letter P in PROVEN is for Passionate for God. Read the article *"How to Write a Psalm"* in Appendix H. Then, in the space below, write out a psalm of your own to God. It's not as hard as you may think. Just let it rise from your heart.

Ask the Lord to reveal to you areas of your life you haven't yet given to God and where you still want to be in control. It may be something like seeking escape or pleasure through pornography and masturbation, or it may be that you hold onto your "rights" of retribution or anger. What areas in your heart or soul are you trying to keep secret from God? Be *open and honest.* Take a good look. Stop fighting the Holy Spirit as He wants to bring them to light so that you can be healed.

PRAY

Select a quiet place away from distractions. It doesn't work to pray in bed after the alarm goes off. You may even need to shower before praying. Give God the first fruits (the best time and the start of your day) in prayer and study. Show God how much you love Him and want to get to know Him. Be attentive to when your mind wanders and begins to think about the person or circumstance about which you are praying. God tells you to take captive every thought and make it obedient to Christ (2 Corinthians 10:5). Practice this in prayer. At times simply uttering the name of Jesus aloud can pull a drifting mind back to focus. At first, five minutes can seem like forever to pray, but with diligence and by relying upon God you'll develop the discipline to keep focused.

READ THE BIBLE

Although you have recently read from Psalm 119, God's Word is active and alive, which makes reading the same passage fresh as you read it again or think on the truths it contains. Allow Psalm 119 to become your friend, comforter, and encourager. Meditate on Psalm 119:1–16. Afterward, go back through and select your five favorite statements in these verses.

MEMORY VERSE

Galatians 2:20: "I have been crucified with Christ and I no longer live, but Christ lives in me. The life I live in the body, I live by faith in the Son of God, who loved me and gave Himself for me."

WEEK 3 DAY 2 (TUESDAY)

Don't rush through today's Daily Reading. Ask God to reveal truth to you. Be patient and quiet before the Lord.

DAILY READING

Initially, most men are uncomfortable with accepting God's unconditional love. You want to feel worthy or try to earn God's love. This is called "performance-based love," which is an attempt to perform for God. The problem is that you cannot earn God's love. There are none righteous—not a single person (Romans 3:10–12). Compared to the Lord's absolute holiness and purity, your best actions are as filthy rags (Isaiah 64:6). You must accept that, apart from God doing the work in and through you, you cannot do a single thing of eternal value (John 15:5). In contrast to God, the world values a man by his deeds; but at the same time the world allows wicked internal thoughts and private actions to co-exist as long as they remain in the closet. What values does the world place on you? Does it applaud your grades in school, performance at work, skill at sports, or another achievement? Is your position or level of salary highly esteemed? The problem is that the ways of the world (i.e., awards, honors, and positions) are all dependent upon human effort and achievements.

The world also promotes an incorrect view of love—love that is earned. This love's physical aspect (or effort) is sex. In truth, the world's mindset is this: Love is sex.[5] Think through, for a moment, how this view clouds and affects your relationships. Can you see how this world-view centered on sex naturally leads to lustful thoughts, a fantasy life, pornography, masturbation, or sex addiction? We all want to be loved. If sex is love, then why not love (lust) continually; love yourself (masturbate), and love others (have sex with them)? God says otherwise. It's time to correct your backward thinking. First, the Lord judges a man's heart and motive, not appearances (1 Samuel 16:7). That's why "playing religion" does not please the Lord. Second, love is a decision and commitment. It involves freely and totally giving of your complete self to another, and is never dependent on any return. Decide right now to love faithfully, not selfishly. Love is not based in flesh, but spirit. Simply stated, God is love (1 John 4:8). Pure love actually sums up the entire written Word of God and your role in life: Loving the Lord with all of your heart, mind, soul, and strength, and loving others as yourself (Matthew 22:36–39).

List key points and record your insights.

____

____

____

____

____

Go to God in prayer right now and admit that you cannot overcome on your own. Recognize and admit areas where you were just pretending to live as a Christian or practicing religion. List them.

____

____

____

____

____

____

What is your view of love? Spend a moment thinking about how you would describe love and then jot down some notes. Look for ways in which it has been based upon sex. Examine how your view of love is based more upon receiving from others than upon giving to them.

HEARTWORK

The letter E in PROVEN is for Eternal in Perspective. What do you think of the Bible's admonition, "Do not love the world or anything in the world" (1 John 2:15)?

Read the above verse again. Allow it to convict your heart. Now, commit to seeking real love based upon real relationships and real decisions to give of yourself. Write down your decision in regard to choosing the ways of God over the ways of the world.

How do you receive God's love? Picture it right now. Are you trying to earn it? Do you need to feel worthy before you will accept it? Are you pushing God away? Not a single person has ever earned God's love, and neither can you. It's time to stop trying to perform for God. That only leaves you empty and alone. It also builds walls between you and the Lord as you refuse to receive His gift. Instead, shift your thinking and take on an eternal perspective.

Gladly receive and open the gifts of God. Although they are born in spirit (not the flesh), the gifts of God are indeed real and fulfilling. The Lord's unconditional love leads you to gratefulness, which opens your heart to loving God and to desiring to give unearned love to others. By simply accepting God's unearned and unconditional love, you become transformed and long to carry out the commands that please Him. Rather than trying to earn love by doing good, when you accept unearned love and the Spirit of God, He empowers you to live a holy life marked by a thankful spirit and love for Him and others.

Have you been performing for God and for others, i.e., trying to earn their love or respect, rather than accepting your true position and being open and honest in your deepest, inmost being?[6] Explain in the space below. You must recognize where you are right now before you can change your location, so take the effort to answer these questions.

____

____

____

____

PRAY

R is for Repentant in Spirit. Ask God for forgiveness of any sins He brings to your mind, i.e., some particular conduct or failure to turn to Him. Ask God to tear down the walls around your heart that prevent you from being open, honest, trusting, or vulnerable. Ask God to give you hunger for real intimacy with Him. You'll need to be persistent and make this a daily request to God. Intimacy is granted only to the humble—those who seek Him first. When you ask for things with zeal and confidence, the Father is pleased to grant them to you. On the other hand, a prayer that is nothing more than "OK God, show me how to..." will seldom rise higher than the ceiling in your room. Jesus is your model for prayer. He got up early to pray and prayed into the night (Luke 5:16; 6:12). In two of His parables, a persistent widow received justice based upon her relentless pleas (Luke 18:1), and a desperate man kept knocking at his neighbor's door at midnight until he got bread (Luke 11:5–8). Your life truly depends upon intimacy with God, so pray like you believe and want it.

- Confess how you have substituted sex for intimacy (and seek God's forgiveness).
- Confess how you have hidden your feelings and built up walls around your heart so no one can enter.
- Confess how you have been running away from (and not openly to) God.
- Seek forgiveness and ask God to show you how to repent and turn away from these things.
- Keep asking God to give you hunger for real intimacy with Him and others.
- Ask God to bless other Proven Men. (Jot down the names of those you pray for.)
- Ask God to heal the emotional wounds in your family.

READ THE BIBLE

Read Genesis 2. Read to get to know and love God. Review the memory verse.

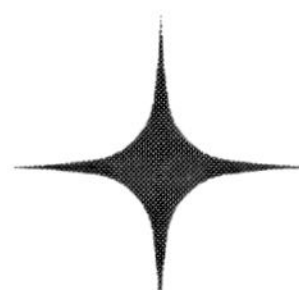

SPECIAL NOTE:

The letter O in PROVEN is for Open and Honest. Do you ever get frustrated, upset, or angry over little things like a slow computer or when someone misunderstands you? Ask God to show you the source of hidden anger deep inside of you. Be still and listen to what He has to say (Psalm 4:4). Now confess any sin that God reveals to you. Forgive those who hurt you. Ask God to give you a heart of gratitude instead of anger and to see the good in others instead of their faults. Practice being thankful.

MEMORY VERSE

Galatians 2:20: "I have been crucified with Christ and I no longer live, but Christ lives in me. The life I live in the body, I live by faith in the Son of God, who loved me and gave Himself for me."

DAILY READING

Ask yourself (and honestly evaluate your answers):

Do I really believe in my heart that God is good—absolutely good?
❑ Yes ❑ No ❑ Maybe

Do I really want to trust God with total control over all areas of my life?
❑ Yes ❑ No ❑ Maybe

If you cannot get past these two questions, stay put in your heart. Don't go on. It's that important. You won't be healed any other way! Cry out to God to change your heart so that you see Him as 100 percent good and absolutely trust Him with your whole life. Even if it takes a week or two, don't jump over these two points; if you do, this study will be of limited value. Build your house upon the only sure foundation. If you cannot mean yes to both questions right now, put two big stars near them and return here every day until you can. Of course, you should keep working through the rest of the study. Meanwhile, pray long and hard for God to (1) change your heart, (2) break your self-will, and (3) transform you into a needy, dependent servant. Wrestle before God and don't give up until He changes you. Start now.

Yesterday's lesson highlighted performance-based love and stressed that trying to perform to earn God's love is not God's way and cannot make you holy. In fact, it actually leads you further from God because you reject His grace. You prefer to receive praise or to boast about your actions. For an antidote, pay close attention to Ephesians 2:8–10: "For it is by grace you have been saved, through faith—and this not from yourselves, it is the gift of

God—not by works, so that no one can boast. For we are God's workmanship, created in Christ Jesus to do good works, which God prepared in advance for us to do." Anything good you do is carried out by God's power and plan. It's God who does the work. It's God who unconditionally loves you, and His love draws you to Himself. His grace saves you from sin and death, and the same grace that has sealed you for heaven changes your heart even now.

There is a long list of things you cannot earn. Here are just a few:

- heaven (salvation)
- forgiveness
- love
- joy
- the presence of God
- life
- health
- peace
- a grateful heart
- contentment
- hope
- mercy

Don't you long to possess these things? If you cannot earn them, how will you experience or enjoy them? The key is accepting God's grace. By its very definition, grace is an unearned gift—totally free. It's offered to all men—not limited to those who "deserve" it (Titus 2:11). Because grace is freely offered and not able to be earned, why do you still refuse to accept it for what it really is? Don't be proud—you're not a special case. God loves everyone, without showing favoritism (Romans 2:11). You need not and cannot earn grace. Period!

Humbly ask God to reveal to you right now any areas (such as lust, anger, or greed) and attitudes (such as pride, selfishness, or judgment) that keep you from living out holiness. Listen to what God tells you, then list anything He points out. Make the effort to listen to God and write down what He reveals.

____

____

____

____

____

____

Slowly read the following verses about His grace, absorbing them into your heart:

> "For all have sinned and fall short of the glory of God, and are justified freely by his grace through the redemption that came by Christ Jesus" (Romans 3:23–24).

> "But the gift is not like the trespass. For if the many died by the trespass of the one man, how much more did God's grace and the gift that came by the grace of the one man, Jesus Christ, overflow to the many!" (Romans 5:15).

> "I do not set aside the grace of God, for if righteousness could be gained through the law, Christ died for nothing!" (Galatians 2:21).

> "For the grace of God that brings salvation has appeared to all men. It teaches us to say 'No' to ungodliness and worldly passions and to live self-controlled, upright, and Godly lives in this present age, while we wait for the blessed hope—the glorious appearance of our great God and Savior, Jesus Christ, who gave himself for us to redeem us from all wickedness and to purify for himself a people that are his very own, eager to do what is good" (Titus 2:11–14).

Grace involves God giving you the faith to believe and to act upon such belief. God gives unmerited grace to the sinner for salvation (Romans 5:2). It's both the power and the desire to do His will. The good news is that you can make yourself available to receive His grace to overcome temptations if you do two things. Both are identified in the following verses:

> "Let us then approach the throne of grace with confidence, so that we may receive mercy and find grace to help us in our time of need" (Hebrews 4:16).

> "But he gives us more grace. That is why Scripture says: 'God opposes the proud but gives grace to the humble'" (James 4:6).

Are you seeing more clearly that you must ask God with confidence (faith that believes) for His gift of grace, and yet be completely humble in reliance upon the Lord? Go to the Lord right now with this attitude, asking for grace.

HEARTWORK

Why is it so important to live by grace? You must take on an eternal perspective about grace in order to shed performance-based living, which keeps you in bondage to all kinds of sins, including sexual impurity. Grace frees you from self-condemnation, worry, and strife. As you accept your position in Christ—an adopted child and heir to the kingdom due solely to grace—your entire world-view and focus changes. You stop striving in your own strength. You no longer feel inadequate. You end the hunt of turning to sex as part of trying to find out what is missing in your life, and you're finally willing to turn and totally yield to the God of unconditional love and boundless grace.

Here's the incredible thing about grace: It can't be earned. Therefore, you're freed from the weight of needing to perform good works to earn God's grace and instead do good works out of a spirit of thankfulness for God's grace. This distinction makes all the difference. Your heart is free to love without worrying about how your deeds will measure up, and you're free to pour out blessings upon others simply by the joy of giving to them. In fact, God has prepared good works for you to do together with Him (Ephesians 2:10)—not alone any longer, but done with and through God. In addition, when you realize and accept the great love and sacrifice God gave for you, your heart melts and you're changed from the inside out. Your will becomes conformed to God's will. You experience more of His nature—the opposite of selfishness and pride. This leads to a desire to worship and praise God, which opens your heart to receiving even more of Him. This creates an amazing upward ascent, counter to the downward spiral you've been trapped in.

Dear friend, choose this day whom you will serve. Will you humbly accept the invitation of the Lord to be friends? Will you receive God's gift of grace? Will you welcome and rely upon His power to say "No" to unholiness? If you do, you'll persevere through trials and temptations (Titus 2:12), and you'll enter into a close and real relationship with God. During times of praise and thankfulness, the Lord will replace the desire for your former ways of thinking and living, which never satisfied and always left you wanting. Enter His rest. Turn and yield completely to the Lord.

PRAY

P is for Passionate for God. If you believe God is good and perfect, you'll not only want to praise Him, but also trust Him with your life. Read over the *"Attributes of God"* in Appendix D. Use them as a form of prayer. While you meditate on them, ask God to deepen your understanding of His goodness. Keep asking the Lord to show you how to trust Him completely with your life. Be persistent and pour out your heart to God. Return here and spend a few more minutes in prayer for others. List them as you lift prayers to the Lord.

READ THE BIBLE

Read Psalm 119:17–40, asking God to give you this kind of a heart! Keep a prayerful spirit as you read, loving and trusting God in these same ways. Pick out a few of your favorite verses from this model psalm.

MEMORY VERSE

Galatians 2:20: "I have been crucified with Christ and I no longer live, but Christ lives in me. The life I live in the body, I live by faith in the Son of God, who loved me and gave Himself for me."

WEEK 3 DAY 4 (THURSDAY)

DAILY READING

Be still for a few seconds, asking God to meet with you.

Have you settled that God is good, and have you turned over your entire life to His control? If not, go to God now and talk to Him. Keep wrestling before the Lord until He changes your heart. Don't take "No" for an answer. Real life in Christ depends upon this!

It makes no sense to the world, but you stop lusting when you stop *trying* in your own strength to stop lusting and instead turn that responsibility over to Christ. Don't misunderstand. You still have a role and duty based upon Galatians 5:16 to live by the spirit. Let's recap for a moment: Who is in you, and who lives for you if you yield completely to Christ? Do you get it? Allow the following word picture to help explain.

THE SHOVEL

Imagine that you were given a shovel when you were born. You use it to dig. A shovel is made for one person to use at a time, so when you are digging, God watches. He waits for you to put down the shovel so that He can pick it up and use His wisdom and strength. The biggest problem you face is a lack of faith that if you set the shovel down, Jesus will pick it up and complete the project. You imagine the shovel sitting there doing nothing, or perhaps you're afraid God will want to do a different project than the one you want to do, so you keep a tight grip on the shovel and dig like crazy. You never let God pick up the shovel because you never put it down and trust that He will pick it up, or you fear He will use it differently than you think it should be used. For the moments you put down the shovel and rest, God doesn't pick it up because you lack faith that He will do the job correctly. You simply don't turn the project over to Him.

Likewise, when you are tempted to lust, you're afraid that lust will overtake you if you "put down the shovel of self-effort" and trust in God. So you keep "digging" vainly, using your own strength to overcome. However, God says you can trust in Him to overcome. Christ will pick you up and give you His strength not to lust. He won't lead you into temptation, but through it. He has a blueprint and power that far exceed your ideas and efforts. In fact, the spot you choose to dig is always at the bottom of a sand dune. No matter how hard you dig, sand keeps pouring back in. If you feel like you are not farther now than you were a year ago, it's probably because you're not! Your self-efforts have gotten you nowhere.

The good news is that God wants to be your oasis. He wants you to put down the shovel and believe that He will pick it up. This is true even for tempting thoughts. *When you trust Christ and give Him total control of your life, you won't lust while He is in charge–guaranteed! Compare your life to a shovel—only one person is in charge at a time, you or God. Stop trying in your own strength.* Put down the shovel and trust God to pick it up. Ask Him. Jesus wants to direct your life. Also, don't try to take back control. No matter how hard it seems, God's plan will work. Five years from now you won't still be up to your ankles in sand, but you will be living in His oasis. Meditate on this word picture. Talk to God about it. Agree that He is good and can be trusted with your life.

Right now, commit to putting down the shovel of self-effort and turn to the Lord. Yield completely. He is the carpenter, the potter, and the master builder. Give Him total control of all areas of your life.

How did the shovel of self effort word picture impact you?

___

___

___

The key to victory is yielding to the One who overcomes. It's only when you are living moment by moment in the power of God that you enjoy victory over the selfish carnal nature (see Galatians 5:16).

Consider the following scripture: "Unless the Lord builds the house, its builders labor in vain" (Psalm 127:1).

After you've put down the shovel, you still have a special role. Although Christ is the Commander-in-Chief, you are the loyal soldier and part of the divine team. In His strength, you carry out His orders (obey) and accomplish His good and perfect will. Of course, at first it will be a big daily battle to stop trying to control life or escape into fantasy. You'll soon find that this isn't such a burden. In fact, when you stop holding back and truly love the Lord with all of your heart, you'll more naturally want to do what God wants. It will no longer be about giving up things, but about choosing the new and wonderful things that you start desiring more! No matter how hard, don't quit. (You'll learn more about replacing self-effort throughout this study.)

Have you made a permanent commitment to put to death (turn away from) performance-based living? It's time to die to pride and self-effort and to start living out grace. Here are two verses to meditate upon. As you read them, ask God to become real in your life. As He does, you'll naturally begin obeying His commands out of pure love and devotion instead of trying to earn His favor.

> "In the same way, count yourselves dead to sin but alive to God in Christ Jesus" (Romans 6:11).

> "I have been crucified with Christ and I no longer live, but Christ lives in me. The life I live in the body, I live by faith in the Son of God, who loved me and gave himself for me" (Galatians 2:20).

Do you see that you first must die to self in order to take on Christ? This is an act of your will. It's a choice. Next, take God at His word. Christ lives in all who place their trust in Him (see *"Why Jesus?"* in Appendix E). When you find yourself trying to perform for God, stop in your tracks. Repent of selfishness and pride. Start seeing "performing" as an attempt to manipulate God. It can't be done! He knows your heart, so stop pretending to be alive with Him while acting in your own strength. *Instead, purpose to live to love Him.* The goodness you desire will be made pure when you follow God's plan (Ephesians 2:10). Goodness to others will begin to flow from your great appreciation for God's grace instead of a desire to receive some praise or blessing. Therefore, ask the Lord for a grateful heart that loves others. As you become humble, the good works you do will no longer be an attempt to earn God's love, but rather to give grace. You'll want to feed the poor because Jesus leads you. You'll want to serve others according to the grace of God. You'll finally begin to see people as God does, no longer as objects for your pleasure, but as souls that you can nurture. This is true freedom that leaves no regrets and no emptiness. Listen for God to speak to you in Philippians 4:6–9:

> "Do not be anxious about anything, but in everything, by prayer and petition, with thanksgiving, present your requests to God. And the peace of God, which transcends all understanding, will guard your hearts and your minds in Christ Jesus. Finally, brothers, whatever is true, whatever is noble, whatever is right, whatever is pure, whatever is lovely, whatever is admirable—if anything is excellent or praiseworthy—think about such things. Whatever you have learned or received or heard from me, or seen in me—put it into practice. And the God of peace will be with you."

Have you fully set your mind on things above? Are you guarding what thoughts you allow your mind to dwell upon? Talk to God about these things and record any insights or decisions.

____

____

HEARTWORK

P is for Passionate for God. Will you make pursuing God and getting to know Him a higher priority than pursuing entertainment, sports, TV, sex, happiness, success, or things that bring you recognition? This is the first step toward intimacy and a real relationship with the Lord and with others. Right now, make a decision to live in total dependence on God.

Did you make this decision?

❑ Yes ❑ No ❑ Not sure

Honestly evaluate your answer and examine your heart for anything holding you back.

PRAY

Talk to God as you would a friend. Share with Him things that matter to you.

- Use this week's memory verse (Galatians 2:20) as a way of asking God to change your heart and break your self-will.
- Tell Jesus that you are putting down the shovel of self-effort and giving Him control of your entire life.
- Tell God that you have the faith that He will complete the project.
- Tell God that you trust Him and will follow His orders no matter what they are.
- Ask God to give you the desire and strength to rely solely on Him for your strength and victory.
- Pray for other men who desire purity and also for your family.

READ THE BIBLE

Ask God for wisdom as you meditate upon 2 Corinthians 4:18: "So we fix our eyes not on what is seen, but on what is unseen. For what is seen is temporary, but what is unseen is eternal." Read this verse again several times, asking God to open your heart to Him. Meditate on the memory verse Galatians 2:20: "I have been crucified with Christ and I no longer live, but Christ lives in me. The life I live in the body, I live by faith in the Son of God, who loved me and gave himself for me." Adopt this as one of your life verses.

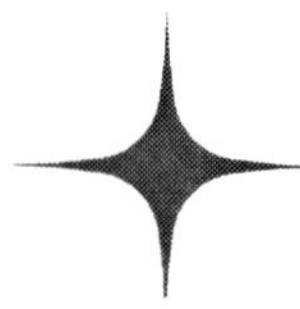

SPECIAL NOTE:

When you become crucified with Christ, you no longer belong to yourself. In fact, you died to the world the moment you accepted His grace. By receiving Jesus, you receive all of Him. You get the benefits of His holiness and righteousness, but you also accept the responsibility of not bringing impure things into the relationship. God is so holy that He cannot tolerate sin. When you fully live for Christ, you won't be able to tolerate sin anymore either! The key is to live out a Proven life daily. Write down what each letter of PROVEN stands for, and as you write it out, commit to putting it into practice.

MEMORY VERSE

Galatians 2:20: "I have been crucified with Christ and I no longer live, but Christ lives in me. The life I live in the body, I live by faith in the Son of God, who loved me and gave Himself for me."

WEEK 3 DAY 5 (FRIDAY)

Read this week's memory verse out loud, hiding it in your heart. (Do you have each week's verse memorized? Jot them down and carry them with you.)

DAILY READING

Read and meditate on 1 Corinthians 6:18–20:

> "Flee from sexual immorality. All other sins a man commits are outside his body, but he who sins sexually sins against his own body. Do you not know that your body is a temple of the Holy Spirit, who is in you, whom you have received from God? You are not your own; you were bought at a price. Therefore honor God with your body."

Why are you to flee from sexual immorality? Record any insights from this passage.

____

____

____

Spending time with God is the only way to get to know who He really is and to shed your performance-based living. Ask God to reveal ways in which you are trying to earn His love rather than accept it. Ponder this for a moment. Stop comparing yourself to others and begin a daily practice of taking the focus off yourself. Commit to following the PROVEN

Model for accepting and enjoying the reality of who you are in Christ. (Passionate for God, Repentant in Spirit, Open and Honest, Victorious in Living, Eternal in Perspective, and Networking with other Godly men.)

Quiet your heart and still your mind. For the next few minutes, you will be asked to mediate on a few things, so don't rush. Ask the Lord to meet with you right now and tell you what He wants you to know. Ask the Lord to show you the things that have been keeping you from accepting His grace (such as pride, a desire to be in control, anger, fear, or lack of faith). Pause right now and listen for God's answer. With true humility, tell the Lord you want to know the full nature of your sins and the roots that keep them alive so that you can allow Him to heal your wounds and usher in restoration, repentance, and revival. Ask God right now to show you your sins. Do not argue with the Holy Spirit as He reveals ways you are filled with pride or selfishness.

____

____

____

What sins did God reveal to you? Confess them as sin. Ask God to give you true repentance and hatred of evil. Lay your sins at the feet of Christ. Be open and vulnerable.

Now, receive forgiveness. That's right, accept God's unconditional love and full forgiveness. God's grace is the gift of forgiveness, and you cannot earn it. There is no penance, only a turning away from sin and turning to the Lord. Real repentance will produce the fruit of God's Spirit in your life, punctuated by a new desire to put the needs of others ahead of your own. You're now free to act as a result of thankfulness for what God has done for you instead of feeling an obligation to repay a debt! In short, you'll experience freedom from bondage to sin and the freedom to live out love.

Consider how grace works. If you owed someone a million dollars, how would you feel? Heavily burdened, I'm sure! If this person does not release the debt, you must make monthly payments out of whatever resources you have, perhaps for the rest of your life. Your debt is always before you. If the entire debt is canceled, however, you would have instant and lasting freedom. You would be so thankful and grateful that you would want to extend grace to others, not because you must, but because your heart is free to do so.

Christ paid a debt for you that you never could have paid. If you try to repay it, you live in bondage to the debt. Consider this analogy: In law, if a borrower fails to repay a debt when it is due and a certain amount of time goes by without the lender bringing a legal action to enforce the debt, then the lender loses the right to get repaid. This is called a statute of limitations. There is an exception, however, to the statute of limitations. The legal right to sue can be revived if the borrower promises to repay the debt after the statute of limitations has expired. In other words, even though the person was legally released from repaying the debt, he can still choose to be bound to repay it. Upon the debtor reclaiming the liability, he once again becomes legally bound to pay it in full.

Fortunately, God does not have a statute of limitations. Rather, He tells us "today" not to harden our hearts when we hear His voice (Hebrews 3:15), and He promises that we are immediately forgiven when we repent (1 John 1:9). However, each time you try to earn God's love or repay the debt that Jesus paid for you on the cross, it's as though you're trying to be responsible for a debt you cannot pay. You keep burdening yourself with a debt that the Lord has released you from. Peace will always escape you as your pride is too thick to accept grace.

HEARTWORK

Spend a few minutes meditating on the cross—the willing suffering and death of Jesus. Ask God to make His suffering real to you and to make you see that all sin, including anger, greed, and lustful thoughts, is ugly and evil. Never forget that sin has a great price.

- Describe your meditation experience—what does the suffering and death of Jesus mean to you?

  ____

  ____

  ____

R is for Repentant in Spirit. Think about what Jesus chose to endure for your sin. He was beaten because you looked at pornography. His hands were pierced with nails because you were not content. He was hung on a cross and mocked because you wanted to lust after the pleasures of the world. The good news is that the blood of Jesus covers all of your sins—past, present and future.

Do you hate sin? Not yet? What will it take for you to hate sin, to hate lust, to hate greed, and to hate your unforgiveness or anger? Consider how Jesus received each lash of the whip in your place. Each drop of His blood was shed for you because Christ loves you and wants you to receive everlasting life with Him in heaven and divine intimacy with Him now. (If you have never seen the movie *The Passion of the Christ* by Mel Gibson, watch it. Allow the visual nature of the pain Jesus Christ chose to endure on your behalf to sink in. Then never doubt His goodness or His love for you again.)

READ THE BIBLE

Read Mark 15:15–39. Read it twice, meditating upon the suffering of Jesus Christ. Now choose to live for Christ.

PRAY

During special moments of meeting with the Lord, be sure to ask God to reveal more and more of Himself to you. God longs to be known by you. Consider using the names or attributes of God as a form of praise (see Appendices C and D). Perhaps read Psalm 119:1–20 aloud. Substitute your name or the names of others as you read it, asking God to make you and others that kind of obedient child.

Make a commitment to pursue and accept God's grace. Spend time asking the Lord to open your eyes to sin. *When you become desensitized to sin or puffed up by pride, you don't see your misdeeds as sin.* Ask for the eyes of Jesus to see as He sees and for the Holy Spirit to convict your heart of sin. Ask God to grant you repentance.

Spend time praying for others. (To overcome self, you need to take the focus off yourself.) List the name of each person you are praying for. If you get distracted or have trouble focusing, use Colossians 1:9–14 as a model for prayer.

MEMORY VERSE

Galatians 2:20: "I have been crucified with Christ and I no longer live, but Christ lives in me. The life I live in the body, I live by faith in the Son of God, who loved me and gave Himself for me."

How will you spend your Saturday night? Will it be honoring to the Lord? If you need to, make detailed plans in advance, but don't allow your old habits or rituals to return. Stop the old way of thinking in its tracks. The bouncer at the door to your mind, if wearing God's armor, is able to crush tempting thoughts. Don't yield an inch. Also, set aside time for worship and praise.

Put into practice some of the new things you are learning from the relational exercises in Appendix A. Read it again this weekend. In addition, openly sharing spiritual matters with family and friends is a very important part of living a Proven life. Make it a priority every day to share spiritual truths with others. Each day, select a point to share with someone. Also, be sure to make time to pray and read the Bible this weekend. Finally, finish any incomplete portions of the study. Don't miss out on what the Lord wants to teach and share with you!

TESTIMONY

"I just wanted to drop you a note of encouragement about one life you helped change.

"This week marks one year since I have been to a pornographic website. While I know we are not to count the days it is a marker in the road that hasn't gone unnoticed to me. Like your study often said, you would occasionally pop your head out and realize you were not in the same place you started.

"I still have daily struggles. Satan has not given up his fight for my heart and mind but there has been a radical change in my life. There is still work that needs to be done and I trust God will not leave His work unfinished in me.

"All the glory goes to God for in my strength nothing is possible. In my strength I am easily overwhelmed but in His strength all things are possible.

"Thank you for your willingness to invest in broken men like me. You are being used by God to restore His children who have gone astray. I have paid an incredibly high price for my sin and now I am trying to rebuild a new life in Christ."

Passionate for God,
Repentant in spirit,
Open and honest,
Victorious in living,
Eternal in perspective, and
Networking with other ***PROVEN Men.***

WEEK FOUR

TESTIMONY

"Today makes 94 days since I started using the Proven Men study and started being pure before the Lord our God. Proven Men has been a blessing to me and I wanted to thank you again. Also I wanted to thank you for directing me to the online group "Free in Christ." It has really been good for me. This study is a big help in our group too. It is one of the very important tools in our toolbox that God has used to rebuild His temple in our lives. Thank you so much for being there when I emailed you and your faithfulness to God. I know if I never get to hug your neck here on earth I will surely ask where you are in heaven so I can do it there."

Passionate for God,
Repentant in spirit,
Open and honest,
Victorious in living,
Eternal in perspective, and
Networking with other ***PROVEN Men.***

MEMORY VERSE

James 1:21–22: "Therefore, get rid of all moral filth and the evil that is so prevalent and humbly accept the word planted in you, which can save you. Do not merely listen to the word, and so deceive yourselves. Do what it says."

WEEK 4 DAY 1 (MONDAY)

This week, you will learn what to do in times of failure or a setback.

DAILY READING

No one is perfect or without sin (Romans 3:23). Even after you chart a course of earnestly seeking the Lord, you probably will experience moments of failures and setbacks. Although God does not grant a license to sin, He instructs you how to respond and be fully restored when you stumble. Failures often occur when you slip back into old routines. Perhaps you had an argument with someone or are tired or lonely and you let your guard down. Instead of turning immediately to God, you allow old patterns to return and trigger a relapse.

Some people even stumble when they get frustrated over the length of time it seems to be taking to be free, so they "help God out." Self-effort fails, however, because it takes back permission for the Lord to work in your life. God won't force Himself on you, and He won't make you live a holy life. Instead, He waits until you grasp that He alone heals and transforms. Don't misunderstand: God does this for your own good. If the Lord allowed your efforts to succeed, you would be puffed up and keep seeking independence. Such rebellion leads only further into the deceitfulness of the world and traps you in bondage to all kinds of sin stemming from selfishness.

Self-condemnation often follows failure. You may want to throw in the towel, but God wants to forgive and renew you. One of the first steps in the PROVEN Model in response to a setback, whether it is a sexual or other pride-based sin, is to put on an eternal perspective. God is in a lifelong process of healing you, changing you, and preparing you for divine intimacy now and in heaven. Perhaps the most important understanding is that the Lord loves you unconditionally. That's right! You cannot earn (Ephesians 2:8–9) or lose (Romans 8:35) God's great love for you. It's this complete and available love that draws men to Christ. Will you open the eyes of your soul to the Lord and permit His love to penetrate your heart? To position yourself to experience His love, you must seek the Lord and truly yield your life to Him. Resolve to put the Lord first.

A victorious life does not just happen. It may take longer than you hope or expect for healing to occur. Remember, you're involved in a battle that requires more than self-will; you must have God-sized strength. This battle actually takes place in the spirit world. Spiritual warfare is real, and if you're not actively engaged in the battle, you can expect to experience regular setbacks. If you're playing a new game with someone and did not bother to read the rules, you would incur a lot of infractions and miss out on many opportunities. The spiritual battles we face are very much the same way.

Later in this study, you'll learn more about spiritual warfare. For now, practice learning to tell the difference between the voice of God, who wants you to succeed, and the voice of Satan, who wants you to be ashamed and turn to yourself or the world instead of God. The Lord's voice is always gently calling you to His home. He is not forceful or hurried, but soft. By contrast, Satan's voice is rushed and immediate. Under his plan, you feel pressured to act quickly and must always remain busy. Consider the difference between two parents teaching a child to ride a bike.[7] The first one is gentle. He tells his son how much he loves him. He tells him not to be afraid as he removes the training wheels. "I'll be right here with you." He holds the bike as the child gets on. He trots slowly by him, giving encouraging instructions: "That's right. You're doing great! Keep pedaling." The second parent is rushed: "I only have a few minutes, so you better be ready to ride this bike. I took off the sissy wheels. It should only take one try unless you are a dope."

When the child tips and falls, the first father is nurturing: "I fell many times when I learned to ride. I think I still have a scar on my leg. Wow, you did so well! I can see you'll be a great rider." The second parent tells the child, "I knew you would fail." He then proceeds to point out that he spent long hours at work to be able to buy the bike. He's demeaning and makes the child feel unworthy of his time. The child ends up thinking his dad cares more for things than he does about him.

Are you getting the picture? God is a gentle, loving Father. He's patient and kind, offering grace and encouragement. Satan, however, is condemning and loud. He wants you to chase instant pleasures and to feel bad about yourself. All he really cares about is that you don't turn to the Lord. The more he can convince you to look to your circumstances, rights, or needs, the easier it is to get you to look to the world for fixes. By contrast, when you fail, God remains kind and forgiving. He gently encourages you to return to Him right away. Satan would have you believe that you are no good and not worth the bother to God. He feeds the feeling, "I may as well give over completely to sin."

In contrast to the lies of Satan, the Lord has good instructions for you to succeed. Will you slow down and listen to God? Will you draw close to hear His gentle voice? Reject Satan's lies. Get to know your loving Father by immersing yourself in His truth (the Bible), spending daily time in worship of the only truly perfect being, and talking openly to the Lord as a friend. The more you do these things, the easier it'll be to hear and discern God's voice and know that you're truly forgiven, reconciled, and deeply loved. You'll also begin to recognize when Satan is trying to tear you down with lies and steer you toward any of the wide roads leading away from God.

What struck you from the reading?

____

____

____

____

____

____

____

Have you recently experienced any failures or setbacks? List them.

- How did you feel when you had a setback? (If needed, turn to Appendix F right now and determine your feelings.) Did you feel abandoned by God? Did you wonder if He really cares whether you overcome or fail? Explain.

HEARTWORK

Consider this verse: "Therefore, there is now no condemnation for those who are in Christ Jesus, because through Christ Jesus the law of the spirit of life set me free from the law of sin and death" (Romans 8:1). Do you believe that God loves you unconditionally, even when you sin, and that He wants you to be healed? Don't confuse God's discipline with rejection.

Stop trying in your own efforts. Make a permanent decision to trust God no matter what the circumstances. Even after a fall, you'll be riding your bike again in no time, carried along by your loving Father. The Lord will pick you up when you stumble and fully restore you, so turn to and completely trust Him.

READ THE BIBLE

Read Hebrews 12:5–13 and record your insights.

Do you believe that God fully forgives you when you repent and turn to Him? Consider 1 John 1:9: "If we confess our sins, he is faithful and just and will forgive us our sins and purify us from all unrighteousness."

Trust that God is not a liar. He not only forgives your sin, but He also replaces it with His own righteousness. Your feelings or emotions, on the other hand, can give the wrong impression. Confess any unbelief and turn to God.

PRAY

Set a timer if you have to, but pray for at least five minutes. (If you have time, pray for ten minutes.) Satan wants to distract you and keep you from meeting with God. Try writing a list of the things that you need God to provide (e.g., soft heart, clean hands, pure mind) and then ask Him. Keep asking God to make you a needy, dependent servant who is hungry for His holiness. Talk to God about transforming you into a person who is grateful and content. Be sure to spend the bulk of your time praying for others. (List them.)

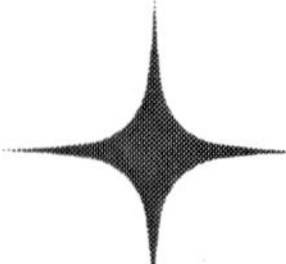

SPECIAL NOTE:

R is for Repentant in Spirit. Do you make it a practice to confess sin immediately and seek forgiveness, or do you beat yourself up instead and withdraw from God? If you delay in seeking forgiveness and restoration with God, you'll grow increasingly distant from the Lord and people. Break the cycle. For instance, be diligent that each time you allow an impure thought to linger, confess it as sin, repent, and accept God's immediate forgiveness. Draw near to God; He promises to draw near to you (James 4:8).

In the past, you may have wallowed in guilt or sought to hide or distance yourself from the Lord and others. Arm yourself now with the truth about His unconditional love and live in freedom as His dearly loved son. Your first reaction to sin should be to recognize it for what it is: A desire to control life or hide from reality. Carefully consider this: It is your turning from God that makes your thoughts and conduct sinful. The cure is to race back to the Lord immediately without giving Satan time to smother you in guilt and shame that perpetuates a feeling of unworthiness. By running to the Lord, you'll be restored right away and will be able to worship and fellowship with God in openness.

In your own words, write out the things you will do the next time you sin.

____

____

____

____

____

____

____

____

MEMORY VERSE

James 1:21–22: "Therefore, get rid of all moral filth and the evil that is so prevalent and humbly accept the word planted in you, which can save you. Do not merely listen to the word, and so deceive yourselves. Do what it says."

DAILY READING

Have you accepted that God's timing is perfect? This applies to all areas of your life (e.g., getting married, finding a job, healing old wounds, or becoming free from certain sins). God has a purpose behind everything. In fact, sexual healing is often slow because the Lord takes you at a pace that you can handle. Just as a loving father would not send a child down a steep hill when his boy or girl was learning to ride a bike, God won't bring you through the healing process at a faster pace than you can learn, appreciate, and accept. God provides lasting healing, not merely a Band-Aid. Therefore, healing is a process with a purpose, and the process of healing goes on for a lifetime.[8] Still, there will be moments of significant progress along the way.

It's time to put on the mind of Christ and confront the tactics of Satan. Surrender to the enemy is not an option in this battle. To deceive you into complacency or setting aside God's armor, the devil will try to fill your mind with thoughts of self-effort and the need to earn God's love or approval. When your guard is down, Satan seeks to turn your thoughts inward and focus them upon your circumstances and rights. The devil also floods your mind with tempting thoughts of chasing after the momentary pleasures of the world while shielding you from the true nature and cost of such things. Life's "little" sins, such as gossip or anger, will seem too insignificant to bother with, but if you give Satan a foothold in small areas, he can gain more overall control in your life. Satan frequently fosters a "stair step" bondage approach,[9] which looks something like this:

- Temptation to lust or fantasize
  - Acting out
    - Feeling guilty
      - Experiencing shame or self-condemnation
        - Turning inward (closing out feelings and friends)
          - Desiring to escape
            - Temptation to lust or fantasize

This never-ending downward cycle can and must be destroyed by the power of God. Leave no root remaining to spring up again later. Confess to the Lord that you turned from Him and were consumed with your circumstances, allowing Satan to lead you far astray. Set your mind and heart on living by God's Spirit and under His direction and control. Each time, at the moment of temptation, reject the so-called "escape" route that Satan offers and recognize it as a lie. Lust and fantasy breed discontent, because they can never satisfy or fulfill. Engage in the spiritual battle and choose to take your place on God's winning side!

To allow God to lead, you must give Him total control. (See the shovel word picture in Week 3, Day 4.) Tell the Lord that He not only has permission to run your thought life, but also has ownership of your mind. When Christ is in charge of your life, you will not lust, guaranteed! Therefore, keep your eyes fixed upon Christ in humility and chase after a real relationship with Him. Replace the thoughts that Satan would have you dwell upon with praise and thanksgiving to the Lord.

Replace self-condemnation with worship of the Lord for His goodness, and accept His righteousness into your life. Practice "truth therapy,"[10] i.e., accept God's promises and statements about His love for you and His purpose for your life, and reject anything that stands opposed to God's Word. Begin with the promises that the Lord does not reject anyone who looks to Him, but heals and forgives (Ephesians 1:7). God's love is unconditional and cannot be earned. You simply possess it. Therefore, get back on the bike right away each time you fall, and then listen for and follow God's instructions. Victory is assured.

Write down your thoughts about this section.

____

____

____

____

____

____

Consider how the downward spiral works. Guilt and shame lead to hopelessness, which sets you up for using sex as a coping mechanism, which leads to temptation and a fall, which leads to more guilt and shame, which again leads to hopelessness, and on and on. God can break this cycle. His love is unconditional (Romans 8:35–39), He freely forgives and does not condemn (Romans 8:1), and He gives hope (Psalm 62:5, Romans 15:13). God does not tempt, but leads you through temptation and picks you up (James 1:13). Therefore, stop turning away from Him. Run to the Lord and accept His healing and power. Reject Satan and hate sin!

List some of the lies Satan uses to deceive you.

____

____

____

____

____

____

Are you sometimes careless in what you allow in your field of vision—you read a swimsuit edition, take a second look at women, scan the horizon for opportunities to lust, tell a dirty joke, or watch a TV show or visit an Internet site that spotlights seductive women? List areas where you know that you are somewhat careless in guarding your mind, then commit to stopping these inputs.

___

___

___

___

___

___

Although healing is a lifelong process, you'll experience great victories along the way. Sure, you'll still have struggles and some occasional failures, but you can walk in victory as you continually repent of any sin and daily turn to and rely upon God. Keep the E (Eternal in Perspective) in PROVEN always before you.

Don't be consumed with how long it takes to see the results; concentrate on today (Matthew 6:34). The real goal is an intimate relationship with God, which is a growing experience. Also, don't be discouraged if you don't feel like a spiritual giant just yet.

If you haven't read *"Joel's and Tim's Stories"* in Appendix Q, take a few minutes to do so sometime this week. You'll discover that four weeks into pursuit of God's healing, Joel still stared at the ground while walking to work because he tended to lust after women during his commute. Yet, he was not consumed with counting the number of days in which he acted, or failed to act, in freedom because he was too busy clinging to and seeking the Lord in desperation and dependency. Joel finally appreciated that he simply could never overcome on his own. Today, be committed to loving God and hating evil. Tomorrow will take care of itself if you trust God!

HEARTWORK

Participate with God. Don't take back control or think you can do it on your own. Rather, truly desire to be transformed. If you secretly want to enjoy the sensual pleasures of pornography or lust, God's transformation process will be thwarted. Tell God of your commitment.

PRAY

List the people you want to pray for, but don't just think about them. Instead, petition the Lord to work in their lives. Your role in prayer is to communicate with God, not to think about others. Prayer releases God to work, whereas thinking of others is based upon self-effort.

- Ask God to guard your thoughts and heart, and then rely on His armor.
- Ask God to give you His power to carry out your commitment to eliminate worldly inputs and to replace them with the things of God.
- Ask God to make you a needy, dependent servant. Keep praying for others, especially other Proven Men and your family.

READ THE BIBLE

Keep reading in order to get to know God. Read and meditate on Romans 7:7–25 and 13:11–14.

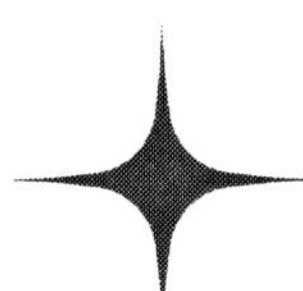

SPECIAL NOTE:

Are you willing to be molded by God? He will not begin to work until you are ready. He waits for you to realize that you cannot do it on your own and that you must depend on Him. Will you look to Him alone for life? You are ready for the potter's wheel when you're willing to have the Lord create in you these six elements:

Passion for God. Without passion for God, your soul will never find freedom and receive healing. It begins with humility—knowing in your inner being that the Lord is the One who created you and that apart from Him, you can do nothing. Deep love and thanksgiving will pour out from you as you begin experiencing His great love.

Repentant in Spirit. Pride is the greatest barrier to knowing and experiencing God. It blocks out intimate relationships with others. True repentance lays down self-interests and rights. It teaches you to freely forgive others. In humility, you realize that your greatest sin is departing from God as you go your own way to carry out your selfish desires. Then you race back to the Lord to be near Him again.

Openness in Communication with God and Others. Talk to the Lord as a friend, telling Him of your struggles and listening when He speaks. Purpose to build relationships with others and allow yourself to have feelings, which are intended for good and can help to signal when you stray from the Lord.

Victorious Living Under His Authority. Each moment you live by the Spirit, you'll be able to master each desire that enters your mind (Galatians 5:16). God wants you to draw near to Him so He can give you His righteousness and power to live in holiness and be united in spirit. Stop striving in your own strength and receive the Lord Himself. Then you will be transformed.

Eternal Perspective. When you look for meaning beyond your circumstances, the sin of selfishness is conquered. As you understand that your home is in heaven, your work on earth takes on new meaning. You look to and rely upon the Lord for strength to fulfill your purpose in life. You no longer need to control life, but gladly submit your will to the Lord and ask Him to carry out His plan as you seek after Him with all your heart.

Neediness for Others. You will never be stamped Proven by standing alone. The Lord uses others in your life to encourage you. Work to develop relationships (networking) with other men who are diligently seeking the Lord and, just like you, are finished with pretending or trying to go it alone.

MEMORY VERSE

James 1:21–22: "Therefore, get rid of all moral filth and the evil that is so prevalent and humbly accept the word planted in you, which can save you. Do not merely listen to the word, and so deceive yourselves. Do what it says."

DAILY READING

Yesterday's lesson touched on God's promise that if you live by the Spirit, you will not gratify the desires of the sinful nature. Today, you will explore some new elements of what it means to live by the Spirit. First, read Galatians 5:16–26.

Think through why it is important to know and obey God in order to live by His Spirit. Write down your insights.

____

____

____

____

Want to know the key to victory—the antidote for lust and impurity? It is spending more time relating with God and becoming a worshiper of the Lord!

Read the above statement again. Now commit to it. Write down how you will spend more and better time relating with God. If you don't take steps now to incorporate worship into your daily life, you'll remain merely a listener and not a doer of the Word—a person self-deceived and stuck in bondage to sin (see James 1:22).

A good first step is living out Romans 12:2, which says: "Do not conform any longer to the pattern of this world, but be transformed by the renewing of your mind." Describe some of the patterns of this world to which you still conform (for example, TV shows, a desire for wealth or power, seeking self-pleasures, boastfulness, judgmental attitudes, or anger).

DECISION TIME

It is time to switch masters. God's pattern is for you to be gentle, humble, kind, forgiving, grateful, content, thankful, and at peace. Read this sentence again, asking the Lord to give you a desire for these things.

Right now, make an irrevocable decision to yield your life fully to God and to allow Him to fill you with the fruit of the Spirit.

Another necessary ingredient for lasting victory is found in Ephesians 4:19–24, particularly verse 23: "...be made new in the attitude of your minds." Romans 12:1–2 similarly commands you to renew your mind so that you can know God's will. Dear friends, there are no shortcuts to renewal of your mind, which once dwelt upon lust and fantasy. You must replace the backward thinking of the world with the truth of God, which is obtained through reading the Bible and openly talking to God in relational prayers.

God wants you to think about things that are true, noble, right, pure, lovely, admirable, excellent, or praiseworthy. Are you replacing worldly thoughts (such as lust, fantasies about being a hero, or getting revenge) with Godly thoughts? Are you also taking captive every thought and making it obedient to Christ (2 Corinthians 10:5)?

Describe how well you are doing in these areas, and list anything you intend to start or stop doing.

____

____

____

____

The rest of today's *Heartwork* will be a little different. You will read a select passage from the Bible and then spend the remainder of the time in meditation and prayer.

READ THE BIBLE

Open your Bible to Romans 8:5–17. As you read and meditate upon this passage, ask God to reveal His truth about living by the Holy Spirit. Won't you allow the Holy Spirit to move in your heart and melt it as wax as you read this Biblical passage? It is written for you! Open your heart and soul to the Lord.

HEARTWORK

MEDITATION AND REFLECTION

Don't rush through the following meditation, but turn your attention toward meeting with God.

- Begin by allowing your spirit to be overwhelmed by God and His great love, mercy, and grace. Open your heart to God and allow Him to transform your will to His.
- Picture yourself fixing your eyes on Jesus, who perfects your faith.
- Contemplate the Lord deeply in your heart right now, knowing that you will not grow weary or lose heart as you remain under His wing (Hebrews 12:2–3).
- Ask God to illuminate your face with the glory of the Lord—the glory that dims as you drift away. Pray that your countenance becomes an ever-increasing brightness as you draw nearer to the source, experiencing more of the likeness of Christ (2 Corinthians 3:18). Purpose to be grateful, thankful, and content.
- Change the way you see and act out love. Choose not to conform to the pattern of this world any longer (Romans 12:2). Make it your goal in life to pursue after and get to know the Lord, who is love and gives perfect love. As you do, you will gladly and gratefully accept His unearned and unconditional love, and you will start truly loving others. Your fixation on sex and the view of love as sex will also change, replaced by an appropriate view of the sexual intimacy God designed for marriage. Single men, too, will cherish real love that is not dependent upon sex or even a spouse, but is birthed in spirit and is fulfilling.
- Right now, confess any sin you have committed this week.
- Confess ways that you have been withholding love from others or not being a friend.
- Confess ways you have been avoiding or ignoring God.
- Ask the Lord to instill in you a deep desire to worship and praise Him. Commit to spending copious hours meeting with God with zeal and passion.
- Ask the Holy Spirit to reveal any areas where you treat God like a vending machine, demanding what you think you deserve or need.
- Ask God to show you ways in which you do not fully turn to or trust in Him.
- Openly discuss with the Lord whether you see Him as good. Keep going to God in prayer and petition, asking Him to open your eyes to His faithfulness, forgiveness, and

unconditional love. Soak in the promise that if you seek Him with all of your heart, He will make Himself known to you. Tell God that you are no longer pretending to trust in Him or simply going through the motions of trying to get to know Him.

- Ask the Lord to cause you to truly believe that His Word is trustworthy and true and that it has daily application in your life. Also, keep reading the Bible to know God, meeting with Him in your heart and soul, and not merely to gain knowledge about Him.
- Ask God to change your inner desires so that you make pursuing the Lord your number one priority in life.
- Desire absolute purity across the board in your life. Spend time talking to God about this and make a commitment to sexual integrity.
- Be still and listen to whatever else the Lord presses upon your heart.

PRAY

Prayerfully read Ephesians 1:15–21, asking God to give other Proven Men the same wonderful gifts in this passage. As you pray this passage of Scripture, replace the pronouns "you" and "your" with the names of others. Keep the focus off yourself, except to ask to become a willing and obedient servant who is humble, content, and grateful.

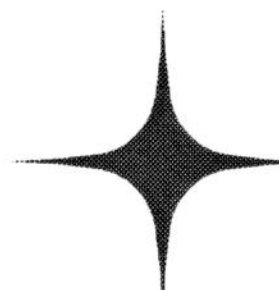

SPECIAL NOTE:

A word of caution: As you begin to experience victory, pride will seek to return. You'll be tempted to think that you're now in good enough shape to continue the battle in your own strength. That's Satan's goal—to turn you away from the one and only real God. As you willingly walk in your own steps outside of God's camp, you'll be ripe for capture. Instead, cling to the Lord. Stay close to Him by living out your greatest purpose in life: To love the Lord with all your heart and to know Him as a friend. Allow God to set your feet on sure ground and heal your wounds. You'll become whole and complete, not lacking anything (James 1:2–4). Imagine having true peace and contentment. Even greater than that, the Lord Himself is being offered to you!

MEMORY VERSE

James 1:21–22: "Therefore, get rid of all moral filth and the evil that is so prevalent and humbly accept the word planted in you, which can save you. Do not merely listen to the word, and so deceive yourselves. Do what it says."

DAILY READING

Prepare your heart to meet with God. Read and meditate on 1 Peter 2:1: "Therefore, rid yourselves of all malice and all deceit, hypocrisy, envy, and slander of every kind." What are you to rid yourself of and why? (See this week's memory verse.) Review the section *"Eliminate selfish practices from your life"* in the middle of Appendix J.

State in your own words how setting boundaries is a good defensive posture in the battle. Explain also why this defense alone will not win the war. See Colossians 2:20–23 for help: "Since you died with Christ to the basic principles of the world, why, as though you still belonged to it, do you submit to its rules: 'Do not handle! Do not taste! Do not touch!'? These are all destined to perish with use, because they are based on human commands and teachings. Such regulations indeed have an appearance of wisdom, with their self-imposed worship, their false humility and their harsh treatment of the body, but they lack any value in restraining sensual indulgence."

Identify as many things as you can that have triggered or led up to moments when you have given over to lust; for example, arguments with your wife, stress at work, alone at home, watching certain TV shows, surfing the Internet, or driving past a certain store.

____

____

____

Record any patterns leading to sin; for example, your feelings and emotions have been shut down, your wife refuses sex, you argued with someone, you are tired, or you did not pray or read the Bible.

____

____

____

List any practical things you can do to:

1) Eliminate or reduce the triggers in your life. Your list might include such things as praying, singing songs, not going to Facebook, YouTube, or Internet chat rooms chat rooms, giving up TV, not talking to women other than your wife about personal matters, or avoiding old stomping grounds.

____

____

____

2) Be more aware of triggers or any signals that your guard is down.

3) React to triggers in a way that pleases God. For example, how does God want you to react when you are having an argument or when you are experiencing stress at work?

Rituals are slightly different from triggers. A ritual is anything you routinely do as part of the process that leads to acting out. Rituals can include purposely going to a favorite Internet site, driving past a park, surfing TV channels, taking a shower with certain music on, or fixating on a specific person or photograph. Identify any rituals you have followed between the point of temptation and completion of the act.

List practical things you can do either to stop rituals before they begin or to catch yourself in the middle of a ritual and break it before you act out. Note that once you've started a ritual, you've probably already decided to ignore God and sin. It's far easier to stop a ritual as soon as you realize you are beginning one than it is to break it in the middle. Some ideas include:

- Carry a memory Scripture card in your pocket and read it before or when tempted.
- Call or text other Proven Men before or during temptation.
- Sing or write a love song to God.
- Stop what you are doing. (For example, get off the Internet now.)
- Confess each sin as it occurs.

____

____

____

Although you cannot always control a trigger, you must commit to ending the rituals that you put into place after a trigger sets you off, even if it means giving up things such as watching all TV or surfing the Internet without someone else in the room. Otherwise, you will remain a slave to sin.

While the healing path may seem like a lot of work, keep an eternal perspective. Trust that God will change your heart and desires as you yield your life to Him and purposefully reject the temporary pleasures of the world. The alternative, staying trapped in bondage to sexual sin, really is no option. It will destroy you and rob you of joy.

PRAY

Talk to God, visualizing His presence as a living being while you are praying. Ask the Lord what is important to Him and listen for a response in your heart. Tell God of your love and thankfulness for Him. Ask the Lord to give you His power and strength to reject temptations to fantasize or lust when you are stressed. Ask for His power to break the grip of sin. Talk to God about your rituals; confess them as premeditated sins and turn from them. Ask God to show you deep in your heart and soul that He loves you unconditionally. Pray for other Proven Men and for family and friends.

READ THE BIBLE

Read the Bible to get to know and experience God; not just to learn information or to check off homework, but to truly join your heart to His. Read Psalm 32.

HEARTWORK

Write a note to God confessing that you have used fantasy as a way of hiding from reality. Turn to the Lord right now in prayer to articulate what is in your heart. Use the space below.

MEMORY VERSE

James 1:21–22: "Therefore, get rid of all moral filth and the evil that is so prevalent and humbly accept the word planted in you, which can save you. Do not merely listen to the word, and so deceive yourselves. Do what it says."

DAILY READING

A companion of passion for God is a repentant spirit. A repentant man grieves over the sin of leaving God's camp to party with the enemy, not out of self-pity, but because he is learning to love the Lord more than he loves himself or the world. As you develop a repentant spirit, you sorely miss God's presence when you sin, and you long to return to Him in your heart and soul. You will want more than anything to be restored in fellowship with God. In essence, you know—and have experienced firsthand—that you can openly communicate with God and hear His voice in your heart. Therefore, you race back to the Lord. You won't allow a setback to keep you from returning to Him.

Not sure this is true for you? The good news is that repentance is a gift from God. Keep asking for it until you receive it! When you draw close to the Lord, you'll become fulfilled and satisfied. Peace and joy will become real, and your life will have purpose. In fact, through passionate praise, you connect to God and actually live out your great need of worshiping a perfectly holy God. The Holy Spirit is released to act. Your walls are torn down and heart melted, your perspective changes, and your life, now hidden in Christ, is renewed and transformed. Through long periods of prayer, talking to God rather than focusing on yourself or blaming others for what went wrong in your life, you will develop the openness necessary to see that you had been pretending to put Christ first while secretly chasing after the lusts of the world. Of course, this type of intimate relationship is developed over time and must be intentional. Today is the best time to start!

List any insights.

V is for Victorious in Living. If you live by God's Spirit, you will be victorious (Galatians 5:16). When you revert to self-effort or self-focus, setbacks happen. Throughout this series, and for the rest of your life, make sure you set your heart upon living by the Spirit. This means turning to the Lord and fully yielding to Him at every point. God promises that when you do, you won't keep falling into sexual sin. How about that! Consider memorizing or recording key verses where God has revealed to you how to live according to His ways and according to His Spirit. Then, when setbacks happen, you'll be prepared and not so overwhelmed that you throw in the towel. Instead, you'll run back to your loving and forgiving Father. Keep pursuing God, and keep living by the Spirit in victory!

Below and on the next page, write out what you will do each time you stumble or experience a setback such as looking at pornography, masturbating, or entertaining a lustful thought. Don't fall for Satan's lie that you may as well give in if you start to slip up. Victories will become easier in the weeks and months ahead, provided that you keep doing battle and putting on the armor of God as described in Ephesians 6:10–18.

You've already studied Colossians 2:20–23, which says that you must die to the basic principles of the world and that setting rules won't restrain your sensual indulgences. In other words setting boundaries is not enough; you must also pursue a love relationship with God. Otherwise your vacant house will be ripe for sin to find a home (Matthew 12:43–45).

Proverbs speaks of a woman sitting at her door inviting men into her house. But listen to the result: "Stolen water is sweet, food eaten in secret is delicious! But little do they know that the dead are there, that her guests are in the depths of the grave" (Proverbs 9:17–18).

• What is your reaction? Write it down.

- Do pornography and other sexual sins still seem delicious to you? God says that those who continue to eat forbidden fruit are blind and deceived and that they will suffer His wrath. To love the things of the world is to reject and even hate God (James 4:4). Ouch! If you don't see that chasing after the things of the world and its passions and pleasures leads to separation from God, it's time to wake up. If you don't choose to hate pornography and other sins, then you'll not overcome the destruction that flows from sexual immorality. You'll also miss out on the joy and blessings of interacting with God.

HEARTWORK

Right now, make a decision to hate (turn away from) all sexual sins, to hate self-seeking, to hate greed, to hate complaining, and to hate all things that are opposed to God. Write out your commitment.

____

____

____

____

____

____

____

The letter O in PROVEN is for Open and Honest. God already knows your heart, so be open with Him. God desires an intimate relationship with you. Will you be devoted to loving the Lord? If you're not open and honest with yourself and others, do you really think you're being open and honest with God? It's time to give up secret and shameful ways.

READ THE BIBLE

Read Psalm 1. Meditate on this passage. Allow your heart to be moved, even melted as wax. Adopt these truths as your own.

PRAY

As part of your prayer time, praise the Lord while reading the *"Attributes of God"* in Appendix D. As you read each one, ask God to reveal to you that He is good and perfect in each of His attributes. Afterward, return here for more suggested topics for prayer.

- Spend a few more minutes asking God to make you humble. You won't experience God if your heart is hard or by seeking to be the one in control.
- Acknowledge that God is good.
- Tell the Lord of your fears or struggles and wait for a response.
- Ask God to reveal to your spirit how faithful He is to you. Allow yourself to feel and know it.
- Ask the Lord how He wants you to respond to His love.
- Pray that others are blessed beyond even yourself. (List their names.)

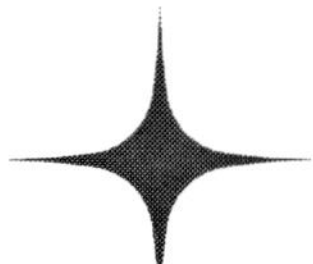

SPECIAL NOTE:

How are you doing on your Friday nights? God can make weaknesses your strengths. If Fridays once were times of defeat, loneliness, and acting upon selfish temptations, turn the night into one of praise and worship of the Lord. From now on, TGIF can mean "Thank God I'm Free." Give each Friday to the Lord and celebrate with Him.

Make a donation. Please consider making a tax deductible donation to support our mission of restoring families one man at a time by helping people embrace a proven way of life that produces lasting victory from strongholds of pornography and sexual addiction. It is our vision to reach one million men and families by helping those who want help through our 12-week study combined with accountability. We can't do this without you. Visit our website: www.ProvenMen.org.

MEMORY VERSE

James 1:21–22: "Therefore, get rid of all moral filth and the evil that is so prevalent and humbly accept the word planted in you, which can save you. Do not merely listen to the word, and so deceive yourselves. Do what it says."

When setbacks happen, don't throw in the towel. Instead, use setbacks as opportunities to see your great need for God. Agree to put the shovel of self-effort down (see Week 3, Day 4). God wants to bring you healing! Finish any *Heartwork*, and review portions that have had an impact on your life. This weekend, be sure to spend time praising and worshiping the Lord. In addition, make time to read Luke 15:10–24. God is calling your name. Run to Him! In addition, plan to set aside some couch time and discuss spiritual matters with others.

Review your battle plan for dealing with triggers, tempting circumstances, and rituals. Does it include confession and repentance if you have a setback? Be ready to confess each and every fantasy, second look, or lustful thought. Make sure your plan also includes repenting of greed, anger, or withholding love. Be aggressive at recognizing every sin and then acting immediately. Give no foothold for plunder by the enemy.

Review all four weekly memory verses. (They are listed in Appendix R.) Get into the practice of writing the memory verses on cards to have available to memorize.

I know that you are going through a spiritual battle and it can be exhausting. But consider writing a short love letter to God, which will release Him to fill your cup and encourage you as you focus on the things above.

WEEK FIVE

TESTIMONY

"My husband, who is in jail, was so overwhelmed at getting the Proven Men study from your ministry. Other inmates are hungry and encouraged by just seeing another Christian man go through the same things. This has helped to ease some shame, and has opened up the opportunity for Godly conversation about sexual issues. The prison chaplin is so excited he is contacting the prison commissioner and requesting your material be made available to all the inmates and he is willing to work with these men in the chapel. My pastor is just as pleased. He got the material this afternoon and called and told me, 'It was a God thing!' as over the weekend, 2 young men in our church came to him admitting problems with pornography. He said as he and my husband work through all of this together via mail, he looks for him to have a Joseph experience from the pit to the palace. Now the officials are coming to him asking how to start this Godly program. Thank You for doing the will of Jesus."

Passionate for God,
Repentant in spirit,
Open and honest,
Victorious in living,
Eternal in perspective, and
Networking with other ***PROVEN Men.***

MEMORY VERSE

1 Thessalonians 5:16–18: "Be joyful always; pray continually; give thanks in all circumstances, for this is God's will for you in Christ Jesus."

DAILY READING

God designed and perfectly created both male and female. A husband and wife complement each other. Marriage is a union, such a perfect fit that two become one (Ephesians 5:31). The master design was for a couple to permanently join physically, mentally, emotionally, and spiritually. When entering into this lifelong commitment, the bride and groom make irrevocable vows that the union will never be broken, neither by divorce nor through the giving of oneself to any other.

How great it was for God to design such a perfect relationship as a representation of our permanent relationship with Christ. However, when we act outside of this union in ways such as premarital sex or wandering eyes, we reject God's gift in order to chase after temporary pleasure, which never really fully satisfies. All forms of lust, such as fantasy, porn, and masturbation, break down the bond of marriage and negatively affect our relationships with God and a spouse.

Why does God want you to live a sexually pure life according to His design? When the Lord tells you to be faithful to your spouse, you can be sure it's for your own good. God wants to protect you from harm. He knows that sexual immorality not only endangers your body but also scars your soul and spirit. You pretend to know better and say, "No one is hurt" or, "She consented, so where is the harm?" But who knows the long-term spiritual damage better than God? Put an end to this ride by believing God and trusting in His Word. Count on the Lord knowing what is best for you. Sexual misconduct harms you in many ways. Surely guilt, shame, and shutting your heart are among them. Other ways are more subtle. The pornographic images are stored forever in your mind and compete with your present real relationships. You carry over perverted and adulterous fantasy thoughts into marriage.

What real person could ever measure up to a fantasy? Your illicit lusts and fanciful expectations are self-centered and anti-relational. Over time you actually train yourself to be selfishly served and instantly gratified. You also discipline yourself to withhold love and feelings. In your mind, you are a king, if not a god.

The evils you entertain also end up blocking your perfect union with God. When you chase after the idols of selfish pleasure, you build a dividing wall. The sign on your heart declares "Keep out!" or "Off limits." By walking in step with the world, you turn away from the One who created you and loves you most. You stop listening to God's voice, and you cannot discern His will. Your requests of God go unanswered because they are selfish and cold (James 4:3). You drift through life self-deceived, thinking that your ways can bring satisfaction.

Even though your soul cries out for divine union with God, turning repeatedly to selfish and prideful indulgences will blind you to the beauty and perfection of God and His ways. Doubt about God's goodness creeps in. Like sheep we go astray, each to his own way (Isaiah 53:6). You deceive yourself into thinking that you know best and all is well, but inside you rot.

What is the cure? *Only by acknowledging and repenting from your sinful and selfish ways and running to God in an open and honest relationship do you allow God to repair the damage.*

Fortunately, God is a good shepherd. He does not abandon the lost. Instead, He gently calls, and He encourages you to return to the safety and fulfillment of His green pastures. The Lord wants to supply every true need. As you respond and move toward Him, God washes you clean and heals your wounds. The Lord perfectly guides and protects His flock. He will renew and transform all who are willing. *Will you respond to His call?*

How you will use these divine truths to make changes in your life?

____

____

____

____

HEARTWORK

- Explain in your own words why all sexual thoughts and activity that do not conform to God's intention grieve Him.

____

____

____

____

____

____

The union between husband and wife was designed by God to be both emotional and spiritual. In God's perfect plan, marriage guides us to an understanding of how much Christ loves the church. Just as Christ is faithful to and loves and nurtures the church, Christian men are to be totally faithful and devoted to loving and nurturing their wives.

Will you agree with God? (This heart shift applies equally to unmarried men.)

Read Ephesians 5:25–33. Does any particular image, truth, or command strike you?

____

____

____

____

____

____

The "test" for purity is not whether it feels good or whether the other person consents, i.e., premarital sex. In fact, all sexually impure thoughts or acts offend God and harm your spirit regardless of your consent. Meditate on this for a moment. Write out any commitments in desiring absolute sexual purity according to God's standards.

____

____

____

____

Because God is good and loves you, He wants the best for you. His command that men have only one wife (including in their hearts and thoughts) is not a burden but a blessing. God knows that if you have a divided heart, you'll never have a trusting, safe, fulfilling relationship with your wife. God also knows that your heart will not have true peace or contentment if you seek to serve two masters or are divided in your love or loyalty (Matthew 6:24; Psalm 86:11).

Will you decide today that you won't be divided between loving the world and loving God?

God wants your heart devoted not just to good works or outward appearances but to Him personally. He doesn't delight in sacrifices, but in a broken and contrite heart He is pleased (Psalm 51:16–17). Be fully devoted to pursuing intimacy with Christ. Keep drawing near to God, and He will draw near to you!

PRAY

O is for Open and Honest. Are you being open and honest in your talks with God about whether you consider lust and porn as sinful, causing God to grieve? Go to the Lord now in open communication. Ask the Lord to reveal the evil of lust and fantasy.

Are you being open with others when they ask you how you are feeling? Talk to God about it. It does no good to hide your feelings or pretend all is well.

- Ask the Lord to loosen your tongue to talk openly to Him and others.
- Ask God to reveal what walls you have built around your heart that block out God and others, and to show you how to tear them down. Be still and listen for a moment.
- Talk to the Lord about what you're afraid will happen if you give control of your life to Him or if you let others into the innermost parts of your heart.
- Ask the Lord to make you a one-woman man who seeks purity in your sexual relationship (including thoughts) with your wife or your future wife. Now commit to it!
- Pray for blessings and protection for your wife or future wife and for your family.
- Keep praying for other Proven Men. (List them as you pray.)

____

____

____

____

READ THE BIBLE

Is God giving you new insights and revealing truth in your heart as you read the Bible? Ask Him! Read Proverbs 5 slowly while asking God to meet with you. As you read, meditate not only on the temporary pleasures of fantasy or immorality, but on the high cost of dwelling on and chasing after the flesh (the world). Agree to listen to the Lord and allow other Godly men to give you instruction as you strive to live out purity.

(NOTE to singles: Don't fall for the lie that you are incomplete if not married. In fact, the Bible says in 1 Corinthians 7:8 that it's good to be unmarried. Also, don't be deceived; sexually impure thoughts and actions will not simply go away when you get married! Therefore, when reading about how married men should act in purity, don't shrug it off. Rather, be all the more committed to living in absolute purity right now by allowing the Lord to renew and transform your mind and by putting into place all six elements of a Proven life!)

MEMORY VERSE

1 Thessalonians 5:16–18: "Be joyful always; pray continually; give thanks in all circumstances, for this is God's will for you in Christ Jesus."

DAILY READING

Meditate on Colossians 3:2–3: "Set your minds on things above, not on earthly things. For you died, and your life is now hidden with Christ in God."

What does this mean to you, and how will you do it? Be specific.

____

____

____

____

The day a person cries out and asks Jesus to be his Savior is not the end point of his earthly life. Rather, it's an open door through which a believer crosses over from death to eternal life. Clearly, it's wrong to think, "I am saved and assured of heavenly salvation, so it doesn't matter what I do in life." In fact, the Bible warns against this false security (Matthew 7:21–23, Galatians 5:13–15, 2 Timothy 2:19).

Although God surely writes your name in the Book of Life with permanent ink, whether you live according to His will and at peace is another matter. While the Holy Spirit does indwell all believers, you can quench the Spirit of God. When you act according to your own desires, expect these things in your life: anger, slander, sexual immorality, and other sins of the flesh. The only position that brings joy, peace, contentment, and other fruit of the Spirit is one of living a Proven life by the power of God. Do you want to experience the deep abiding love of the Father? It begins by choosing life.

Jesus said that this is life: To "know" the Father (John 17:3). Life isn't being constantly happy, living in good circumstances, or having an abundance of possessions. Rather, life is knowing God the Father intimately. How well do you know the Father? Your response will say a great deal about the freedom you experience from the grip of sin. The Bible says, "Today, if you hear his voice, do not harden your hearts" (Hebrews 3:7). It's time to go to the Father, not to ask more selfish requests, such as to take away temptations or to make your life easy, but to know Him. Seek the Lord with all of your heart.

What holds you back? Are you afraid of God? Do you view Him as a harsh taskmaster? Perhaps your own father or another authority figure was mean, distant, cold, or abusive. The Bible tells you to fear God, but not in the same way you fear or avoid a mean-spirited man. When you hide away from God you miss out on healing, peace, restoration, and a clean conscience. Life without God is a life devoid of hope, stuck under the power of the world. Yes, you're to fear God, but in a healthy way. As you turn to and trust in God, peace will replace ugly, destructive fear and anxiety, and the true fear of God will safeguard your soul and bring you peace.

Even though proper fear of God is healthy and desirable, you'll probably have a hard time replacing the destructive kind of fear (or even anger) you may have for your father or other authority figure. The only way to make and maintain the switch is to get to know God the Father. Once you see and experience Him as He really is, you'll be changed in all areas of your life from the inside out. *Make the decision to get to know God.* Spend regular time talking to Him with openness and honesty. Read His Word, the Bible. He gave it to you so that you could get to truly know Him. In fact, the Scriptures are active and alive, capable of penetrating and changing your heart (Hebrews 4:12).

Worship and praise the Lord with passion. He is due your praise. Worshiping God the Father also frees your heart and opens a direct link to Him. You'll be transformed by mutual love, and the walls in your heart will start to tumble.

Consider how another ministry describes the role of knowing God the Father: To be healed from sexual addiction, you must know God intimately. "For it is from that relationship that all of the answers and meaning in life flows. We need to experience the deep abiding love that proceeds powerfully, yet gently from God's heart. We need to experience His love for us—not simply read about it and intellectually agree that it is true."[11] It's time to choose real life—to choose to live by, for, and through Christ.

- Have you made it a practice to skim back over the Daily Reading and record key points or insights? Keep digging for nuggets of truth to apply. Jot them down.

____

____

____

____

There's a big difference between doing good deeds and loving the Lord. God cares about the distinction.

- Do you sometimes seek to do good rather than love God? Explain.

____

____

____

- What hinders you from drawing close to God and experiencing the full depth of His love for you?

____

____

____

____

Read the following list, looking for ways that each item may be a barrier in your life:

- Pride
- Selfishness
- Time spent doing for God, rather than time spent being with Him
- Rules obeyed to control your action, and commands performed out of a sense of duty
- Greed
- Attempts to earn God's love (performance-based living)

____

____

____

____

Divine intimacy is not obtained by doing works for God but through loving the Lord with all of your heart. Your actions will be guided by such love—empowered and directed by God. Therefore, set your heart upon knowing God and pursuing Him with all of your might.

HEARTWORK

Do you see how God allows trials and difficulties in your life, not because He wants you to be afraid of Him, but so that you will grow and mature, becoming complete and whole, not lacking anything? (James 1:2–4) God doesn't want you to stop short in healing. Trust that He knows the perfect way for you and that His timing is right. Embrace that living for God is more precious than anything else you have ever asked from Him.

Commit to seeking the Lord with all of your heart. Make this the number one priority in your life: To intimately know your heavenly Father. Participate with God. Don't take back control or think you can do it on your own. Rather, truly desire to be transformed. If you secretly want to enjoy the sensual pleasures of pornography or lust, God's transformation process will be thwarted.

PRAY

Are you "experiencing" God when you pray? Do you find that five minutes is not enough time? Consider extending your morning prayer time to 10 minutes. Will you begin your study sooner even if it means rising five minutes earlier each day, in order to use the time to get to know God better?

- Go to God in relational prayer right now, asking Him to reveal Himself in deeper, more personal ways.
- Confess and repent of any ways you sought to serve God in your own strength instead of loving Him and relying upon Him.
- Confess how you have not made pursuing an intimate relationship with the Lord your top priority.
- Ask God to humble your spirit and transform you into a willing, obedient servant.
- List each person as you lift them before God, seeking His grace in their lives.

____

____

____

READ THE BIBLE

Read Psalm 23 twice. Keep seeking to know God and to experience His love for you.

P is for Passionate for God. If time, write a short psalm to the Lord (see Appendix H).

____

____

____

MEMORY VERSE

1 Thessalonians 5:16–18: "Be joyful always; pray continually; give thanks in all circumstances, for this is God's will for you in Christ Jesus."

DAILY READING

Instead of a Daily Reading you will spend the bulk of your time doing *Heartwork*.

HEARTWORK

By now, it should be clear that sexual integrity is obtained through an intimate relationship with God the Father. Instead of a formal Daily Reading today, below are some new attitudes to consider and some suggestions for boosting your new walk with the Lord. Use this outline as a platform for meditation right now. Open your heart to God. As you do, ask the Lord to change you by giving you His strength.

- Take the focus off yourself. Before you can be filled by God, you must empty yourself. Let go of your circumstances, rights, and expectations (1 Thessalonians 5:16–18).
- Put all of your attention on God (Psalm 63). Purpose to get to know the Lord. Put into practice meditating on His names and attributes, dwelling on His mighty works, reading the Bible (which was written for you), and communicating (praying) in a relational style of meeting with Him.
- Be still (Psalm 46:10). Set aside time to simply quiet your mind. When your mind is quiet before God, open your spirit to hear what He has to say, asking Him to reveal truths to you and waiting upon the Lord with the expectation that you will experience Him. During quiet times of reflection and while reading the Bible, seek God with a heart longing to be filled. (Practice it right now. Be still for a few moments.)
- Take captive every thought, including sexual fantasies, thoughts of being a hero, or dreams of winning the lottery (2 Corinthians 10:5). Diligently practice cutting off all

unwholesome or impure thoughts. Don't enjoy them or allow them to remain for even a second. Immediately recognize such thoughts as sinful. They drag you away from God and try to convince you that your ideas are better than following God's perfect plan for you. Repent, accept His forgiveness, and turn to God in praise and worship.

- Accept that God's Word is true—even the portions of Scripture you don't fully understand (see 2 Timothy 3:16). Commit to relying upon God's truths instead of your own ideas or experiences (Proverbs 3:5–8). This means trusting His Word even above the finest minds of men. We are all fallible and can make incorrect assumptions, but God is never wrong. The Lord will continually reveal more insights, sufficient for you to have peace, if you believe in Him and hunger for more of Him.
- Spend time with God. Be vigilant in developing and protecting your time of meeting with the Lord each day (a *"quiet time,"* see Mark 1:35). As you grow spiritually, keep increasing your time of prayer and communion with the Lord. Put a plan into place for reading the Bible daily, including various times and places during the day. Also, start scheduling devotions with family or friends.
- Eliminate TV or Internet browsing and other time stealers. Your desires will change as you meet with God and experience more of His character. Add into your life things that will build relationships with God and others (Ephesians 4:22–24). It's counterproductive to your healing to spend time flooding your mind with anything that promotes a selfish life or sexually immoral practices.
- Include God in every decision you face (James 1:5; Ephesians 6:18). When choosing one thing over another, be sure you are testing your motives and actions (James 4:3). Always ask, "Is this God's will and plan for me?"
- Continually assess your spiritual condition. Your feelings may serve as signals of when you are going astray. Anger, bitterness, loneliness, and anxiety are all red flags that you are acting in your own strength (Galatians 5:19–21). Don't suppress your feelings; rather, talk to the Lord about the underlying issues. An emotionless person feels numb and misses out on a wide range of positive feelings, including joy and contentment (Galatians 5:22–25), so practice knowing your feelings (see Appendix F).

- Network with other believers (Ecclesiastes 4:9–12; Proverbs 27:17). Where two are gathered in the name of the Lord, God is present (Matthew 18:20). Accept that God uses others to strengthen you and permits you to strengthen them (Luke 22:32; 1 Thessalonians 3:2). Don't reject or neglect this blessing.
- Read the Bible daily, expecting that God will turn the desire of your heart and spirit toward Him (Psalm 1:2; 119:97). Don't be hurried, merely trying to get through a set amount of pages. It's about quality, not quantity of time spent reading the Bible. Focus on meeting with or hearing from God. One approach is to read the Bible until the Lord impresses a point on your heart, and then meditate and dwell on that notion, inquiring how you can and will apply it in your life.
- Pray for things God wants to accomplish, not for the things you selfishly desire or think you deserve (see 1 John 5:14–15). Pray especially for others (1 Samuel 12:22; Romans 15:30). Be selfless in asking of God. When you catch yourself going to God for favors, stop and reorient your spiritual compass (James 4:3).[12] Set it again upon knowing and loving the Lord with all your heart and doing His will.
- Adopt this as your motto: "I have been crucified with Christ, and I now live for and through Him."

Jot down what impacted you or decisions you made.

____

____

____

____

____

____

____

Listening and doing are two separate disciplines. Consider the wisdom in Psalm 85:8, which says, "I will listen to what God the Lord will say; he promises peace to his people, his saints—but let them not return to folly." How true. Be aware that if you only hear with your ears, you will return to folly. List ways in which you will do the things you meditated upon.

____

____

____

____

____

- How will you adjust your time in order to spend more of it with God? List the things that you will eliminate. What about watching TV or surfing the Internet? Ask God for direction regarding whether you should give up all TV or all Internet browsing. For instance, Joel decided to stop watching TV when he began doing business with sexually addictive behaviors. It wasn't for an entire year that Joel determined that he could watch some TV again. Many other Proven Men found it necessary to give up TV and the Internet for a season.

PRAY

Extend your time in communication with God to 10 minutes. Do you have a burden for someone? Pray passionately for this person.

- Ask God the Father to accomplish His will in this person's life.
- Ask the Lord to pour out rich blessings upon this person according to His mercy and grace.
- Ask God to give you a burden for another person and then pray for him. (Repeat this process several times daily, praying specifically for others.)
- Keep talking to the Lord as your friend and as a living being.
- Ask God to press upon your heart the things He desires.

READ THE BIBLE

Read all of Psalm 27. Read it twice slowly. Listen for God while you read. Ask Him questions, and let Him reveal profound things. Go back to Psalm 27:1 and meditate on this verse. Let it sink in.

What three things is the Lord teaching you from this passage? Think through how God acts in these ways in your life. Reread Psalm 27:4. If you could ask the Lord one thing, would it be the same request as this? Consider adopting this as your new greatest desire and petition to God.

Does your heart long to seek God's face (Psalm 27:8)? Ask the Lord to teach you how to know Him (Psalm 27:11). Begin a practice of waiting upon God to lead you and relying upon His strength (Psalm 27:14).

MEMORY VERSE

1 Thessalonians 5:16–18: "Be joyful always; pray continually; give thanks in all circumstances, for this is God's will for you in Christ Jesus."

DAILY READING

Although it may seem easier to ignore people than to forgive them, you'll carry the scars of anger or hate forever if you don't release them.[13] (You also need to stop beating yourself up for your failures and accept God's forgiveness.) The Lord modeled perfect forgiveness. While you were yet a sinner, and even an enemy of God, Jesus died on the cross as a substitute for your sin (Romans 5:8).

God's perfect nature is to forgive every time we ask (Psalm 86:5), and because His Spirit lives in you as a believer in Jesus Christ (Ephesians 1:13), you have His power to overcome evil with good and to release others of their sins. If you refuse, your fight to keep God out of control of your life—just so you can hold onto anger or withhold forgiveness and love—will leave you exhausted. In the end, you'll go through life anxious and worried as you live by your strength. Right now, mentally tear up the lists of sins committed by others and forgive them.

Recall the discussion of role models. The influence of your father cannot be overstated. He was (or should have been) not only one of the most important models for living out a Proven life, but also a person in the best position to guide you into a loving relationship with your heavenly Father. The problem, however, is that your earthly father isn't perfect. Perhaps you have some painful memories of hurts and pains caused by your dad. Maybe he was absent. How you respond today to these wounds deeply affects how you now are relating to God. The good news is that the Lord can bring healing into your life. Today's lesson is twofold: To learn to release the sins of others (including your dad) and to start seeing and experiencing God the Father as He really is so that your heart will be free to engage in pure love again. These are important aspects of your freedom from sin.

HEARTWORK

Are you ready to release the sins of others, regardless of who they are or what they've done? It will take the power of God to do so. Therefore, ask the Lord for His strength right now. Ask Him to soften your heart and reveal truth and wisdom to you. Start with this: How would you describe your relationship with your dad? Do you have any feelings of anger or resentment? Have there been disappointments? Ask God to reveal any buried feelings.

Write out your feelings toward your dad. (Plan on using your own journal for this exercise, because it may require more time and space than permitted here.)

____

____

____

Because of the way you are designed—for relationships—you must forgive others and do all you can to restore broken or damaged relationships. Ask the Lord to enable you to let go of any anger, bitterness, fear, or other bad feelings you may have against your dad. This is not the same as stuffing feelings or pretending they don't exist. It doesn't mean that you must pretend he was perfect or ignore your pain. Instead, make a decision to forgive him even if he doesn't deserve to be forgiven. (Do this even if your father has passed away or otherwise is absent.) This is for your benefit, not just his. Your soul needs to forgive so that it can release the anger and rage locked inside. Otherwise, bitterness and anger will leave no room for God or for His healing in your life. Right now, talk to God about opening your heart to these feelings and ask for His mercy, grace, and strength to forgive your dad. As you release anger, you actually make room for peace, joy, and love. *Do you hold anger against anyone else?* Anger may be the reason you shy away from certain people. *Do you withhold love from anyone?* List them.

____

____

____

R is for Repentant in Spirit. Have you repented for harboring anger or for withholding love from your parents or others who hurt you? Freedom in your spirit comes only after you first repent from your sins (including refusal to forgive), followed by forgiving others of their sins. Confess these things to the Lord right now. Openly seek forgiveness for closing off your heart and ask for the gift of reconciliation with those you listed above. Think through ways you will reach out to them.

Some people have difficulty seeing God the Father as perfect, good, and loving because they cannot see past their earthly fathers or father figures. Right now, take a moment to think about how you view God. Describe your mental picture of God the Father.

____

____

____

____

____

Write out your response to the two items below[14]:

1. "When I think of God as my father, I feel":

____

____

____

____

____

2. List the good and bad things you think about God the Father:

___

___

___

___

What similarities do you see between how you feel about your dad and how you view God the Father?

___

___

___

___

Note: Even though you may tend to judge God like you judge your earthly father, God did not sin against you. He doesn't need your forgiveness because He is perfect and sinless, unlike your earthly father. Confess to God how you have judged Him. Ask God the Father to forgive you and to change you so that you can see Him as He is—perfectly good.

Have you ever made a judgment about someone and later on, after you got to know this person better, realized you were wrong about them? Well, that's one of the most common mistakes man makes about God. We think that He has harmed us or withheld love, so we harbor anger, make incorrect judgments, and try to keep a safe distance from Him. The problem with staying away from God is that you'll never be able to correct your error about Him. You'll remain stuck up to your ankles in sand as you hold tightly to the shovel of self-effort, refusing to give up control. You'll never see God as perfect, good, and loving (and therefore trust Him with your life) without spending time with Him. You won't change until your attitude toward God changes, and your attitude won't change until you spend enough time with Him to see His perfect nature and find that He is good. As you meet with God, your anger toward Him and toward others will melt away because the Lord's gift of grace and forgiveness will overshadow you. Your eyes will be open to the truth about God, and you'll taste His goodness and experience His love, mercy, and grace. The fruit of the Spirit will replace the acts and thinking of the sinful nature (Galatians 5:19–25).

Ask yourself again: Do I really believe that God is good, and have I turned over my entire life to His control? If you cannot honestly say yes, stay in daily prayer, asking God to change your heart and focus in life. Keep going to the Lord daily to meet with Him. Approach the daily *Heartwork* not out of a sense of duty, but with a determination to experience God. During your quiet times with the Lord, keep asking Him to soften your heart and to conform your will and desires to His.

PRAY

Spend a moment asking the Lord to reveal to you anything that prevents you from making Him the center of your life and keeping the pursuit of intimacy with God the Father your top priority. Tell Him of any confusions, fears, or concerns you have. Listen for His response.

- Keep praying for others, especially those who have hurt you. Ask God to show you how to forgive them and bless them.
- Keep praying for other Proven Men. They too must forgive others and let go of anger.
- Ask God for forgiveness for judging Him in the same way as you have judged others.
- Ask God to give you eyes that see God the Father, Jesus Christ, and the Holy Spirit as perfect and good, as loving and forgiving, and yet as a living Triune Being who wants to have an intimate relationship with you.

READ THE BIBLE

Read Luke 11:2–4. Although this may be a familiar prayer, meditate on each word. Ask God to give you fresh understandings and insights on how to talk with Him and how to forgive others.

MEMORY VERSE

1 Thessalonians 5:16–18: "Be joyful always; pray continually; give thanks in all circumstances, for this is God's will for you in Christ Jesus."

DAILY READING

Have you remembered to confess and repent of (turn from) every fantasy, second look, or lustful thought? Do this the moment they occur. Putting into practice a plan of taking captive every impure thought right away is vital in the process of breaking the grip of lust. A word of caution: *Don't throw in the towel if you have setbacks.* Stay the course. You're on the winning team! (If you do have a setback, revisit Week 4.)

Read and meditate on Colossians 3:5–14. Listen for what God wants you to experience. Record your insights.

____

____

____

Do you see that you are to "put to death" both sexual immorality and greed (Colossians 3:5)? Both share a common root sin issue, namely selfishness. They are detestable idols that take God's place in your life. To overcome such selfish roots, what things will you rid yourself of (see Colossians 3:8)?

____

____

- Have you ever noticed how little things can anger or annoy you? List the things that set you off.

  ____

  ____

  ____

Be mindful that each of these things is fed by the same roots of selfishness and pride that keep sexual immorality alive. With Colossians 3:5–14 in mind, explain in your own words what effect replacing (putting to death) the old nature (such as anger, malice, and lies) with the new nature (such as humility, gentleness, and kindness) will have on whether you continue to engage in sexual immorality.

____

____

____

____

Shifting gears for a moment, do you have a good handle on what God's will is for you? Would you like to know what the Bible has to say about it? Read and meditate on 1 Thessalonians 5:16–18: "Be joyful always; pray continually; give thanks in all circumstances, for this is God's will for you in Christ Jesus." (Have you memorized this weekly memory verse yet?)

List the three things this passage says are God's will for you.

____

____

____

- Why do you think these three things are listed as God's will for you? Ask the Lord to open your heart to what He wants to reveal to you right now.
- Are you aware that always being joyful is not the same thing as being happy all the time or living free from troubles? Think through the difference right now.

____

____

____

E is for Eternal Perspective. Love is a decision, not a temporary feeling that fades in and out. Similarly, joy isn't based upon circumstances. Joy flows from the eternal knowledge and hope of the Lord's unconditional love and your position as a forgiven, adopted, treasured son of God. That's why you can be joyful always. Joy flows from the promise that the Lord will never leave you nor forsake you and that your inheritance in heaven is guaranteed. Take on this view yourself.

Continual prayer is attainable because true praying is all about being with God, not merely asking Him for gifts or miracles. It's dwelling upon the Lord throughout the day, the same as young lovers constantly anticipate being together. It's a new way of thinking and acting, keeping a constantly open line of communication between your heart and God's. Jot down ways you can be thinking of God at all times throughout the day.

____

____

____

____

Giving thanks in all circumstances is a tall order. It requires a firm commitment to God and the eternal perspective that you're just passing through this world. It also helps to remember that, although you deserved hell, Jesus not only paid that price but reserves a place for you in heaven, complete with a new mind and body—free from sin. Through unmerited grace, mercy, and love, the Lord showers you with goodness. Resolve to start noticing all He provides and thanking Him for it. You'll find that giving thanks is contagious; it will replace the habit of complaining and discontentment that leads you to search out fantasy.

Did you notice the pattern in these points? You are to be joyful, praying, and giving thanks continually in all circumstances, not just when you feel like it. You know this is possible, because God doesn't tell you to do things you can't do. If you're self-seeking, you won't come close. However, you'll begin to experience joy and be thankful as you seek after God and allow Christ to be in control of all areas of your life. When you give up your rights and expectations for how things should turn out, the outcome of events isn't so important anymore. You won't be angry, because you gave up your expectations.

- Will you yield your heart completely to God? Will you give up your rights? Write your commitment.

____

____

____

____

HEARTWORK

Spend a few moments asking God to open your eyes to His absolute goodness and His wonderful faithfulness, love, and kindness. Talk to Him now. Tell Him what has prevented you from turning every area of your life over to His control and for His purposes. Ask God to change the way you view Him and to soften and transform your heart.

Another Friday is here. Are you prepared? Will you keep moving toward having a heart of worship? Plan right now to make tonight (and Saturday night) a time spent on things true, noble, right, pure, lovely, admirable, excellent, and praiseworthy (Philippians 4:8, your memory verse for Week 2).

PRAY

Are you able to stay focused during prayer? Sometimes you may need to write out your prayers. Other times try using the Bible to keep your attention focused. For example, pray-read Colossians 1:9–14 as a format for lifting others up to God. Open your Bible to Colossians 1:9–14. Read the name of a loved one in place of pronouns such as "you" and "us." Speak from a heart that's truly asking God to work in this person's life to give him that type of a heart and desire.

It will take several minutes to do this, but go back and pray-read these verses again, using the name of your wife, if you're married, or a close friend. Then insert the names of your parents, your siblings, or any children. Don't race, but truly desire these things for the people you bring before God. Model future prayers with similar earnestness and selfless petitions for others.

READ THE BIBLE

Read Proverbs 12. Let God's truth penetrate your heart.

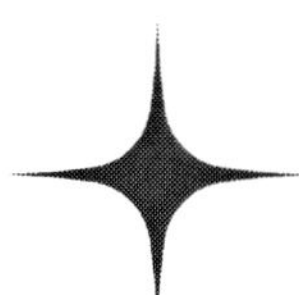

SPECIAL NOTE:

What is your number one priority in life? God wants to be your top priority! Record any commitment to switching masters and making intimacy with your heavenly Father your new goal.

E is for Eternal Perspective. Are you beginning to embrace the bigger picture? Are you seeing that life is so much more than seeking to satisfy sensual desires? What is something you see differently?

MEMORY VERSE

1 Thessalonians 5:16–18: "Be joyful always; pray continually; give thanks in all circumstances, for this is God's will for you in Christ Jesus."

Have you ever set aside "couch time" with your wife or a friend? Schedule time where you just talk. Don't be distracted by TV, children, or anything else. Plan some topics and have a few open-ended questions ready, but also be spontaneous. Some ideas include discussing or setting mutual goals, learning about your wife or friend's likes or dislikes, and planning for upcoming events. Plan to have a weekly couch time. The key is to make it a priority and schedule it.

Do you want to know God better and to love Him more deeply? Tell Him. Then make a commitment to love the Lord with all of your heart. State ways in which you will take action to pursue God.

Make it a mission to be *passionate for God*. Read aloud the *"Names of God"* in Appendix C, being reverent while you say them. Write the Lord a love letter.

WEEK SIX

TESTIMONY

"I think there needs to be a warning at the start of the workbook. I would suggest something like, 'This book will stir up emotions and reveal things to you that will not make you happy, and show you how you really live.' When I first started the workbook I was so convicted over seeing for the first time my selfishness (wanting to be first), self-sufficiency (wanting to be in control), self-gratification (wanting to be served), greed (wanting more), and pride (wanting in on my terms), that I closed the book and ran and hid in pornography. But the Holy Spirit drew me back to Christ, the only One who can save and heal me. I felt such a longing to return to the Lord, so I returned to the study and am using it to go to Jesus and am making it a part of my daily prayer time."

Passionate for God,
Repentant in spirit,
Open and honest,
Victorious in living,
Eternal in perspective, and
Networking with other ***PROVEN Men.***

MEMORY VERSE

Romans 12:1–2: "Therefore, I urge you, brothers, in view of God's mercy, to offer your bodies as living sacrifices, holy and pleasing to God—this is your spiritual act of worship. Do not conform any longer to the pattern of this world, but be transformed by the renewing of your mind. Then you will be able to test and approve what God's will is—His good, pleasing and perfect will."

DAILY READING

Who are your heroes or role models? We all have them. In fact, God created you to model behavior after others. Of course Christ was the perfect role model, but you can and should also model your life after other Proven Men. Indeed, the apostle Paul said, "Follow my example, as I follow the example of Christ" (1 Corinthians 11:1).

Whether or not you are aware of it, you constantly model your behavior after others. Similarly, others model their behavior after you. One need only watch a toddler mimic an older sibling to see this principle acted out at the earliest stages of life. Teens also wear the latest clothes of their models. Often, though, role models are not Godly, and we pick up sinful practices. Even a parent's sins are passed down to the third and fourth generations by the modeling of bad behavior (Exodus 34:7). Yielding to Christ, however, breaks the chain and establishes a good model.

How about it? Are you ready to break the mold and to live a Godly life? Right now, meditate on how your parents and favorite teachers, friends, sports stars, or actors modeled certain behaviors that glorified selfishness and pride.

Most TV shows highlight premarital and extramarital affairs. Advertisements use sex and greed to sell products—feeding a "gotta have it now" attitude. Many of your role models may have succumbed to the pressures of the world and followed in the footsteps of their role models. Now you face the same pressures. Many of the actions, attitudes, and beliefs of others are pressed upon you. The area of sexual relations is no exception. In fact, it is heightened. Every generation goes through some form of sexual revolution that opposes God's perfect design for marriage.

The actions and attitudes of friends and family also aid in shaping your own view of sexual integrity. Sex education largely occurs outside of the classroom through repeated observation.

For instance, boys are often exposed to porn from classmates, older brothers, or even their dads. They are taught that it's routine entertainment. We're all influenced about the virtue of premarital sex by the exploits of family members or our peers, i.e. it's a badge of honor or a symbol of manhood to have sex on dates. Knowing that a friend or relative regularly masturbates conditions us to accept it as an ordinary part of our own lives. Each time we observe others talking about or acting upon sexual impulses invites us to view porn, masturbation or another form of sexual activity simply as an opportunity to escape or feel good. It also trains us to treat women as sex objects. In short, those who have influence in your life often are contributing factors in your own bondage to sexually compulsive thoughts and actions. Of course, ultimately it's your own deceptive heart, filled with pride and selfishness that feeds and waters the impulse to make sex the master over your life.

Have you lived with a poor role model? Did you follow others just to fit in? Undoubtedly, you have picked up some bad habits, values, and beliefs from others, but now you're responsible for the actions you choose each day. The good news is that God promises to break the cycle if you turn to Him. Will you fix your eyes on God and look to Him as your model? He has a plan to reprogram you. You'll find it in this week's memory verse. "Therefore, I urge you, brothers, in view of God's mercy, to offer your bodies as living sacrifices, holy and pleasing to God—this is your spiritual act of worship. Do not conform any longer to the pattern of this world, but be transformed by the renewing of your mind. Then you will be able to test and approve what God's will is—his good, pleasing and perfect will."

The Lord wants to renew your mind. That process begins with putting an end to chasing after sexually immoral practices with your mind and body. Begin viewing your body as a temple of God. Allow the Lord to take control. Next, stop lusting after what the world lusts after. It begins by blocking out the unhealthy inputs of the world. This means ending the barrage of messages. It may be that you should stop watching certain or even all TV programs or movies. What other patterns of the world are you following? Do the lyrics of the songs you listen to promote godliness or selfishness? **Holiness requires an all-out shift of priorities and actions. Only when you refocus your energies upon getting to know the Lord and following His ways can you break free from the grip of lust.** The end result is that you're changed. You'll actually be able to see and follow God's will. It becomes a replacement for the things you are now chasing after. Honestly consider what role models you follow. Are they Proven Men or lovers of the world? You do have a choice, but if you don't choose your master, the pressures of the world will choose for you. The Bible is filled with great role models, as well as model rules for living. If you don't have a close Godly male friend, then seek out Godly men. *Networking* with them is not the same as throwing around names. It involves true and unselfish friendship. You enter into relationships to serve others and open yourself to the Christian life.

HEARTWORK

Ask God to break the grip of the world and the ungodly influences of certain people in your life. Then choose this day to serve only God. Fix your eyes upon Jesus. Allow Him to become your greatest role model and friend (while also including other Godly men in your life).[17] Christ won't lead you astray, and there's no guilt or shame in His ways. Record any insights from the Daily Reading.

If you were told by doing a list of things that you would never commit a sexual sin, would you be eager and committed to doing those things? Well, the Bible has a list of eight things that it says will keep you from falling. *Interested?* Read 2 Peter 1:5–10. List the eight things:

Describe what it would require to live out all of these things.

____

____

____

____

____

____

____

Did you notice how hard it would be to perfectly do just one perfectly, let alone all eight? *How does this make you feel?* The point is not to be discouraged, but to realize the need for Christ to perfect you and give you His heart, mind, and strength.

Although following a list of things to overcome sin might seem like a good idea for living out holiness, you would be weighed down beyond what you could bear if you tried to be perfect with just these eight things, let alone the many other commandments in the Bible. Recall the admonition in Colossians 2:20–23, which says; "Since you died with Christ to the basic principles of the world, why, as though you still belonged to it, do you submit to its rules: 'Do not handle! Do not taste! Do not touch!'? These are all destined to perish with use, because they are based on human commands and teachings. Such regulations indeed have an appearance of wisdom, with their self-imposed worship, their false humility and their harsh treatment of the body, but they lack any value in restraining sensual indulgence." Following lists won't stop your inner desires to chase after fantasy! It's time to agree with God that apart from Him, you can do nothing (John 15:5). That's why you must live by the Holy Spirit instead of relying upon your own strength. That's also why a victorious life only occurs by the Spirit of God (Galatians 5:16). How about it? Are you ready to put down the shovel of self-effort and give total control to God? It's time to begin putting into practice all six elements of a Proven life!

Getting back to these eight things for a moment, notice the overlap in themes between these items and your purpose in life. Recall that, first and foremost, you were created to love God (see Week 1, Day 5). This means you cannot keep secret sins (picking up your own shovel to dig your own hole when you think no one is watching) and expect God to keep building your oasis as though He were fooled by your double-mindedness (Hebrews 4:13). You must remove your former way of thinking and exchange it for God's eternal perspective and will. You must be fully devoted to and living in complete reliance upon God. Only then can you bask in the oasis He builds, and only then will you be able to be joyful always, praying continually, and thankful in all circumstances (1 Thessalonians 5:16–18). It's only by yielding 100 percent to God that you can accomplish the list of eight things in 2 Peter 1:5–10, and be kept by Him from stumbling. Right now, commit to trusting God with every area of your life. Hold nothing back this time!

READ THE BIBLE

The commands of God, such as the passage you just read in 2 Peter 1:5–10, can easily overwhelm you. Just trying to live out the eight things that God says will keep you free can lead to exhaustion, yet the Lord promises, "For my yoke is easy and my burden is light" (Matthew 11:30). Right now, for some really good news, read 2 Peter 1:3–4.

Isn't it wonderful how all Scripture is intertwined! Before asking you to incorporate into your life eight principles needed for living victoriously, God reminds you that He gives you His power, strength, knowledge, wisdom, glory, goodness, and promises. That's right, the power to do God's will is waiting for you. True freedom rings when you participate with God in clothing yourself with these eternal qualities that set you free from the evil desires that have constantly dragged you down. Simply put, the Lord offers you His divine nature so that you can be renewed and transformed, being stamped Proven, and therefore escape the corruption of the world. It's time to put down the shovel of self-effort and yield completely to the Lord!

PRAY

Spend five or ten minutes in prayer. Do so with the mindset of meeting with God. Listen for His voice and experience Him as you talk in relational style prayer.

- Thank Him for His precious promises and for the Holy Spirit that supplies your strength.
- Keep asking God to give you hunger for real intimacy.
- Ask the Lord to break your self-deception and stubborn pride.
- Right now, list the names of several people you want God to touch. As you pray separately for each person, ask the Lord to pull him to Himself, to open the eyes of their hearts to the emptiness of living apart from Him and the futility of acting in their own strength, and to make their hearts receptive to His perfect love. Talk to God about anything else on your heart and ask Him what is on His heart.

___

___

___

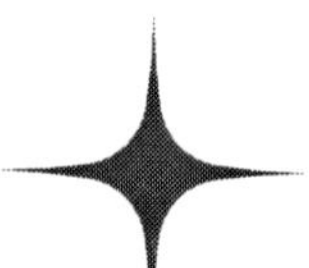

SPECIAL NOTE:

E is for Eternal Perspective. Entertaining lust and fantasy are red flags indicating that you're not fully trusting God and giving Him 100 percent of your heart right now. You've taken back the shovel of self-effort. You're giving room for pride and self-reliance.

MEMORY VERSE

Romans 12:1–2: "Therefore, I urge you, brothers, in view of God's mercy, to offer your bodies as living sacrifices, holy and pleasing to God—this is your spiritual act of worship. Do not conform any longer to the pattern of this world, but be transformed by the renewing of your mind. Then you will be able to test and approve what God's will is—His good, pleasing and perfect will."

DAILY READING

To many, image is everything. What other people think of them matters greatly. They want to fit in. They want the outside of their cup looking sparkling clean for others to see and admire. The inside, however, is kept secret. What a terrible battle rages in our souls! Often, the constant struggle is kept hidden from view.

Have you ever thought of friends, co-workers, and acquaintances: "If they really knew me, they would not like me"? Those of us who have made vows to "never reveal the real me" live with chains around our souls. We would rather die than be found out and rejected. What a pitiful state we chain ourselves to out of fear that we may be seen as imperfect. Right now, open yourself to finding out how you ended up in this plight and what is the way out.

As touched upon earlier, much of our perceived self-image was formed when we were young. Our parents may have branded our souls with unhealthy words and actions. Friends also exert tremendous influence in how we see ourselves. Their importance to us determined what we were willing to sacrifice in exchange for their approval. We could not shield ourselves from all criticism, gossip, jokes, or exclusion from those from whom we desperately sought love or affirmation. Their mean-spirited or careless words or actions were like hot coals withering young reeds. They often produced harmful self-judgments. Each time we failed, we believed these negative statements about our worth. This recurring pattern fueled either a poor self-image or a desire to keep from revealing inner thoughts or feelings, which have loaded more weight on our backs to carry through life.

Fortunately, what others say or even our own self-perception does not reflect how God views us. When the Lord examines each person, He does not look at the outward appearance. There's no rating system based upon height, weight, or other aspects of physical appearance that we call beauty; nor is God's view dependent upon IQ, status, position, income, what school we attended, the number of our friends, or the style of our clothes. No, all people are created in God's image, and all are equally loved. God doesn't show favoritism (Romans 2:11).

What matters to God? He searches the world for people who are devoted to Him in heart and soul (Psalm 14:2; 53:2). The Lord longs for you to turn to Him in this way. Stated differently, "The Lord is far from the wicked, but he hears the prayer of the righteous" (Proverbs 15:29). Therefore, stop saying "Lord, Lord" with your lips while keeping your heart from Him. Be devoted to knowing and pursuing Him.

Is your heart beating after the Lord? That's what matters to Him. Your healing begins when you choose to accept God's view of you, that you're preciously and wonderfully made. The Lord longs for your individual attention and love. Accept that God the Father considers you a treasure given as a gift to Jesus. The day you were received by Christ, all of the angels in heaven shouted out in rejoicing (Luke 15:10). How about that description of the pleasure of Christ upon receipt of you as His adopted son, brother, and friend!

As you meditate on God's tremendous love for you and His desire for fellowship, you'll be irresistibly drawn to Him. God loves you unconditionally, just as you are. He will not force change upon you. Rather, your desires change as you are in His presence, seeking His will and gladly following His ways. For instance, during worship and praise, the Lord melts away bitterness and anger. You become holy as He is holy when you spend time meeting privately and openly with God. It's then that you willingly yield to the Lord and experience more of His nature and character. Humility, in a Godly sense (and not based upon self-contempt), redefines your self-perception. You not only invite God to see the inside of your cup but ask Him to wash it clean.

Jot down your thoughts about the Daily Reading. (Remember to keep making notes in the margins while reading.)

HEARTWORK

Think through what it means that God does not show favoritism. How does that make you feel?

Did you contemplate how God loves others as much as you, and you as much as others? Did you notice that healing is available to you, not just to others? Great spiritual awakening and deep communion with the Lord are at your doorstep. God's view of all people as equal means that you must put aside pride and stop judging others or comparing yourself to them.

The Lord is looking for hearts devoted to Him in relational ways, not people who have the greatest skills. You're capable of surrendering your life to God and journeying with Him. Won't you enlist? All that's required is to stop relying on your own strength and turn to and trust Him.

Be sure that you don't shrug off self-examinations of your life. Right now, be still. Ask the Holy Spirit to press upon your heart any ways in which you have backward, incorrect, or worldly thinking. Spend a moment asking the Lord to reveal what you are holding on to instead of giving up all control to Him.

____

____

____

____

____

____

____

____

When you look at a rubber stamp with the letters P-R-O-V-E-N on them, they look backward. The letters are reversed, i.e., the N is first, followed by the E, the V, the O, the R, and then the P. **ИƎVOЯꟼ**

Only when the stamp is placed in the ink (a symbol of the red blood of Jesus) and stamped onto an object (a symbol of your willingness to let God write your life) does the word become correct. That is the spirit of Proven Men Ministries. The red ink of the letters P-R-O-V-E-N are stamped over the word "Men" to symbolize that we each have been stamped by the blood of Christ and are correcting our thinking and actions.

E is for Eternal Perspective. Stay the course, but make sure the course is set for loving God. Remember, the by-product of a right relationship with God is the loosening of the grip of lust and other sinful desires.

PRAY

Spend time today communicating with God. Talk to God about any childhood offenses you suffered or caused.

- Ask for God's mercy and healing.
- Ask for His ability to forgive those who hurt you. Rely upon God in forgiving others.
- Ask God to make you a needy, dependent servant.
- Ask God to lead you into holiness and purity.
- Now, spend time praying for others, especially those who hurt you.
- List each person as you ask God to expand their hearts and fill them with mercy and grace.

____

____

____

____

- Pray that other Proven Men in your life will be humble, grateful, and content.
- Pray for the leaders of your church.

READ THE BIBLE

Read Nehemiah 9:1–11.

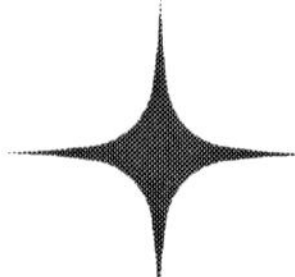

SPECIAL NOTE:

The entire book of Nehemiah provides a vivid analogy of how to repair a broken spiritual condition. When you have time, read the rest of Nehemiah with the following thoughts in mind. For now, think through the following outline and how you can allow the Lord to rebuild your life.

The walls of Israel lay in ruins and the people were afraid to rebuild them. The physical condition of the walls parallels the spiritual condition of the people, and the rebuilding parallels the restoration of the people after seventy years in captivity. The aspects of rebuilding the walls also parallel how a person who suffered abuse or has a broken life is restored. Some things you can learn from this book and apply to your life include:

1. Examine the damage. Before the city walls were repaired, a damage assessment was made; see 1:3 and 2:11–20. It's okay to assess damage from childhood abuse or other harmful events. Just don't stay there. Examine the areas that are damaged and plan a repair. Also, be sure to tear down the false walls around your heart that block out relationships, block out forgiveness, and block out passion and love. Examine the damage in your life right now.

2. Allow yourself feelings. Nehemiah mourned over the ruins; see 1:4. It's okay to mourn over damage or abuse. Go ahead and weep or mourn. Practice being aware of your feelings.

3. Tell God about it. Nehemiah met with God; see 1:5–11. Talk openly to God in relational prayer. Confess your failings as an adult to live for God. Thank Him for His mercy, kindness, and forgiveness. Pray with supplication and earnest, heartfelt petitions.

4. Ask God and others for help. Nehemiah told the king he was sad and asked for help in rebuilding a Jewish city; see 2:1–18. The Jewish culture did not permit being sad around the king. Nehemiah risked wrath by talking about it. Our culture doesn't permit men to talk about feelings, about being weak, or about being needy or dependent, and it certainly leaves little room for talking about masturbation or childhood abuse. However, these are not God's ways. Rely upon God's strength and courage. Ask God and others for help.

5. Let others help (network with other Proven Men). Nehemiah sought assistance; see 3:1–32. Proven Men are to be needy, dependent servants of God. We are to give control to God, which means letting Him control our lives. We are to be *open and honest* with others and accepting of help. Link up with other Proven Men and allow them to help, support, and encourage you.

6. Expect opposition from outside. Israel faced stiff opposition to rebuilding the walls; see 4:1–5. Satan, the mortal enemy of God and man, doesn't want you to turn to Jesus for healing because that means you'll love and serve the Lord. Satan will seek to put stumbling blocks in your way to keep you trapped in bondage.

7. Expect opposition from within. Many Israelites mocked the effort to rebuild; see 4:10–5:13. You'll face scoffers.

8. Pursuing holiness will disrupt the lives of others as your time and energy is diverted from activities, such as TV, that people in your life still find routine. Some have an attitude of judging, making light of your problems or giving pat advice like, "Just pray about it." Your wife may not want any involvement in the healing process, and she may even tell you to just work on your own issues. Don't lose heart. God is your fortress and strength. Also, don't judge those who resist your efforts, and don't withhold love from them. Instead, remain committed. Pray for others and reach out to them.

9. Long for renewal and revival. Nehemiah and others didn't give up. They had faith and did whatever it took to rebuild and repair. They sacrificed greatly and truly placed their trust in the Lord. In the end, the walls were repaired, and the Israelites (and even their enemies) saw that the work was done with the help of God (6:15–16). The people began confessing sins (Chapter 9), and a revival took place. If you long for freedom, trust in God; then die to yourself (giving God control of your life) and resolve to do whatever it takes. God will restore your relationship with Him and with others as you repent of your sins and experience His healing. As you live by the Spirit, the noose of sexual sins will be removed.

MEMORY VERSE

Romans 12:1-2: "Therefore, I urge you, brothers, in view of God's mercy, to offer your bodies as living sacrifices, holy and pleasing to God—this is your spiritual act of worship. Do not conform any longer to the pattern of this world, but be transformed by the renewing of your mind. Then you will be able to test and approve what God's will is—His good, pleasing and perfect will."

DAILY READING

Life is like climbing a moving ladder that's always descending. If all you do is hang on, you'll be pulled down. It takes great effort to go against the flow of the world, but that's where victory is found. You'll encounter sharp rungs, such as harsh words spoken by people who are withholding mercy. Many other obstacles will tear at your grip. You'll even receive advice from well-intentioned people on how to try jumping off or how to increase the comfort while sinking. Such advice, while sounding good, relies upon self-effort that always fails because it actually is moving you in the wrong direction. What you need is to keep climbing up the ladder toward the Lord. Instead of looking around or comparing yourself to the status of others, tilt your head upward. Rely upon the Lord for His strength and His direction. When trying to decipher in which direction you're heading, ask yourself if you truly desire holiness and purity in your inmost being. Openly examine whether you truly want to meet with God. If you secretly want to remain in the world because some temporary pleasure has captured your attention, you won't outpace the speed of descent. The ladder won't stay put for you while you're playing the games of the world. Even if you're not actively seeking out impurity, the ladder never stops pulling you downward.

The same is true for those who have reached new heights. You cannot rest. You probably are strides ahead of where you were just five weeks ago when you began meeting with the Lord through this study, but each moment you end your journey of climbing toward and with the Lord, you begin to lose what you've gained. It won't take too long before you're backsliding. That's why you cannot rest upon yesterday's efforts, no matter how noble they were. *Remember, this is not a twelve-week program but a tool for beginning a new, lifelong journey of intimacy with and dependency upon the Lord in a real relationship as Proven Men.*

Rather than be discontented that the ladder of life is constantly on a downgrade, be excited that the Lord has revealed this knowledge to you and that He has provided you with His strength to overcome. Won't you commit the rest of your life to striving for absolute purity as part of your ascension toward Heaven? The Lord is calling you to journey with Him to higher places, into His inner courts and into His very presence. Join Him! Record any insights.

HEARTWORK

It's now time to conquer self-judgments and other evaluations, placed on you by society, that hinder your relationship with the Lord and your spiritual growth. Allow God to reveal ways in which words and actions of others or your own assessments have influenced you as opposed to how God views you.

- What memories do you have of your parents or others withholding love? What scars are left behind from people telling you that you're inadequate, no good, unworthy, inferior, or defective? Spend time thinking about it. Jot down what God reveals to you.

Now turn to God. Allow truth therapy to bring healing. Recall the true way God views you by considering the following names He uses for you:

- Royal Priest (1 Peter 2:9)
- God's Holy People (Ephesians 5:3)
- Wonderfully Created (Psalm 139:14)
- Brother to Jesus (Hebrews 2:11)
- God's Possession (Ephesians 1:14)
- Dearly Loved (Ephesians 5:1)
- Adopted Son of God (Ephesians 1:4)
- Image of God (Genesis 1:27)
- Chosen by God (Colossians 3:12)
- Future Judge of Angels (1 Corinthians 6:3)
- God's Heir (Galatians 4:7)
- Ambassador of Christ (2 Corinthians 5:20)
- Friend of Jesus (John 15:14–15)
- Saint (Psalm 34:9; 85:8)
- Child of God (1 John 3:1)
- Salt and Light of the World (Matthew 5:13–14)
- Righteousness of God (2 Corinthians 5:21)
- New Creation (2 Corinthians 5:17)
- God's Workmanship (Ephesians 2:10)
- Temple of the Holy Spirit (1 Corinthians 6:19)
- Member of God's Household (Ephesians 2:19)
- Citizen of Heaven (Philippians 3:20)

Mark this page and return here whenever you doubt God's love for you or when you want to be strengthened in faith. Keep your eternal perspective!

Purpose to learn more of God's promises and truths about who you are in Him. Use them to spur your heart to live for and together with the Lord. Allow this truth to set you free:

Your sins have been removed as far as the east is from the west (Psalm 103:12). Praise be to our perfect, loving Father!

Won't you allow God to retrain your thinking? You have a choice either to accept and embrace truth or to listen to lies and mean-spirited words of Satan and others. You also have a decision to make in responding to evil—to overcome it with good by God's power or to descend into the pit to join in with it. Right now, talk to the Lord, asking Him to:

- Give you power to forgive those who hurt you.
- Heal the wounds caused by lies.
- Reshape your thinking and regenerate you by His love and the infinite worth He places on you.

Commit to relying upon God's power to immediately reject condemning thoughts and replace them with the robe of Christ's righteousness, which He gave to you as an adopted, dearly loved son (Romans 8:1–2). Consider one ordinary man, Joel, who had spent twenty years seeking self-pleasures through pornography, masturbation, fantasy, and other forms of false intimacy. He had thought himself better than others, he was quick to find fault, and he thought he deserved all that he had and more.

The fruit of Joel's life was similar to the "acts of the sinful nature" described in Galatians 5:19–21. When he finally admitted chasing after fantasy brought no peace or lasting joy, he turned to Christ, this time for good. He chose to begin climbing toward the Lord and leaving the world behind. It was a long, hard mountain, but he never stopped immersing himself in prayer or Bible reading and study in order to get close to the Lord and to know Him intimately. He finally grasped the depth of his need for the Lord, so he engaged in daily confession and opened himself up to God's gift of repentance. He began learning how to rely upon God's strength for each step he took. He turned away from the world, eliminating TV for an entire year, plus ending other inputs that favored the love of the world over the love for God. Importantly, he also began openly engaging with other men who were seeking the Lord with all of their heart. He purposefully connected with other men who wanted to climb toward the Lord and meet God on His holy mountain. Only when he totally switched masters and teams did God begin healing him from the inside out.

Won't you choose to move toward the Lord this and each day? Link up with other Proven Men, just like you've seen in a picture of a team of mountain climbers. They long to make the trip with you!

DAY 3

Review this week's memory verse: Romans 12:1–2: "Therefore, I urge you, brothers, in view of God's mercy, to offer your bodies as living sacrifices, holy and pleasing to God; this is your spiritual act of worship. Do not conform any longer to the pattern of this world, but be transformed by the renewing of your mind. Then you will be able to test and approve what God's will is—his good, pleasing and perfect will."

Look for connections between memory verses weeks one and six. You already know that the greatest command is to love God with all of your mind, heart, and soul (Matthew 22:36–39). In Romans 12:1–2, God teaches you how to begin understanding and knowing His will as you live out the greatest command with your whole being! Here's an approach:

- First, take an interest in knowing and appreciating God's mercy toward you (2 Corinthians 4:1; Ephesians 2:4). Let it sink in.
- Second, offer your body back to God as a form of a living testimony to Him (Romans 12:1).
- Third, remove the influences of the world from your heart. Transform your mind by opening it to see more of God's mercy, which, in turn, makes you want to offer your body again, worshiping with your soul and guarding your heart (Ephesians 4:22–24).
- Fourth, worship God passionately with your soul in order to be connected to Him (Hebrews 12:28–29).

This continual upward moving pattern brings you into the reality of the purpose of your life. You're changing from the inside out and becoming holy as the One who lives in you and now directs your steps is holy (1 Peter 1:15).

God wants you to know Him and His will, just like a best friend does. Did you ever have a friend whose likes and dislikes you knew almost instinctively and sometimes you thought you could read his mind? (If not, imagine it now.) To get to know another person's will, you must spend lots of time with him. It's the same for getting to know God and His will. You must spend lots of time with God. There are no shortcuts to friendship.

- Will you spend time getting to know God and His will? Time does matter. Compared with meeting with the Lord, how much time do you spend with TV, the Internet, or the newspaper? What are your big time killers? Jot them down.

  ____

  ____

  ____

  ____

Write out any commitments to reduce or eliminate entirely time killers and any commitments to use that time in pursuing God.

____

____

____

____

A word of caution: Don't judge your relationship with God based only on the amount of time you spend. If you're doing the daily *Heartwork*, you're spending quite a bit of time with disciplines for holiness. Nevertheless, be certain that you're being devoted to loving God and being His friend. We read in the Gospels that many of the Pharisees and spiritual teachers of the law didn't have an intimate relationship with God despite scanning over Scripture and mouthing prayers for hours a day. They didn't have a heart that panted after God or one that really wanted God to control their lives. Therefore, they didn't know God's will, and they didn't have their minds renewed.

As for you, stay committed to spending lots of time with the Lord while also desiring His will. Study the Bible to get to know God. *Keep seeking to please and enjoy Him. Remember, if your heart is not passionate for God, it won't be open to His healing, which He longs to give.* Instead, you'll stop short of transformation and give up on what's perceived as a "religious" route to freedom from sexual bondage. Those who don't truly surrender fail to see results. Losing heart over a lack of progress, many return back to old ways, giving their life over to the carnal nature or simply moving on to find another program in a quest to control their own healing. Don't be fooled: Healing comes only through an intimate relationship with God, one in which you love Him with all of your heart, soul, mind, and strength.

READ THE BIBLE

Read Psalm 147. Read with a desire to know God's heart.

PRAY

Spend five or ten minutes in prayer and praise. Let it rise! If you haven't been panting after God during the *Heartwork*, confess that to Him. If you haven't been taking captive every thought during the day, confess that too. Then get down to business, choosing to reject the "escape routes" offered by Satan, which are really roads leading away from God and into the devil's dark domain.

- Ask God to change your heart and to give you an eternal perspective.
- Commit to loving (not just serving) God.
- Pray for others, that the Lord will renew their minds and draw them to His side. (List them.)
- With any remaining time, write your own psalm (see *"How to Write a Psalm"* in Appendix H), sing a praise song to God, or meditate on the *"Attributes of God"* in Appendix D.

MEMORY VERSE

Romans 12:1–2: "Therefore, I urge you, brothers, in view of God's mercy, to offer your bodies as living sacrifices, holy and pleasing to God—this is your spiritual act of worship. Do not conform any longer to the pattern of this world, but be transformed by the renewing of your mind. Then you will be able to test and approve what God's will is—His good, pleasing and perfect will."

DAILY READING

Comparison to others is a trap that keeps people from living out sexual integrity. We know that pride is one of the roots that keeps sexual immorality (including porn and masturbation) alive in a person's life. What we often miss, however, is that each time we judge someone else's sin as worse than our own, we are feeding our own pride. For instance, we justify ourselves by thinking, "At least I don't go to prostitutes" or "I only look at porn once a week, not every day like John." Watch out. Judgmental attitudes demonstrate that pride still remains welcome and alive in your life.

Right now prepare your heart to conquer judgmental attitudes. In Matthew 7:1–5, you are told, "Do not judge, or you too will be judged. For in the same way you judge others, you will be judged, and with the same measure you use, it will be measured to you. Why do you look at the speck of sawdust in your brother's eye and pay no attention to the plank in your own eye? How can you say to your brother, 'Let me take the speck out of your eye,' when all the time there is a plank in your own eye? You hypocrite, first take the plank out of your own eye, and then you will see clearly to remove the speck from your brother's eye."

Describe how you think or act when you see sins or faults in others.

____

____

____

At whatever point you judge someone, God says you condemn yourself because you do the same things (Romans 2:1). No matter what fault you find in another, in the Lord's eyes you have the same type of fault in your life, so stop judging or comparing.

God warns us not to be deceived because neither the sexually immoral nor idolaters nor adulterers nor prostitutes nor sexual offenders nor thieves nor greedy nor drunkards nor slanderers nor swindlers will inherit the kingdom of God. (1 Corinthians 6:9–10.)

This is a hard passage to accept. We tend to make up our own rules. We also create grades of sin. Yet the perfect design God has for us is to avoid all forms of sexual activities outside of marriage. Did you see that lustful thoughts and pornography are in the same category as prostitutes and adulterers? In other words, the man who looks at Internet porn when he is bored is in a similar broken relationship as those cruising the streets looking for prostitutes or a husband having an extramarital affair with a co-worker. This Bible passage is not so much about what particular area a man falls short in regards to sexual integrity, but about the heart. If you judge and don't extend mercy to the person turning to what you view as a worse sin than your own, on what basis should God show mercy to you? Don't misunderstand; God's not holding back on you, but revealing that it's your own judgmental heart that is the real issue. The good news is when you show compassion and freely forgive, then God pours out His mercy and grace upon you because you are finally ready to receive it.

Dear brothers, we all fall short of God's standard of absolute purity. So stop comparing and stop judging. Repent and turn to God. Seek His face and ask for His righteousness and holiness.

Ready for some good news? Immediately after describing how man falls short, God gives us this hope: "And that is what some of you were. But you were washed, you were sanctified, you were justified in the name of the Lord Jesus Christ an by the Spirit of our God." (1 Corinthians 6:11.) God is declaring that those that are now washed clean by the blood of Christ are the very ones, like us, that had engaged in every type of sexual sin one can imagine! The very people for whom the Bible was written included those who had given themselves over to orgies, prostitution, and affairs. Rather than view the Bible as a book condemning you or even those that may have strayed into deeper areas of sexual sin, rejoice that the Bible was written as an encouragement to all men. What greater hope than to see God choosing to encourage all who turn to any sinful behavior that they can be healed by turning to Him. The Lord desires that none should perish, but all come to Him for life (John 10:27–29).

The reality is that the Bible does not condemn sexual offenders. That's right. God does not slam the gates to heaven shut on what we consider a serious sin. Instead, it's only those who reject God's love and forgiveness and continue to refuse to turn to Christ for life that actually condemn themselves (John 3:18). It's the choice to stay away from God that condemns, not the particular sin we stray to.

God's in the business of restoring and redeeming lives. But He won't force you to accept Him or even to believe that His ways are the only ways to bring true contentment. Purpose to stop comparing your life to others. Instead, open your own heart to God. Purpose to get to know Him. He has so much to teach you if you are only willing. Accept that God won't simply take away the temptations to lust. Accept that change is hard. In fact, recognize that you cannot heal yourself or even stop sinning without His help.

Freedom for anyone suffering from any form of sexually compulsive thoughts or actions is the same. It doesn't matter if your particular choice is sexual fantasy, pornography, masturbation, premarital affairs, extramarital affairs, masochism, sadism, voyeurism, exhibitionism, or bestiality. First and foremost, you must want to be changed by God. The Lord will not force anyone to submit to Him or give up his selfish ways. In fact, God allows us to give ourselves over completely to all kinds of depraved practices. Consider Romans 1:28–32, which reads: "Furthermore, since they did not think it worthwhile to retain the knowledge of God, he gave them over to a depraved mind, to do what ought not to be done. They have become filled with every kind of wickedness, evil, greed and depravity. They are full of envy, murder, strife, deceit and malice. They are gossips, slanderers, God-haters, insolent, arrogant and boastful; they invent ways of doing evil; they disobey their parents; they are senseless, faithless, heartless, ruthless. Although they know God's righteous decree that those who do such things deserve death, they not only continue to do these very things but also approve of those who practice them."

There are three things I want you to focus upon from this passage. First, did you notice that God reveals that we sink only when we stray from Him? God is reminding you that it's the refusal to turn to and rely upon God that's the real heart issue and reason we stay stuck.

Second, at the end of the passage God alerts you to the fact that when you get out of tune with Him you tend to seek out and find comfort by others that do the same things we do. It's almost as if you want others to masturbate or look at porn so that you can justify yourself.

Third, what is also fascinating about this passage is the long list of seemingly unrelated sins that are lumped together. Why do you suppose that all of these sins are listed here? Think back to the hand analogy from the article "Freedom from Sexual Bondage" located at Appendix J. Recall that it is pride and selfishness that are the roots that fee all sin, including lust, porn or sex addiction. Our battle is not against a particular sin we find disgusting, but the condition of our own heart. It's your own pride and selfishness that feeds every sin.

Record any notes, thoughts, or commitments.

____

____

____

____

____

____

____

____

HEARTWORK

Ask God what He wants to teach you. Let the Holy Spirit speak to you as you ask yourself:

- Do I think it worthwhile to know and follow the ways of God?
- Am I ready to receive God's healing and be restored to Him?
- Do I really want to change?
- Am I willing to do whatever it takes?

PRAY

Be sure to spend time meeting with God in prayer. Spend your time confessing or praying for others.

- Ask God to have mercy on people who are deceived and trapped in forms of sexual bondage including homosexual behavior, fantasy, or lust.
- Confess and cry out to God to forgive you for judging others.
- Repent from any prejudices or any judgmental attitudes you had or still have.
- Ask God to reveal to you all areas where you compare yourself to others, put others down, or think of yourself as more important.
- List the names of others and earnestly pray for them.

____

____

____

____

READ THE BIBLE

Read Psalm 119:1–20 (or through verse 37 if you have time). Open yourself to God, allowing each word to penetrate your heart, soul, and mind.

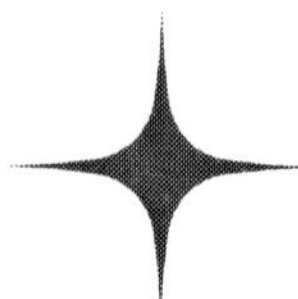

SPECIAL NOTE:

The PROVEN Model for healing begins with passionately seeking after God and clinging to Him. Healing demands that you develop an intimate relationship with the Lord! The problem is that you have been looking in all of the wrong places, even behind doors you never thought possible, because you wanted to control your life and be independent; yet the hole in your heart reserved for God remains empty. As you *praise* and worship God, however, you become positioned to receive His purity and holiness. By fixing your gaze upon the Lord, you literally become so focused and connected to Him that you experience His character and nature. Over time, your will, wishes, and desires become His, and you become holy.

Repentance must occur for you to turn from prior sinful practices. You must experience Godly sorrow for living apart from God. Ultimately, all sexually immoral acts are based on selfishness and pride. It's pride that tells God, "You were wrong in the way You made me" or "I know what is best for me." It's also selfish to pursue fantasies and sexual activities not intended for you. Again, pride tells you that you deserve this pleasure or that God is wrong in saying it will lead to harm. Selfishness and pride are so tightly woven into your thinking that you even deceive yourself into thinking you're not proud or selfish. Whatever the reason you're acting according to fleshly desires, you must acknowledge that God is right and that your thoughts and actions are wrong. Otherwise, your pride will block God from working in your life. A proud man will not really want to change or give the Lord permission to transform and renew his heart, mind, and soul.

Begin today in open and honest communication with God. Talk to Him about your past. Tell Him of your hurts and pains. Talk also to a trusted confidant about your childhood hurts. Do so, however, with the goal of moving forward. Seek out other Proven Men who will not judge or betray your confidence. God will release the weight you were never meant to carry (Matthew 11:29).

A victorious life results when you put down the shovel of self-effort and give the Lord permission to act in all areas of your heart, mind, soul, and will (Galatians 5:16–25). Please note that illicit sexual desires are not instantly or permanently taken away. In short, you'll still be tempted and even have setbacks. But remember, victory is not based on the length of time of your last sin, but how you respond to a setback. God is much more interested in a daily relationship with you than keeping score regarding sins for which Christ already paid the punishment. Victory occurs when a man turns over control—complete control—of his heart and life to the Lord.

A Proven life is also facilitated by replacing the temporary focus you have with an eternal perspective. If you believe that this world is all there is, then surely your attitude toward sinful behavior is affected. But when you believe that God exists, that He created and loves you unconditionally, that Jesus left heaven to die in your place, and that you will receive a heavenly body and live with Him forever in heaven, your circumstances are viewed very differently. Contentment, thankfulness, peace, and joy are just a few new feelings that melt away the anger, bitterness, and self-pity you harbored for years. You also want to obey your loving heavenly Father.

As you cling to and seek hard after God, Christ becomes your true meaning and purpose in life. Please note, you won't win the battle alone. You must be networking with other men who are striving for sexual integrity (Ecclesiastes 4:9–12; Proverbs 27:17). Thus, get out of your comfort zone and connect with others. Allow them into your life. It's the final punctuation mark so necessary for lasting healing.

MEMORY VERSE

Romans 12:1-2: "Therefore, I urge you, brothers, in view of God's mercy, to offer your bodies as living sacrifices, holy and pleasing to God—this is your spiritual act of worship. Do not conform any longer to the pattern of this world, but be transformed by the renewing of your mind. Then you will be able to test and approve what God's will is—His good, pleasing and perfect will."

DAILY READING

Yesterday you learned about not judging others, regardless of the type of sin. This point hit Joel hard years ago when he read a scenario describing a man going to an adult bookstore to watch pornography in a booth. While that man was sexually excited, another person entered the small booth and asked to take care of him. In a moment of weakness, he gave in. The next trip to the adult bookstore was more planned as a place to have a hookup.

This scenario made such a big impression on Joel that he fell before the Lord in brokenness. You see, Joel had been to such a booth in an adult bookstore to sneak a peek at a movie clip. He finally realized what God meant by not judging others. Joel saw that he was not so far away from having affairs or anonymous sex himself. It was then that Joel settled in his heart that he could never and would never judge anyone regardless of any sin whatsoever. Please know that sin never satisfies, and in the continual hunt for more pleasures, who knows where it can lead? Record your reaction to this point.

____

____

____

____

Throughout the study, you're reminded that an intimate relationship with the Lord is the doorway to healing. Intimacy with God is available to all who seek Him with all their hearts. It works this way: As you meet with God for the purpose of knowing Him, you start hearing God in your inner soul. At times, there will be a still, small voice upon your heart. You might have images in your mind directing your thoughts. Perhaps events will seem orchestrated as the same theme keeps recurring throughout the day.

Another way you can experience God is through meditating on Scripture. Certain passages will be fresh and new to you. The Holy Spirit will reveal truth and give you insights as you hunger for closeness to the Lord. At such times, your heart may race with excitement—this is a direct experience with God! As you stay connected with the Lord and seek after Him, He will continue to guide your life by opening your eyes and ears to the same message through a variety of sources. Train yourself to look for these "God sightings." Earnestly desire to know God and to commit to following His will and plan for you.

By now, you know that you must remain in God's camp and under His authority and command to keep on living in victory. Practically speaking, it means avoiding certain people, places, and things that entice you to follow the world, while at the same time immersing yourself in the things of God. Perhaps the enemy's camp is a magazine rack, bookstore, TV show, Internet site, or health club. Maybe its enticement includes particular friends who constantly talk about sex, greed, or other idols. Even hugging people in certain ways can give ground to the enemy. Will you also stop looking for vulnerable people to focus upon for selfish pleasure?

HEARTWORK

Oh, child of God, repent and turn away from anything that hinders and distracts you from passionately pursuing the Lord and seeking Him in His court in divine unity. Replace your former practices with true prayer, focused Scripture reading, spiritual songs, and open communications about things noble and pure. Do you truly desire to change and be changed by God? Unless you do, you'll keep being drawn to the same stench of the world masked only by your own self-deception. Give up control to the Lord. God is not holding out on you. He wants to unveil your eyes and unplug your nose so that you choose that which is edible. Feast upon the Lord. Hate evil and cling to good. *Don't you know that healing will evade the proud and be delayed in those self-seekers who try to control their lives?* On the other hand, your passionate desire to live for God and get to know Him enlists God to permeate your entire life and heal wounds. It's time to assess your true motives. Whether you really want to receive God may become clear from *open and honest* answers to these questions:

- Am I simply reading the Bible out of a sense of duty rather than to meet with God?
- Am I following a program to end sinful practices instead of seeking to be in a relationship with God?
- Do I want healthy relationships so much that I will reach out to others in openness and vulnerability?
- Do I hold onto control of my life (i.e., am I afraid of what God might ask if I yield fully to Him rather than put down the shovel of self-effort)?

It's time to make a heart-shift. It's time to stop posing and start living for Christ.

In addition to intimacy with the Lord, you were designed for open relationships with others. In fact, being lonely or bored are common triggers that lead toward the false intimacy of pornography. Dear friend, are you sometimes lonely? Chasing after the world will leave you empty. However, don't expect an immediate change the moment you say no to lust. A battle will take place. You can expect feelings of loneliness to temporarily intensify as you transition away from a life centered upon yourself and the ways of the world. The Bible notes that your old friends may abandon you once they know you are serious about turning to God (1 Peter 4:3–4). They won't be able to stand the presence of the Holy Spirit, who is being released to act in your life. Remember, however, that they are not rejecting you, but God. Have pity on them, not yourself, because they are choosing an independent life, whereas you are seeking a true life in God. Your open and vulnerable relationship with the Lord convicts their soul, and they run from you to try to hide from God.

Don't be afraid, and don't regret your decision for Christ and His ways. Your home and allegiance is heavenly. All children of God are aliens and strangers in this world (1 Peter 2:11), but God does give you brothers in the Lord to encourage you. Allow the Lord to give you some new friends (Proven Men) and rest in the fact that God Himself is your friend. Purpose to *network* with and be friends to other Christian brothers who are also rejected by the world for choosing purity and holiness.

Expect other trials. Learn to appreciate them. Trials are how you become purified and mature (James 1:2–4; Romans 5:3–5). God says that all who love Him will be persecuted (2 Timothy 3:12; John 15:18). When such difficulties and persecutions arrive, consider yourself a reflection of Christ! You have become a target of the enemies of Christ because it's not you who lives, but Christ who reigns in your life (Galatians 2:20). Others may want to destroy the Master living within you and will do all they can to get you to renounce the Lord and quench the Holy Spirit. Rejoice, because God has accepted you as a son fit to carry out His will. In fact, He entrusts you with His very essence, which others are beginning to notice. Don't turn back, but race forward.

As the battle rages (and these spiritual struggles will not completely end), you must constantly wear God's armor (Ephesians 6). The key is to always keep the focus off yourself or you'll risk self-pity and old feelings that once enslaved you to selfish, sexually immoral practices. Instead, fix your eyes on Jesus, the author and perfecter of your faith (Hebrews 12:2). Choose to serve others out of gratitude and with a willing spirit supplied by God. Plan for times alone, such as reading the Bible, praying, listening to Christian praise music, reading and writing psalms, or doing acts of service for others. Give up TV and other activities that feed your mind with the ways of the world that once ensnared you. Spend time with other Proven Men. Take the initiative to call them or write them encouraging notes. Also, include God in all you do. When you are lonely, tell God about it. Ask Him to fill any voids in your life. The Lord knows how to fill your spirit with that which the world cannot. The Lord wants you as His daily friend. Engage with Him!

- *Will you accept that sexual healing takes time, energy, and a commitment to engaging in the process of relying upon God to supply the grace and power?* State how you will incorporate this into your life.

  ____

  ____

  ____

  ____

- Have you dedicated Friday nights and Saturdays to the Lord, making your weekend a time of worship and praise instead of an opportunity to hunt for worldly pleasures?

READ THE BIBLE

Read Psalm 119:41–72. List five things that struck you.

____

____

____

____

____

PRAY

Spend five or ten minutes with the Lord. Use the names or attributes of God as a form of prayer and praise (Appendices C and D).

- Ask God to break any sins passed down from your parents.
- Commit to forgiving your parents and extending them grace.
- Pray for your family.

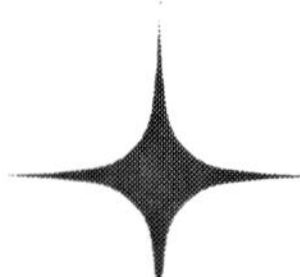

SPECIAL NOTE:

Unless you desire to passionately worship God and are actively spending time and effort developing relationships with others, to what end will your religion rescue you? Consider how much grace God pours out on needy, humble servants, those He calls friends. The Lord bestows such rich mercy on all who have repentant spirits! Turn to God now. He will not reject you. If you hear His voice today, don't harden your heart (Hebrews 4:7). God will replace all you have "lost" and will supply your true needs. The Lord will remove bitterness and anger from hearts that freely forgive others in acceptance of Christ's unconditional love and unmerited forgiveness of their own sins.

MEMORY VERSE

Romans 12:1–2: "Therefore, I urge you, brothers, in view of God's mercy, to offer your bodies as living sacrifices, holy and pleasing to God—this is your spiritual act of worship. Do not conform any longer to the pattern of this world, but be transformed by the renewing of your mind. Then you will be able to test and approve what God's will is—His good, pleasing and perfect will."

WEEK 6 SATURDAY & SUNDAY

This weekend, meditate upon Matthew 5:1–16. Do you want to live by the Spirit? People often reject the teachings and truths of Christ because it means they must give up self-centered expectations and their so-called rights. What camp do you want to be in? Why not be sold out to Jesus? This weekend, begin a practice of using Sunday morning as a time to encourage your family and to prepare your heart for corporate worship in church. Make time to review all of your weekly memory verses and share them with someone. (See Appendix R.) Also, keep sharing with others the exciting truths God is revealing to you daily.

Do you blame others for your circumstances? Blaming God or others for your sexual immorality may seem supported by statistics. For example, a person who was abused as a child is more likely to engage in sexually immoral practices, and those exposed to pornography at an early age are more likely to become addicted than those not exposed. However, anger and bitterness will destroy you if you begin to fix blame. This doesn't mean that you were not a victim or abuse didn't have an impact. God promises, however, to heal and free you from the effects of sin if you turn to Him.

Regardless of the factors leading to your situation, you will remain in sin and bondage if your choices are not God-centered. Satan wants you to be focused on anger, rage, guilt, and shame; to shift blame, and to withdraw from God. The healing God offers is based upon the unconditional love of Jesus. God immediately forgives you when you repent (1 John 1:9). There's no need to feel unworthy of His love or to hide in shame. God also gives you His power to let go of your "rights" and to forgive others. As you deepen your relationship with Christ, you'll increasingly enjoy God and desire the things He desires. That's why you are asked to do a lot of daily *Heartwork*. The strategy is to spend a lot of time developing and maintaining a relationship with God. Be on guard though: Just learning information or checking off homework won't change your heart.

Ask God to reveal any ways in which you have blamed others or shifted responsibility for having false intimacy or shallow relationships. Talk to God and listen to Him.

TESTIMONY

"I had no clue how selfish and prideful I was in my life. This may be a 12-week study, but I'll be reviewing and praying with this material for a long time afterward."

Passionate for God,
Repentant in spirit,
Open and honest,
Victorious in living,
Eternal in perspective, and
Networking with other ***PROVEN Men.***

WEEK SEVEN

TESTIMONY

"I was down one time because of my recurring tendency to sin against purity. It was such a time when I had repeatedly done it that my shame was overwhelming but my pride seemed to get the best of me. Then I just randomly checked the Internet for help sites for my problem and I clicked your site. It was such a blessing for me to have done that. I read through the site and found myself crying and realizing the things written there were all true. I thank God for that encounter and would just like to thank you guys for showing me the real way out of sin. You never know how much it helped me."

Passionate for God,
Repentant in spirit,
Open and honest,
Victorious in living,
Eternal in perspective, and
Networking with other ***PROVEN Men.***

MEMORY VERSE

James 1:19–20: "My dear brothers, take note of this: Everyone should be quick to listen, slow to speak and slow to become angry, for man's anger does not bring about the righteous life that God desires."

DAILY READING

Chances are pretty good that you have experienced some form of abuse (emotional, physical, or sexual), that has contributed to (1) walls still being around your heart, (2) you shying away from vulnerable and intimate relationships and engaging in unhealthy styles of interaction with people, or (3) hidden anger. This may sound like a shocking thing to say, but, it's important to realize that sexual abuse is not limited to forced intercourse. It can take many forms, including exposure to pornography, instruction on how to masturbate, seeing naked adults, uncomfortable touching of your body by another, enemas, or teasing about your body. Emotional abuse, such as shame-based criticism, withholding love, and not permitting feelings to be expressed, can be very destructive. Perhaps you were teased a lot as a child or called names. Maybe your dad was mean or physically abusive. The effects of all forms of abuse frequently carry over into adulthood. The key to healing is a commitment to being *open and honest* about these issues, not locking away your feelings. You must allow God to usher in healing.

Have you been the victim of abuse, whether physical, emotional, or sexual?[18] Most people have. Sadly, adults who had been inappropriately used by others in a sexual manner as children often find it hard to acknowledge that they were victims. Many incorrectly view the abuse through the lens of adulthood. For instance, if someone showed you pornography or touched your groin when you were ten or twelve years old, you may not appreciate that you were not in the same position to say no as you are today. Abuse can have aspects that feel good, and thus you may not view the inappropriate behavior as abuse. But it still was abuse that carries scars.

Take the time to watch the behavior of boys. At moments, they seem all grown up; but as you watch longer, you'll see them as children in need of protection. They are vulnerable and impressionable. That's how you were as a child, but it could be that others violated you and used you for their selfish pleasure without regard to the lasting emotional harm it would bring you.

You didn't commit a sin if you were abused. A victim is never the guilty party, and you're no exception. Even if some later aspects do become sinful, God understands and freely forgives. The unconditional love of Christ awaits us all, drawing us to Him. It permits us to live again. When you open yourself to the Lord and to His healing and soothing love, His mercy and grace melt away self-condemnation, bitterness, and apathy.

Many, if not most, children exposed to some form of inappropriate sexualization (such as pornography or physical touch) develop unhealthy self-judgments. It also opens the door to all sorts of unhealthy sexual responses, ranging from chasing after sex as a form of vindication or viewing sex as dirty even while married. Abuse victims often cast blame inward. They think they brought it on or attracted the sexual advance. Others blame God for not stopping the abuse. In each person, a battle rages inside. Victims suffer deep wounds to their souls, having self-respect torn from them. Anger—even hatred—is planted. Many build thick walls around their hearts, vowing never to be vulnerable. Therefore, relationships remain shallow and unfulfilling. The walls once designed to protect now constrict. While you seek to keep out pain, you also block out love, and you won't let anyone in. How about you? Do you run from real intimacy because of hurt from past relationships or the fear of being harmed again?

Can you trust again? In your own strength, you won't. Instead, you'll constantly turn to false forms of intimacy, ones you dictate and control—ones that don't require giving completely of your soul.

The healing path for victims of abuse begins by embracing God the Father in a real and vulnerable way. Will you turn to God and trust Him? Perhaps you have nagging thoughts, such as "Where were You, God?" or "Why did You let it happen?" You may never have full answers to these questions, but you can trust God when His Word promises that "in all things God works for the good of those who love him" (Romans 8:28). Maybe you'll find consolation in knowing that God can and will use your pain in the healing of others as you can compassionately listen to and love another hurting soul (2 Corinthians 1:4). God also says that the trials in life build you up and make you complete and whole (James 1:2–4).

You don't have to live with bitterness or rage. The more time you spend getting to know God personally, the softer your heart will become. You'll be able to trust again, and you'll be drawn irresistibly to the Lord. As you do, you'll experience more and more of His character, including the richness of His mercy, grace, kindness, and love. He will give you the gift of forgiveness, and you'll even want enemies to be blessed as you keep the focus off yourself. This isn't a fairy tale that only happens to others. God chose you before the creation of the world to be His blessed and dearly loved child (Ephesians 1:4–5). Angels also rejoiced when you turned from sin (Luke 15:10), and the Lord has a kingdom prepared for you, and many good works to do together with Him now (Ephesians 2:10). The solution to a lifetime of hurt is to gaze upon the beauty of the Lord and fix your attention upon Him. You'll be constantly transformed more and more in likeness of your perfect heavenly Father, guaranteed. So fix your hope and trust in Him.

List highlights or any decisions made.

____

____

____

____

____

HEARTWORK

Isaiah 50:10–11 says, "Who among you fears the Lord and obeys the word of his servant? Let him who walks in the dark, who has no light, trust in the name of the Lord and rely on his God. But now, all you who light fires and provide yourselves with flaming torches, go, walk in the light of your fires and of the torches you have set ablaze. This is what you shall receive from my hand: You will lie down in torment."

God warns that those who walk in the darkness apart from God, who light their own fires (self-effort) and follow their own ways, will not experience His healing but instead remain in torment. The firelighters include those who carry the scars of the past, vowing never to be hurt again.[19] Firelighters also are those who live a life of independence from anyone or anything, including God.

The deepest need of a wounded person can only be met by a path of dependence on God. You're deceived and following the wrong road if you think you can be healed or protected from further harm by yourself. Will you dip your own torch into God's cool stream of living water and extinguish your flames of retribution, anger, a closed heart, independence, and bitterness? Will you now begin to walk in God's light and power? Honestly evaluate whether you are an independent torchbearer, and determine to discover what holds you back from being dependent upon God as your source of light and strength.

PRAY

Right now, go to God in relational prayer.

- Ask Him to show you what walls you have around your heart. What are you trying to protect? Now ask Him to tear down those walls.
- Give the Lord permission to take control of all areas of your heart and life. This means you'll have to give up the right to remain angry, the right to run away from conflict, and the right to flee from vulnerable love and true intimacy. God will heal you if you let Him. Go to Him.
- Tell God you want to experience feelings. Now give Him permission to open your heart.
- Spend time pouring out your heart to the Lord. Talk to Him as your Lord, One who is listening.
- Pray for those who persecute you or want to tear you down, asking God to bless, not curse them.

- List some people who annoy you or who you don't like very much. If time, pray for them as Paul prayed for others, using Colossians 1:9–14 as a model.

READ THE BIBLE

Read Psalm 103:1–22. While reading, keep asking God to heal the wounds in your heart. Meditate on this passage, asking the Lord to soften your heart.

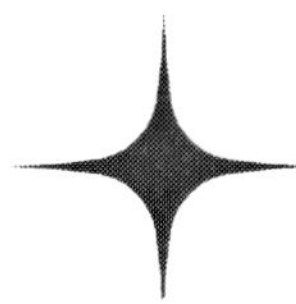

SPECIAL NOTE:

A spirit that's free is one that freely forgives, but a soul that focuses upon self is never satisfied. It cannot tolerate another receiving unearned mercy and grace. Won't you repent over your self-focus and refusal to allow Christ to carry your burdens? Lay down the shovel of retribution and anger. The needy and humble are satisfied because their field of vision is fixed upon the Lord.

Look back to see how you are bitter over, angry with, or adversely affected by hurts of the past, but do so in order that you can forgive those who hurt you.[20] If you hold it inside, the anger against another will constrict your heart and spirit, and you will remain a slave to the ways of the world. Forgiving others is difficult. In fact, one of the hardest things in life is to forgive, but it's essential for healing and freedom from bondage to sin. Forgiveness is why Jesus willingly went to the cross to die for the sins of those in need of forgiveness. Jesus didn't pretend that people did not sin against Him; He did not ignore the real pain and consequences. No, the price of forgiveness was high but totally necessary to restore broken relationships. Love does win out over evil.

MEMORY VERSE

James 1:19–20: "My dear brothers, take note of this: Everyone should be quick to listen, slow to speak and slow to become angry, for man's anger does not bring about the righteous life that God desires."

WEEK 7 DAY 2 (TUESDAY)

DAILY READING

God is just, and He punishes evil (2 Thessalonians 1:5), but vengeance is His alone (Romans 12:19). Those who have been harmed in life are not to seek revenge or hold onto bitterness. Instead, rest in the Lord. God will comfort your wounded heart. He will ensure that ultimate justice prevails.

Why not seek to punish others? Bitterness and anger will gain a foothold. Wanting to become the judge and executioner is selfish and prideful. These often affect your spirit more negatively than the harm inflicted by others. You'll never be truly satisfied by taking revenge or witnessing pain inflicted on others. It won't heal your soul.

If you're honest in your self-evaluation, you'll see so much need for forgiveness in your own life that you'll stop looking at the faults in others (Romans 2:1). If you fail to show mercy to a person who sins against you, you actually bar yourself from receiving forgiveness for your own wrongs. God warns in Matthew 6:14–15 that if you don't forgive, you won't be forgiven.

Don't misunderstand: God isn't withholding forgiveness from you as some form of punishment. He promises to forgive all who humbly ask. Here's how to reconcile the scripture that says if you won't forgive others, God won't forgive you, compared to those He freely forgives who seek forgiveness. If you refuse to forgive others, it signifies that you're quenching the Holy Spirit, who prompts you to forgive as Christ forgives. If you're quenching the Holy Spirit, you're acting out of pride (holding onto the shovel of control) and are in a state of rebellion against God. Therefore, you're not in a state of true repentance regarding your own sin, and hence you're not truly seeking God's forgiveness. That's why He cannot forgive you; you haven't asked in humility for grace.

The good news is that as you allow the Holy Spirit to reign in your heart and soul, He gives you the ability to forgive others while at the same time granting you the gift of humble repentance for your own sin. Think of it in this way: Don't you ask the Lord to spare you from the full measure which your sins deserve? Mercy must be granted to all sinners, including yourself. The Lord fully knows that you simply cannot live at peace while filling your mind with judging thoughts.

If an evil person shot you with a gun, would you decline medical treatment? Would you ask that the bullet and infection remain in order to keep the pain sharp so that your hatred could thrive? Of course not! You don't want your physical body to remain damaged in the hopes that the abuser is somehow punished by it. Instead, you seek healing. Similarly, when others wound your soul, you need a healer. Don't reject the healing of your wounded spirit. Turn to the Lord, the only true spiritual healer. He is the One who created you, and He loves you dearly. The Lord wants to give you a completely well soul, not just a Band-Aid to mask the pain.

What does a healthy spirit look like? The fruit of the spirit is love, joy, peace, kindness, goodness, faithfulness, gentleness, and self-control (Galatians 5:22–23). On the other hand, an unhealthy spirit carries lustful desires for sexual immorality, impurity, idolatry, hatred, discord, jealousy, fits of rage, selfish ambition, dissensions, envy, and the like (Galatians 5:19–21). What fruit do you see in your life? If you've turned to sexually immoral activities such as pornography, lust, fantasy, or masturbation, it's an indication that your spirit is damaged and that you've refused spiritual healing. The same is true if you judge or withhold love and forgiveness from others.

HEARTWORK

It's time to stop refusing the healing power of God. Forgiveness is a key part of restoring your own wounded soul. By truly releasing the sins of others, you stop trying to take on God's position of judge, and you'll be able to appreciate His great forgiveness of your own sins. While you were yet a sinner, Christ loved you so much that He died for you (Romans 5:8). As you now forgive the debts of others, God is released to work in your heart. No longer is it "off limits" to the One who heals and restores. Passion and open relationships will blossom. As you set others free, you actually set your own heart free. Again, the person who refuses to forgive others can only do so by closing out God from his heart and soul, thereby turning down God's healing and forgiveness.

You might ask, "But how can I forgive?" Well, in your own strength, you can't. Your refusal to forgive is a red flag that you're withholding some part of yourself from God. You're refusing to allow the Great Physician to heal your wounds. When God says that apart from Him, you can do nothing (John 15:5), that includes forgiving others. Repent not just from refusing to forgive others but also from your refusal to yield and turn to God. Your heart gets hardened because you haven't fully turned to and trusted in the Lord.

Know this: Forgiving others doesn't mean you're saying that their action was okay. Neither does forgiveness act to release them from all consequences of their sin. The point is that you must not desire their condemnation or take revenge. Rather, seek healing from the Lord for yourself and them. Ask the Lord to heal their broken hearts that have turned away from God and opened the door to the evil they inflicted upon you. Open all areas of your heart to the Lord for cleansing. Turn complete control and authority of your life to God. He will deliver you from your fears and anger. His love will set you totally free.

Dear friend, desire healing of your soul over holding onto vengeance. Because you cannot control the ultimate consequences of others or change their hearts, you'll never be satisfied desiring ruin upon another. Vengeance only breeds discontentment and bitterness as well as damaging your soul further. Yield to God. He won't ask you to muster up forgiveness in your own strength. As your soul is healed by the Lord, the fruit of God's Spirit will free you. Make it your goal to place your soul and heart in the Lord's care. Live out your true purpose in life together with the One who created you and loves you.

Record any insights and decisions.

Have you forgiven as Jesus commands? As hard as it seems, in order to tear down walls you must forgive those who abused you as a child. Also, choose to forgive those who hurt you as an adult.

Forgiving one another was so important that Jesus addressed it over and over again when He was on earth. His disciples asked Him many questions about forgiveness, including how many times they must forgive a brother who offends them. "'Up to seven?' they asked. Jesus answered, 'Not seven, but seventy-seven times'" (Matthew 18:21–22).

Right after giving this answer, knowing that it was hard for them to understand or accept, Jesus told a parable about forgiveness. Read Matthew 18:23–35 and record your insights on forgiveness.

____

____

____

____

- Self-evaluation: What unanswered questions do you have in life that keep you from fully trusting God, e.g., Where were You when I needed You?

  ____

  ____

  ____

  ____

PRAY

Open yourself in vulnerability to the Lord. Ask God to give you His power to totally forgive those who you've been unable to forgive. Trust that Jesus will supply the strength and desire to do this.

- Talk to God about those you haven't forgiven. Ask Him to reveal what is holding you back from forgiving them. Be willing to be *open and honest* and hear from the Lord.
- Ask God to show any anger you have toward Him or toward your family.
- Ask God to reveal truth about hidden anger in your heart, its roots, and the cure.
- Pray for those who have hurt you the most. Ask God to bless them.
- Pray for your family and for other Proven Men. (List them.)

____

____

____

____

READ THE BIBLE

Read through the following verses on anger, meditating on them:

> "In your anger do not sin; when you are on your beds, search your hearts and be silent" (Psalm 4:4).
>
> "Refrain from anger and turn from wrath; do not fret—it leads only to evil" (Psalm 37:8).
>
> "A gentle answer turns away wrath, but a harsh word stirs up anger" (Proverbs 15:1).

"A fool gives full vent to his anger, but a wise man keeps himself under control" (Proverbs 29:11).

"Do not be quickly provoked in your spirit, for anger resides in the lap of fools" (Ecclesiastes 7:9).

"In your anger, do not sin: Do not let the sun go down while you are still angry, and do not give the devil a foothold. He who has been stealing must steal no longer, but must work, doing something useful with his own hands, that he may have something to share with those in need. Do not let any unwholesome talk come out of your mouths, but only what is helpful for building others up according to their needs, that it may benefit those who listen. And do not grieve the Holy Spirit of God, with whom you were sealed for the day of redemption. Get rid of all bitterness, rage and anger, brawling and slander, along with every form of malice. Be kind and compassionate to one another, forgiving each other, just as in Christ God forgave you." (Ephesians 4:26–32).

SPECIAL NOTE:

Find a trusted confidant who will be gentle and non-judgmental in listening to and loving you during times of struggle as you revisit any childhood trauma. Remember and trust that the Lord will heal your hurts as you go to Him and accept His love and healing. God already knows your pain and your needs. Talk to Him, but be patient. It likely will take time to see all of the aspects of your present sinful response as an adult (e.g., bitterness, a closed heart, or withheld love). It may also take time to see the fruit of healing in your life and to give up some of your ways of coping. Keep your faith, and keep going to the only One who can truly heal.

Continue moving toward the Lord for His healing. If you or your spouse have prior childhood abuse in your life, then after this twelve-week series is over, read one of these two books, *Rid of my Disgrace* by Justin and Lindsey Holocomb (Crossway) or *The Wounded Heart* by Dr. Dan Allender (NavPress), which exposes how inappropriate childhood sexual influences lead to restricted relationships that carry over into adulthood and discusses how to tear down walls. Many men avoid reading this book because they don't want to revisit old memories or learn to forgive. However, if you're willing, you can allow the Lord to use one of these books as a tool for bringing healing in your life and opening your heart further in true intimacy and passion for God and others.

For many, the knowledge that God will ensure that justice occurs is enough to free their soul (Romans 12:19). Ask the Lord to give you this peace. Please, however, do not simply stuff anger, hatred, or bitterness inside yourself upon the pretense that you are to give it over to the Lord. Forgiveness needs to be released. Ignoring pain is not the same as trusting God. When you hold onto a desire that harm befalls on another, you restrict portions of your heart from God and others. Your very soul decays and becomes corrupt because it remains apart from the Lord. Your greatest sin is allowing your wounded heart to fester, e.g., you refuse to go to the Great Physician. The wound once caused by others is now worsened by your rejection of God's treatment. It's time to switch masters, giving the Lord complete access to and control over your wounded soul. Talk to God about it right now.

MEMORY VERSE

James 1:19–20: "My dear brothers, take note of this: Everyone should be quick to listen, slow to speak and slow to become angry, for man's anger does not bring about the righteous life that God desires."

DAILY READING

Right now, seek a broken and contrite heart before the Lord (Psalm 51:16–17). Set your heart on accepting God's healing from your anger and His power to forgive others. Review the memory verse.

When you display anger, it might reveal that you don't really believe that God is good or you can trust Him with your life. Maybe you're attempting to run your own life, caring more about your circumstances and rights than about seeking the Lord and enjoying Him. However, self-seekers will always remain trapped in bondage to some form of sin, whether it be sexual impurity, pride, greed, bitterness, or anger. They'll constantly feel the weight of frustration.

Meditate upon Romans 2:8–9: "But for those who are self-seeking and who reject the truth and follow evil, there will be wrath and anger. There will be trouble and distress for every human being who does evil." Write down how it speaks to your heart.

____

____

____

____

You cannot just focus on the ugly aspect of anger to evict it from your life. You must be committed to holiness and righteousness across the board—in every area of your life.[21] This means that your heart needs to be given over to love, forgiveness, and intimate, open relationships with God and others. It means that you must dedicate your emotions to the Lord daily. For instance, in times of anger, cry out: "Lord, rescue me! I give You my anger." Consider Ephesians 4:31–32: "Get rid of all bitterness, rage and anger, brawling and slander, along with every form of malice. Be kind and compassionate to one another, forgiving each other, just as in Christ God forgave you."

Will you rid yourself of bitterness and malice (i.e. evil thoughts toward others) and then replace them with kindness and compassion? The replacement aspect is the true test of forgiveness. You want God not only to forgive you of your sin, but also to bless you. Make no mistake: As you learned yesterday, if you forgive others, God forgives you, but if you don't forgive, God cannot forgive you for similar sins (Matthew 6:14–15). Proven Men want to be forgiven for the sins they commit against God and others. Therefore, they're willing to forgive the sins committed against themselves. Will you choose not only to forgive but also to bless those who have wronged you? (See Luke 6:27.) Tell God.

Anger often is the outpouring of energy in response to a goal that's blocked. You get frustrated over needs or expectations that aren't met. Anger can also result from being threatened or afraid of being used. Most of the time, your anger is not righteous, and it leads to sin and harm. In short, the ground you plow is so hardened by anger that the land cannot yield the fruit of peace, joy, love, or forgiveness (compare Galatians 5:19–21 with Galatians 5:22–24). Moreover, the damage is compounded by a fear of intimacy, pushing others away and refusing to accept intimacy with the Lord.

Uncontrolled anger, which the Lord detests, is more than an outburst of rage, which is merely one way anger is acted out. It includes many forms of inwardly focused self-protection or acts of self-righteousness. Don't be deceived, and don't merely seek to control fits of rage and other outward expressions that are easy to detect. Rather, openly and honestly evaluate your true motives and heart condition. Keep in mind that when you're focused upon your rights and circumstances, you will harbor ungodly forms of anger.

WHAT SHOULD I DO WITH MY ANGER?

God tells you to put away anger, and therefore it's possible to do just that (Psalm 37:8; Ephesians 4:31; Colossians 3:8). God also says that He works for the good of those who love Him (Romans 8:28). Therefore, you can and must put down the shovel of self-effort (see word picture in Week 3, Day 4). Stop trying to defend your so-called rights and trust fully in God to protect and provide for you. Ask God to complete the work in and through you.

HOW CAN I PUT AWAY ANGER?

God experiences anger, although it is always righteous. You can model your behavior after God and follow His directions given to you in the Bible. Consider God's anger:

- God is always slow to anger (Psalm 86:15).
- God gives others room and time to repent before He becomes angry (Revelation 2:21).
- God's anger lasts only a moment (Psalm 30:5–6).
- God's anger is replaced by favor, which lasts for a lifetime and brings love, forgiveness, mercy, grace, compassion, and faithfulness (Psalm 30:5–6; 86:15).
- God doesn't treat our sins as fully as they deserve (Psalm 103:10).
- God removes our sins and restores us (Psalm 103:10–12).

FOLLOW GOD'S MODEL IN YOUR LIFE BY:

- Overlooking small transgressions (giving up your rights) and trusting that God is good.
- Giving others room and time to come around or to see their wrongs. Don't react quickly. Take time to think it through and process your feelings. Perhaps write a note, but don't send it. Take a walk or engage in some other activity before responding. (Don't send off a quick email or text message when you're angry.)
- Taking on an attitude that acknowledges you don't have to win this fight right now. As you cool off, you may even be ready to say you don't have to win the fight at all!
- Admitting to yourself and others that you're angry. Don't bury your feelings.
- Resolving your anger by working through it rather than ignoring it. Also, admit your role and seek forgiveness.
- Replacing anger toward people with favor, i.e., loving them, forgiving them, and being kind to them.
- Not being harsh or giving others what they deserve for their transgressions.
- Forgiving freely, then restoring your heart toward them completely.

Write out any insights you have regarding anger, and state how you will address it in your life.

____

____

____

____

____

____

HEARTWORK

Just like experiencing freedom from sexual sin, you won't break free from a heart of anger on your own. You must decide to give control to the Lord over the wrongs others caused you. Each day you should say, "Today I give You, Lord, control over my rights and emotions, including when I am angry."

Then, when anger arrives, you'll be ready to put down your shovel and turn your anger over to the Lord. Please note that it's okay to experience anger. Just don't act sinfully with it. It's sinful to cross over into rage, revenge, or otherwise allow the anger to simmer for long (Ephesians 4:26). These things lead to bitterness, which festers like a wound that was never cleansed. Therefore, release your anger and turn over control of each situation to the Lord. Of course, you must still seek to reconcile with those who hurt you instead of lashing out with mean-spirited words or actions. God will enable you to do so as you trust in Him fully.

PRAY

The Bible says, "Rend your heart and not your garments" (Joel 2:13). It's not enough to simply admit that a wrong or sin occurred and then react to it. God wants your heart to be soft and loving toward Him and people. You must repent of your sins and restore your relationship with God and with others. Where is your heart? Is it broken over sin and longing for restoration?

- Ask God to open your eyes and heart to Him. Ask the Lord to reveal truth to you today about anger and then to release you from the root issues that fuel your anger.
- Ask God to open your eyes and heart to unresolved anger in your life.
- Ask God to show you how you have refused to recognize or express feelings of anger or how you have sought to disguise it as something else.
- Ask God's forgiveness for being quick to become angry with others or not being willing to forgive as He forgives you.
- Commit to following God's model for anger.
- Commit to holiness and the pursuit of God across the board in your life.

READ THE BIBLE

Read and meditate upon these teachings regarding man's anger, and plan ways to apply them in your life: "You have heard that it was said to the people long ago, 'Do not murder, and anyone who murders will be subject to judgment.' But I tell you that anyone who is angry with his brother will be subject to judgment. Again, anyone who says to his brother, 'Raca,' is answerable to the Sanhedrin. But anyone who says, 'You fool!' will be in danger of the fire of hell" (Matthew 5:21–22). Will you stop wishing harm on others?

- "Love is patient, love is kind. It does not envy, it does not boast, it is not proud. It is not rude, it is not self-seeking, it is not easily angered, it keeps no record of wrongs" (1 Corinthians 13:4–5). Will you stop boasting? Will you put away the record of the wrongs others committed?
- "But now you must rid yourselves of all such things as these: Anger, rage, malice, slander, and filthy language from your lips" (Colossians 3:8). Will you stop complaining? Will you stop gossiping or putting others down?
- "I want men everywhere to lift up holy hands in prayer, without anger or disputing" (1 Timothy 2:8). Will you concentrate on developing your relationship with God, leaving vengeance to the Lord?

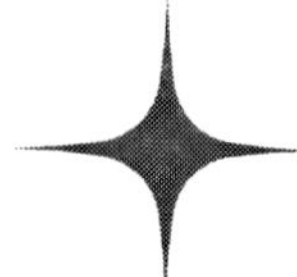

SPECIAL NOTE:

Your anger deeply wounds others.

- Anger intimidates.
- Anger blames others and judges them.
- Anger drives others away from you.
- Anger prevents intimate fellowship.

Your anger harms you.

- You sometimes seek to get what you want by force or intimidation.
- You isolate yourself.
- You build up walls to prevent feelings because they can include criticism, pain, sadness, or other undesirable emotions.
- You withhold yourself (and love or kindness) from others.
- You hide from God, the Source of healing and love.

Read these hindrances to resolving anger and allow God to correct your thinking.

Fear: I won't get what I want without being angry; I will be seen as weak if I don't get my point of view across; if I let others too close, they won't like me.

Isolation: I won't let others be close to me; I don't care how others feel; I can do it myself; I don't need anybody; no one understands me; no one loves me.

Minimize: I don't get angry that much; I am good to others most of the time; I had a bad childhood and have a lot of baggage to carry; it could be worse, I could be doing ______; deep down, I really do love God and others.

Unbelief: God won't or can't change me; I am a bad person; God will make me do things I don't want to do; I am better off being in control of my own life; I have tried before, but it did not work out; my wife won't listen to me unless I get angry.

MEMORY VERSE

James 1:19–20: "My dear brothers, take note of this: Everyone should be quick to listen, slow to speak and slow to become angry, for man's anger does not bring about the righteous life that God desires."

Based upon the memory verse, list the three things you are to do.

___

___

___

Describe how anger is a stumbling block to your relationship with God and why it doesn't bring about the righteous life that God desires.

___

___

___

___

___

___

___

DAILY READING

Below are a few less obvious triggers of anger. Focus on those that fit you and jot down others.

- Listening to the news and reacting to what you hear.
- Failing to do a daily Bible study (and not wearing God's armor each day).
- Being overly busy, tired, or hungry.
- Dwelling on your present circumstances or problems.
- Replaying in your mind what someone said to you.
- Facing tight finances or worrying about bills.
- Focusing on ways you're not getting your way.
- Now add to this list other situations that trigger your anger.

____

____

____

____

Some obvious signs of anger include outbursts, throwing things, and yelling. Often, though, anger is subtle:

- Being rude
- Giving others the silent treatment
- Withdrawing from or pushing others away
- Gossiping or putting others down
- Boasting or building yourself up
- Being critical
- Swearing
- Brooding or sulking

Did you know that one common reaction to internal anger (and to the things that lead to anger) is drifting into fantasy? This escape mechanism takes many forms, such as dreaming of revenge, fantasizing about being a hero, or dwelling upon sexual activities. Perhaps you never realized just how much anger leads you to turn to sexually compulsive activities.

Anger is often a companion of sexual impurity. In fact, if you engage in sexual immorality, the chances are great that deep inside of you there's anger. The root issue might stem from being treated unfairly or suffering some form of abuse as a child. The list of reasons or contributing factors to your anger may be quite long and varied, but the results are the same: *You have a hidden fear of being vulnerable, so you hold onto your rights, always wanting to be in control and keeping others from getting too close to your heart.*

However, you're not able to control life, circumstances, and others, which can bottle up anger deep inside of you. Whether or not you admit it, there's deep-seated anger that you must address and release at the root source. Otherwise, you'll continue to close out God and others, making you ripe for bondage to some selfish type of sin, the same root that feeds sexual impurity.

If you choose to focus on your "rights," you'll experience anger fairly regularly. An angry man has the following things to look forward to in his life:

- Continual bondage to the never-satisfying selfish desires of his heart.
- An ineffective and hindered prayer life.
- A life marred by damaged relationships.
- Acting with harshness instead of kindness.
- Constant impaired judgment.
- Making foolish mistakes.
- Being controlled by feelings instead of truth.
- Judging and condemning others for similar shortcomings.
- Being controlled by feelings of worthlessness.
- Being stunted by a restricted heart that won't give or accept unconditional and pure love.

The good news is that the Lord can and wants to free you. Yesterday, the study introduced the need to live by the Holy Spirit. Some practical things about living by the Spirit with respect to anger include:

- Accepting and trusting God's promise that He will care for you.
- Confessing all self-promoting thoughts as sinful (i.e. anger, revenge, or fantasy).
- Repenting and turning away from sinful thoughts and actions.
- Seeking forgiveness from those you've harmed.

- Trusting God to do the work in your life (putting down the shovel of self-effort and yielding to Him).
- Learning to be content and rejoice in all circumstances.
- Forgiving others based on how God forgave you.
- Accepting that you're not better than others. (Put their interests ahead of yours!)
- Taking captive every thought and replacing it with things true, right, noble, or praiseworthy.
- Being kind to others, even those who harm you, and planning in advance how to do this.
- Reading Bible verses that encourage love, forgiveness, mercy, and kindness.
- Being passionate in loving the Lord, singing praise songs, and reading psalms in Scripture.

God wants to give you these new spiritual clothes to wear instead of anger: Patience, kindness, and humility; bearing with and forgiving others; being self-controlled; and loving God and others (Ephesians 4:31–32). Try them on. They'll make a great fit!

READ THE BIBLE

Meditate on these verses, which is your Bible reading for today:

- "Therefore, as God's chosen people, holy and dearly loved, clothe yourselves with compassion, kindness, humility, gentleness and patience. Bear with each other and forgive whatever grievances you may have against one another. Forgive as the Lord forgave you. And over all these virtues put on love, which binds them all together in perfect unity" (Colossians 3:12–14). Will you seek (and allow yourself to have) compassion for others and desire that they succeed? Ask God to give you this kind of a heart.
- "In your anger do not sin; when you are on your beds, search your hearts and be silent" (Psalm 4:4). Will you respond to anger by going to a quiet place and searching your heart silently and openly, and letting the Lord speak to you about your anger and about your circumstances? Also, stop fantasizing in bed at night.
- "Refrain from anger and turn away from wrath; do not fret—it leads only to evil" (Psalm 37:8). Will you take captive all fretting or worrying about wrongs done to you? Fretting leads to evil.

- "A gentle answer turns away wrath, but a harsh word stirs up anger" (Proverbs 15:1). Will you respond to others with gentleness and be quick to listen and slow to speak?
- "A fool gives full vent to his anger, but a wise man keeps himself under control" (Proverbs 29:11). Will you stop reacting to everything that bothers you and instead live by the Spirit under God's control?
- "Do not be quickly provoked in your Spirit, for anger resides in the lap of fools" (Ecclesiastes 7:9). Will you be slow to be provoked? Will you give up your desire to always being right?
- "In your anger do not sin. Do not let the sun go down while you are still angry, and do not give the devil a foothold" (Ephesians 4:26–27). Will you make it a point to resolve anger and restore relationships right away, on the day of the transgression? Do not let anger boil overnight. It doesn't just go away. This gives Satan a foothold in your life.
- "I want men everywhere to lift up holy hands in prayer, without anger or disputing" (1 Timothy 2:8). What holds you back from lifting up your hands to the Lord, and why do you keep quibbling and arguing with others? Do you desire God's will and purpose in your life? You must trust Christ with all of your life. Be *passionate for God* and seek to love and serve God with all of your heart and with all of your life. Lift up your hands in holiness, not in anger!

Always seek a repentant heart without regard to who was right. Some ideas for processing your feelings in light of Scripture include examining:

- What am I feeling about God while I am angry, and is it based on truth?
- Is my anger a self-protection mechanism?
- Why was I offended or upset?
- Do I want to hold tightly to my rights, vent, and grumble, or do I want to be restored to that person?
- How did my actions cause or contribute to the situation?
- Do I have a log in my own eye that I cannot see because I am focused on the speck in someone else's eye?
- Have I turned to God, or do I choose to sit and stew by myself?
- Am I trying to rally people to my side of the argument in order to win a fight, or am I asking for Godly advice to be able to forgive and reconcile?

- Have I sought wise counsel and accurately stated the facts without trying to make myself look good?
- Do I want to love others because they are people made by God in His image and because God tells me to love them, or do I want to see some people as idiots or unworthy of my love?
- Am I ready and willing to go to the person who offended me so that I might be restored not only to him but also to God?

Mark this list. Next time you are angry, return to this list and process your feelings and attitudes using it as a guide.

HEARTWORK

Use a separate sheet of paper and prepare a game plan for dealing with anger. Start with one situation when you have been angry and think through how you will respond next time. Take time right now to practice a fire drill in your mind. Walk through it several times so that you will be self-controlled, putting on the Lord's armor and His righteousness.

PRAY

Spend five or ten minutes in prayer. Talk to God as though you could see Him beside you. Meet with the Lord and pour out your heart. Be sure to keep praying for others each day.

- Lift up others, listing them as you are praying for them.
- Pray for your church leaders.
- Pray for missionaries your church supports.
- Pray for the homeless and hungry in your community and worldwide.
- Pray for others the Lord brings to your mind, but guard against simply thinking about them.

MEMORY VERSE

James 1:19–20: "My dear brothers, take note of this: Everyone should be quick to listen, slow to speak and slow to become angry, for man's anger does not bring about the righteous life that God desires."

The goal of forgiveness is reconciliation and restoration between you and God and also with others. You'll be applying these principles in your daily life, so be sure this scripture is hidden in your heart. Every one of us has been hurt by others, and it's hard to forgive. State why you think God asks you to forgive others.

____

____

____

____

Sin incurs a debt that must be forgiven. You need to be forgiven by God for all of your sins, which are wrongs against our perfectly holy God. You also need to be forgiven by others for sins against them. They too need such forgiveness from you. By definition, sin is a debt that cannot be repaid in full. Therefore, forgiveness involves the voluntary cancellation of a debt. Right now, read Luke 7:36–47.

Record any insights or prayers to God on the topic of forgiveness.

____

____

____

HEARTWORK

You may have committed thousands of sins, all of which God freely forgave despite you not deserving it. You've also been forgiven countless times by others. When others sin against you, on what authority do you withhold forgiveness? Were your sins against our sinless Lord less deserving of punishment than the sins others committed against you, a sinner? Do you have rights greater than God? Of course not! Don't listen to Satan's lies about needing to protect your rights or demanding that others earn your forgiveness. God knows what occurred, and He is the one who judges. God knows that if you judge, become angry, or withhold forgiveness, you'll withdraw from Him. Satan wants you to be angry so that you'll withdraw from the Lord. Dear friend, God wants you to maintain a constant intimate relationship with Him. Give up your rights and retribution and cling to the Lord.

DAILY READING

Most people who act upon the temptation to retreat into fantasy (sexual or other forms) have anger deep inside. Some will not admit it, and most refuse to examine their hearts. When you fantasize, it's to pretend to live a different life from the one God has for you. You use fantasy as a way to compensate for abuse, unfair treatment, or other shortcomings in life, but the anger hidden deep inside is not released in a fantasy world, and your fantasies don't stay separated from your real life or outward actions. No matter how good you are at pretending or leading a double life, you're deeply affected by your fantasies, because that which fuels them affects you in other real ways.

Often, fantasy is used to block pain. You allow fantasy to occur (and even look to it) rather than acknowledging your anger, bitterness, jealousy, unforgiveness, or other true feelings and emotions. However, you cannot truly block out all of the pain. The fantasy world doesn't alter reality; it merely kills time. Worse yet, it kills your soul by drawing you further and further away from the source of peace, joy, and the healing of your underlying wounds.

Eventually, you act upon some of your fantasies. Just as a pornographic image doesn't satisfy for long, neither will your fantasy world. A progression almost always occurs when you turn to sex as a solution, which will ultimately include things such as flirting, flings, affairs, voyeurism, exhibitionism, or prostitutes. Nothing you try will ultimately satisfy because the root problems have not been addressed.

When you retreat to fantasy, you're really running from God. Maybe you don't believe that God is good or just. In essence, you want to be in control of your life. In your perfectly created fantasy world, you can become rich, heroic, witty, or a perfect lover. You can have fame and fortune; you have no shortcomings and are always right.

You include others in your fantasy, but they are subservient to you; they pander to your every whim and desire. In your fantasy world, they rejoice to receive any morsel from you and gladly center their lives around you without receiving your true love and devotion (except in the twisted way you think your perfection satisfies them).

In essence, you are like God, the center of the universe. Followed to its logical conclusion, your fantasy world eliminates God from your life as you seek to live independent of Him. This is the exact opposite of why you were created. No wonder that in real life your heart aches and you feel as though your needs are unmet. They are!

The cure is not more sex or fantasy. Rather, it's purposing to lead a Proven life by seeking hard after the God of the universe (being *passionate* for God); putting on humility, considering others more important than yourself (being *repentant* in spirit); communicating your feelings, emotions, needs, and desires to the One who can supply them (being open and honest); leading a *victorious* life through Christ; viewing life through God's eyes (having an *eternal perspective*); and serving others rather than being served (*networking* with other Proven Men). You'll only be content when you're living out this real purpose in life.

Don't think that God has shortchanged you. He has great plans for you (Ephesians 2:10). In fact, He has given you more valuable things than anything you can conceive in a fantasy. He has given Himself. First, Christ died on the cross as a substitute for your punishment so that you could be adopted as His son (Ephesians 1:4–5). Second, He gives you His righteousness (2 Corinthians 5:21) and holiness (Ephesians 5:3) so that you can enter His courts (Psalm 96:8; 100:3–4) and become intimate friends with Him (John 15:14–15). There's nothing greater that God can give you than Himself. Won't you accept His invitation?

Dedicate today and tonight as a day to honor the Lord with your mind and body. Play Christian praise songs and select items from the *"Relational Exercises"* in Appendix A.

PRAY

Spend five or ten minutes communicating with God using these examples:

- Ask God to show you how much you need His mercy and forgiveness and how much He has already given these to you so that you can be broken and sorrowful and can then forgive others.
- Accept God's forgiveness for your sins.
- Ask God to change you so that you no longer seek revenge or to pay back evil with evil.
- Commit to the Lord not to seek revenge, but to freely forgive. Ask God for His strength to carry this out.
- Express forgiveness and mercy toward anyone who has hurt you. Turn to God for His strength to forgive.
- Ask God to bring to mind any abuse you have suffered for which you have not forgiven the abuser. Don't let Satan keep this ground and enslave you to bitterness and anger.
- Pray for those who have hurt you. Forgive them in your heart and ask God to bless them.
- Pray for other Proven Men and your family. (List each one.)

____

____

____

READ THE BIBLE

Meditate on the following verses:

- "Therefore, if you are offering your gift at the altar and there remember that your brother has something against you, leave your gift there in front of the altar. First go and be reconciled to your brother; then come and offer your gift" (Matthew 5:23–24).
- "If your brother sins against you, go and show him his fault, just between the two of you. If he listens to you, you have won your brother over. But if he will not listen, take one or two others along, so that 'every matter may be established by the testimony of two or three witnesses.' If he refuses to listen to them, tell it to the church" (Matthew

18:15–17). Be sure that your goal in this process is reconciliation and restoration. Don't misuse this command as a way of rallying the troops or to vindicate yourself. Be 100 percent blameless.

- "Confess your sins to each other and pray for each other so that you may be healed" (James 5:16).
- "Then Peter came to Jesus and asked, 'Lord, how many times shall I forgive my brother when he sins against me? Up to seven times?' Jesus answered, 'I tell you, not seven times, but seventy-seven times'" (Matthew 18:21–22).
- "Do not take revenge, my friends, but leave room for God's wrath, for it is written: 'It is mine to avenge; I will repay,' says the Lord. On the contrary: 'If your enemy is hungry, feed him; if he is thirsty, give him something to drink. In doing this, you will heap burning coals on his head.' Do not be overcome by evil, but overcome evil with good" (Romans 12:19–21).
- "Forgive us our sins, for we also forgive everyone who sins against us" (Luke 11:4).

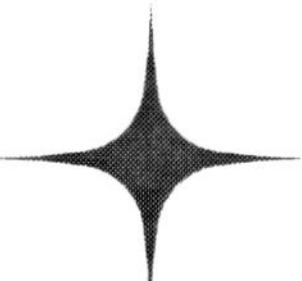

SPECIAL NOTE:

It's difficult to embrace that although you were harmed or even abused as a child, the sinful way you respond today is harming you rather than the abuser. In large ways, the harm to your spirit can be greater now than the harm caused by the abuse because you are running from God and from intimate relationships.

Are there people whom you have not been able to forgive? What reasons do you use to justify your refusal to forgive? Compare them to Scripture. Are they honest? Will you choose love over hate, forgiveness over anger, and life over death? God wants the best for you. You cannot get peace or joy on your own. Holding on to bitterness or withholding love and forgiveness will destroy you, not the abuser.

MEMORY VERSE

James 1:19-20: "My dear brothers, take note of this: Everyone should be quick to listen, slow to speak and slow to become angry, for man's anger does not bring about the righteous life that God desires."

True life comes only from God. Are you fully devoted to Him? Have you turned over complete control of all areas of your life to the Lord? Talk to God about these things. If you were sexually abused, consider seeking help from a competent Christian counselor—one who relies upon the healing power of Christ and is patient and gentle in pointing you to the Lord for healing. Plan also to work through one or two difficult, but wonderful books, *Rid of my Disgrace* by Justin and Lindsey Holocomb (Crossway) or *The Wounded Heart* by Dr. Dan Allender (NavPress), which are designed to guide those who experienced sexual abuse. Face painful memories in order to develop an unrestricted heart. Allow God to restore you. Understand that some of your responses to abuse are sinful because they restrict your heart. Willingly forsake your rights and turn away from judgmental attitudes, condemnation, blame, an inward lifestyle, or self-protection. Run back to the Lord. As a child of God, you can be victorious in living. Ask God to give you His power, and then rely on it. This weekend, make time to praise and worship the Lord. Perhaps write Him a love letter (see Appendix H). Don't forget to set aside couch time to talk to your wife (if you're married) and others.

Starting Monday, you'll be asked to do a mini-fast over lunch. Although not a magic formula, it's a lost art. Fasting can be a way of preparing to yield to the Lord and see yourself as a needy, dependent servant.

Read through Appendix A again this weekend, putting one or more activities into practice.

WEEK EIGHT

TESTIMONY

"I am currently working on the study and it is making some unbelievable changes in my life! Well actually, God is making the changes but the devotional is helping me right my relationship with Him! THANK YOU VERY MUCH for following God's leading you to do this!"

Passionate for God,
Repentant in spirit,
Open and honest,
Victorious in living,
Eternal in perspective, and
Networking with other ***PROVEN Men.***

MEMORY VERSE

2 Corinthians 7:10: "Godly sorrow brings repentance that leads to salvation and leaves no regret, but worldly sorrow brings death."

Sorrow is not the same as repentence. What is the difference between Godly sorrow that brings repentance and worldly sorrow that keeps you separated from God? List some personal examples of each.

____

____

____

Have you ever cried about your circumstances? Well, being sorry or even crying isn't the same as being repentant. For example, Judas was sorrowful about betraying Jesus and then went out and hanged himself rather than truly repenting (Matthew 27:3–5).

Examine the following verses, asking the Lord to open you to Godly repentance:

- "For I desire mercy, not sacrifice, and acknowledgment of God rather than burnt offerings" (Hosea 6:6).
- "They do not cry out to me from their hearts but wail upon their beds. They gather together for grain and new wine but turn away from me" (Hosea 7:14).
- "See that no one is sexually immoral, or is godless like Esau, who for a single meal sold his inheritance rights as the oldest son. Afterward, as you know, when he wanted to inherit this blessing, he was rejected. He could bring about no change of mind, though he sought the blessing with tears" (Hebrews 12:16–17).

Right now, explain why feeling bad or even crying is not the same as experiencing Godly repentance.

____

____

____

____

DAILY READING

FASTING

This week can be a giant step forward if you are committed to doing whatever it takes to be healed and if you really want to live a Proven life. Make this decision now. Ask God to reveal truth to you about sexual addiction, its roots, and its cure. Have you made a decision to do "whatever it takes" to be free from bondage to sinful ways of relating to people and responding to difficulties, and to receive God's healing? Are you ready to start your engines and get going? Well, this time you're going to cut back on your fuel and take on more of God's.

First, if you are physically able, do a mini-fast every day this week by skipping lunch. Go ahead and eat a normal (or light) breakfast and a normal (or light) dinner, and then only liquids for lunch. Each time you feel at all hungry, pray and ask God to change you and fashion you as He sees fit and to take total control of your life. During the day, frequently contemplate how you are recommitting and solidifying decisions of making loving and pursuing after God your number one priority for the rest of your life. (Note: A fast isn't a magic formula. It won't remove sin. It can, however, help you focus and learn to become more dependent upon God.)

Second, give up all television this week. Use the time to listen to praise music, go for walks, and do other activities with family or friends. Devote the week to prayer and holiness.

Third, don't let any unresolved anger remain in you. Make a decision to be at peace by the gift of reconciliation.

Fourth, freely forgive each and every transgression you have suffered, no matter what.

Fifth, practice being content and grateful for everything.

HIDING OR SURRENDERING?

When a person turns to sex or other escape mechanisms, he never brings about the desired result. Many keep increasing the activity in a vain attempt at trying to force it to work.[22] Some will eventually spend hours a day viewing Internet pornography, and others even masturbate up to ten times a day.

Regardless of what you turn to, you'll always be on a constant hunt for more, newer, and better ways to feed the desire for a moment of pleasure. Although you think that you receive temporary relief from the issues of the world that you are hiding from, you're ultimately left feeling empty. Guilt and shame lurk beneath the surface. You often lack any real sense of contentment and purpose. Your double life also creates loneliness because you don't let others in.

Sin never satisfies. How true, and yet how distant the principle. Just knowing in your head that fantasy, pornography, and other sexual sins don't truly satisfy your needs brings little relief. This is especially true if you still don't clearly see the true source of your hidden pain. Instead, you remain caught in a flight from real intimacy. Some don't see any need to revisit old painful memories or look for the deep roots; yet to obtain healing, you need to confront these underlying issues and the source of pain.[23] For instance, if your hand feels numb and you refuse to look for the cause, how can it be treated or healed? Perhaps you have a thorn under the flesh from an old accident or injury. How long will you pretend all is well? When will you surrender and allow the doctor to remove it?

As hard as it is to accept, you have deep wounds in your spirit. The intense pain gives way to escape and coping methods, but your shots of Novocain wear off, and you keep going back to the same numbing activities. Now is the time to end the pretense that you're okay. Admit that you're hurting inside, that the pain of prior relationships hasn't simply gone away, and that you fear intimacy. Your escapes to fantasy, masturbation, pornography, or other anesthesia give you away. Stop hiding your true condition from yourself. Tell God about your fear of real intimacy, and that you're afraid to let others get close. Ask Him to show you how you've equated sex with love and therefore are trying to live without vulnerable and intimate love.

You may have experienced horrible abuse or neglect as a child. Even the harsh teasing by others left scars. The memories may be painful, yet the Lord asks you to open up to Him and others. Part of the healing process is redeveloping *open and honest* communication with others. Seek out a trusted confidant, such as other Proven Men, with whom you can talk about your pain without fear of rejection. Even if some men fail you, don't give up. The Lord will supply you with someone else to talk to if you're willing to do whatever it takes to be healed and fully restored in your relationship with God and others. Also, if, after many attempts, you simply cannot locate someone with whom to openly share, it doesn't mean that God cannot or will not heal you. It just may take longer and require even greater time spent in open communication with the Lord. Once you establish one, tell your *networking partner* of your pain. Admit that you have a hard time showing or receiving love or trusting others. Diligently build relationships with him and several other men. Earnestly ask God to give you someone to whom you can be a friend.

Live out a Proven life, purpose to:

- Recognize the pain of the loss of a relationship with a loved one.
- Forgive the abuser of all harm and release him.
- Form new relationships with other Christians.
- Purpose to see God as good.
- Pursue the Lord with all your heart.
- Trust the Lord completely.

Stop acting upon what you don't know about God and begin seeing how the Lord has proven His love. Jesus' taking your sins on the cross is proof positive! Now seek to get to know the God who gives Himself to you. Record any insights, prayers, or commitments.

____

____

____

____

HEARTWORK

The primary root cause of your lack of intimacy and turning toward sexual immorality is pride and selfishness. In your own words, describe how pride and selfishness keep sexual sins alive in your life. Don't brush this off, but ask God to open your eyes.

Make sure you grasp that "sexual addiction involves relational sins"[24] and meditate on the remedy of turning to God in passion, repentance, and openness. Rebellion and anger must be dealt with before healing occurs; you're in a flight from real intimacy. Meditate on how to pursue real intimacy with God and others, and record any commitments.

____

____

____

Don't forget to fast over lunch. Consider kneeling in your work space and spending some time in prayer, asking God to change you and fashion you as He sees fit. All day long, keep telling the Lord that you are His and that He now has total control over all of your life. It's very liberating to let go of control and allow God to be in charge. Today, or sometime this week, read the *"Network Partnership"* article at Appendix P. This is an essential part of living out a Proven life.

PRAY

With a soft heart, meet with the Lord.

- Ask God to reveal how you are afraid of, in rebellion against, or angry with Him.
- Ask God to cause you to believe that He is perfect and totally good.
- Ask God to forgive you for not trusting Him with all areas of your life.
- Ask God to open your heart to Him and others.
- Ask God to heal your wounds.
- Accept God's healing and unconditional love.

- Forgive those who have hurt or abused you.
- Pray for others. (List them.)

____

____

____

READ THE BIBLE

Are you hungry for the things of God? Keep reading to get to know God and to apply His truths in your life. Read Psalm 22. Jesus quoted from this psalm while on the cross. The next time you feel overwhelmed, recall that your risen Savior can empathize with you and is ready and able to comfort you.

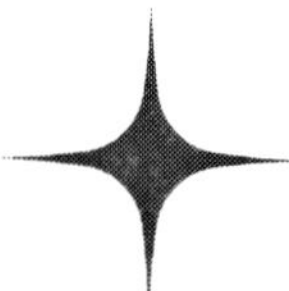

SPECIAL NOTE:

Sexual addiction involves relational sins. You choose not to engage in vulnerable relationships because the wounds of your past lead you to fear more wounds in the future should you let anyone so close again. Therefore, you hide in sexual activities and fantasy. Although you include others in parts of your life, you do so only up to a point you determine, and you have walls others cannot see over or penetrate. On the other hand, the essence of healing from sexual addiction is developing relationships, starting first with God and moving toward others.

O is for Open and Honest. Use discussions with others to aid in the healing process of renewing relationships. Risk telling a trusted friend of the rejection and abuse you have suffered and of your fears. Ask them to listen without offering fixes, and ask them to affirm you. Some deeply wounded men may find it useful to talk to a Christian counselor, but it is important to guard against becoming dependent upon him for hope or healing, which comes only from God. Allow him to help uncover the root pain issues so that you can move toward freedom expressed through forgiveness of others. Look for ways in which you have learned to shrink from intimate relationships. Then seek to be *open and honest* in your real relationships.

MEMORY VERSE

2 Corinthians 7:10: "Godly sorrow brings repentance that leads to salvation and leaves no regret, but worldly sorrow brings death."

WEEK 8 DAY 2 (TUESDAY)

DAILY READING

The biggest battle a person trapped in sexual bondage faces is turning the focus from himself and onto God.[25] Read this statement again. Will you engage in that battle? You must rely upon God's strength to do this!

Powerlessness or a lack of control can be uncomfortable or even scary because you're at the mercy of others. Unfortunately, people sometimes abuse authority and can inflict serious pain, such as child abuse. List ways in which you are powerless today (e.g., addiction, controlling boss or spouse, or debt).

____

____

____

Describe how you have felt in times of powerlessness. (See the *"Feelings Chart"* in Appendix F.)

____

____

____

Many men never like being out of control. For instance, Joel chose not to drink alcohol, not because he thought it was Godly, but because he so desperately wanted to always be in control. How about you? Do you hate powerlessness or lack of control? List what unhealthy walls you have built for self-protection.

____

____

____

____

Men often seek rock solid control over emotions as a way of coping with a sense of powerlessness. We are even proud of feeling nothing (e.g., no fear, no pain, no exuberance—nothing). However, God made us emotional beings with feelings. Suppressing those feelings becomes a full-time job. It's time to reverse course. Start recognizing your feelings and sharing them with others.

Pornography and fantasizing are tempting substitutes for your need for intimacy, but they are a false intimacy that never satisfies. The addiction grows deeper and leads to places you never imagined. Anger is also always just around the corner since you never really gain the control you seek.

One of the most common characteristics of people who turn to pornography, masturbation, or other sexual escape is that they want to control life. You subconsciously rely upon a chosen form of sexual activity to avoid the pain of open, vulnerable relationships. While you cannot fully control others or cause them to love you, you can control your fantasies, the person in the picture, and your own sexual body.

You also control how much of your life you open to others. For instance, you can have sex with someone but not allow them to know your spirit. You probably run from real relationships, or at least those at a certain vulnerable level, because relationships are a source of pain. It seems better to squeeze any pleasure you can from self-focused sexual activities, even enduring the resulting guilt and shame, than to risk the hurt or rejection associated with real intimacy. You end up depersonalizing the object of your lust and thus turn sex, which is a valid aspect of intimacy with a spouse, into an inward, self-pleasing form of phantom relationship.[26] Frequently, even a spouse is treated as an object of pleasure rather than a spiritual partner with whom to grow in deepest intimacy and vulnerability to the point of being transparent and single-minded in heart. Consider the following passages from the recommended book *False Intimacy: Understanding the Struggle of Sexual Addiction* by Dr. Harry Schaumburg (NavPress 1992, pages 22, 31, 38, 72, 80):

> "Sex addicts think and plan their lives around sex... A sexually addicted person becomes fully absorbed with sex, for it becomes the greatest need—not the greatest desire. Sex is wanted, demanded, and will be pursued at any cost."

> "The truth is, however, that when we try to bury the core reality of emptiness, the result is false intimacy, not genuine. When we insist that our needs for intimacy be fulfilled and ignore the reality that loneliness is always present, we get the very opposite of what we're demanding: We're left alone to stare with open eyes at the harsh reality of nakedness."

> "But at its core, sexual fantasy is a worship of self, a devotion to the ability of people to fabricate in their minds the solution to what they know is a need and believe they deserve."

> "Simple recognition of addictive behavior is not on its own enough to accomplish healing. Sex addicts who stop living in denial and recognize that they have hurt others and turned away from God may not always have an urgent desire to change. Their tears of sorrow over their addictive behaviors may spring more from the fear of being rejected and feelings of ridicule than from genuine brokenness and repentance."

> "You must pursue God on His terms, in brokenness and humility, facing the sinful condition of your heart and inviting God to begin healing you. A sex addict truly changes when his or her relationship with God changes."

Record any insights.

____

____

____

____

The fundamental underlying problems that sex addicts face include:

- A reluctance to be in a passionate, dependent relationship with God.
- The use of sex (i.e., pornography, fantasy, or masturbation) as a method of avoiding pain.
- A longing for love but without intimacy.

These, and the other problems associated with sex addiction, are hard to swallow. *Right now, are you beginning to shut down your emotions rather than face these difficult issues?* Instead, will you accept truth revealed by God and seek change? Real change will only come through God and by an intimate relationship with Him. Your other relationships thereafter can be healed and restored.

It's worth repeating that fantasy is focusing selfishly upon yourself. It's time to switch masters.

HEARTWORK

God is perfect, and His mercy is real and good. He can be trusted. Therefore, being under God's control need not be uncomfortable or scary. It's a lot safer than being under your own control. Sexually addictive behavior is an attempt to control life. Explain what this means to you and how it is true in your life.

____

____

PRAY

Turn your attention to God in prayer.

- Review the memory verse.
- Admit and repent over how you have sought to control your life instead of giving control to the Lord.
- Seek brokenness and humility so that you can offer your life as a pleasing sacrifice (Romans 12:1–2).
- Ask God to give you a heart that loves Him and hates your sin.
- Ask the Lord to soften your heart so that you can hear His voice and follow His commands.
- Confess any anger or ambivalence (numbness or competing emotions) toward God or a family member then repent and turn away from it.
- Ask the Lord for His strength and grace to forgive others completely.
- Meditate on the goodness of God and praise Him for being holy and just.
- Seek first the kingdom of God, and pour out your heart in worship.
- List others to pray for and earnestly ask the Lord to open their spiritual eyes to His rich mercy.

____

____

____

____

Don't forget to fast over lunch. Spend time in prayer, asking God to change and fashion you as He sees fit. Continue to keep telling the Lord that you are His and that He now has total control over your life. Perhaps kneel in your work space (if you have privacy) to be more reverent and focused on God.

READ THE BIBLE

Read Psalm 36. Don't rush, but meet with God.

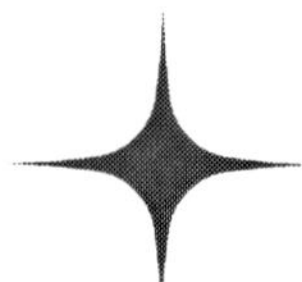

SPECIAL NOTE:

O in PROVEN is for Open and Honest. You're supposed to have feelings. Don't confuse suppressing anger with resolving anger. Suppressed anger leads to unrest and even violent explosions. Resolved anger leads to restored relationships and unrestricted hearts. Go to the *"Feelings Chart"* in Appendix F. You'll see that at times, you feel angry, mad, hateful, incensed, bitter, furious, and enraged. If you lock up these feelings, you'll not be free to love God or love others. Face your feelings and then respond to them as God intended.

MEMORY VERSE

2 Corinthians 7:10: "Godly sorrow brings repentance that leads to salvation and leaves no regret, but worldly sorrow brings death."

Reject performance-based thinking and legalism, which concentrate on following rules rather than focusing on loving God. Stated another way, legalism is conforming to a code or system of deeds and observances in the energy of the flesh, hoping to gain the blessing and favor of God or man. Legalism invariably denies the principle of grace and exalts the pride of man. For example, you set aside 10 percent of your income so that you can say that you tithe versus truly desiring to give God your first fruits. (Of course, there are times that you simply must be obedient and ask God to give you the desire to go with it.)

A warning bell should ring in your mind anytime you catch yourself checking off this series of homework instead of performing *Heartwork*. Nothing will sap the life out of your passion for God more than being legalistic or performance-based.

List ways in which you have been legalistic or performance-based and state how you will allow God to change you in these areas.

____

____

____

____

P is for Passionate for God. One good way to keep a check on legalism is to stay *passionate for God.* Make knowing and loving God (instead of following rules) your goal. Obedience to God necessarily flows from a heart that pants after Him.

DAILY READING

Which is a sure foundation, sand or rock? No one builds a house upon sand. How about your spiritual foundation? Is it built upon self or God? The only sure foundation for a life free from the grip of sin is to stand upon the Rock of Christ (1 Corinthians 10:4). How do you reinforce your relationship with and dependence upon God? You must desire to know and love the Lord. It's a choice. You must choose to accept Him, because He won't force Himself upon you. You cannot have two masters (Matthew 6:24). Either you are acting apart from God or He is Lord of your life. When you examine the building materials carefully, you'll want to choose the best foundation. The more you see God's perfection, power, and might, the more you'll know that He is capable of guiding and protecting your life. The more you see His real and unconditional love, mercy, and grace, the more you'll understand that He has your best interest at stake and can be trusted as the builder.

Intimacy with God occurs and grows when you spend time with Him in worship and praise. This is more than an opportunity to receive an emotional high. When you meet with the Lord to give of yourself in times of worship and praise, He fills your heart and feeds your soul. Your intimate knowledge of the Lord is also fed by reading His Word daily with a mindset of experiencing Him. Your relationship blossoms while serving others and seeing them as dearly loved souls and children of your heavenly Father. While serving others, you step outside of self-consumption and gratefully give without expectation to receive anything other than an opportunity to live out worship. Choose to *network* with other Proven Men, where acceptance and encouragement in the ways and thoughts of the Lord are given and received. When pain knocks at your door, make a choice to turn to the Lord (standing beside other Proven Men), rather than retreating inward and toward sexual behavior. Stop treating the world as a mirror in which you only look at yourself, and quit agonizing over your circumstances. Focusing on yourself is like sticking your head into a barrel. It blocks out the reality and beauty of God and all He created. Rather, open the eternal eyes of your soul and look upward to your precious Lord in heaven. You'll find out that joy doesn't depend upon circumstances.

As you look to God for purpose and fulfillment, you'll soon discover that He has a plan for you. You won't know or achieve it when your eyes don't look beyond your selfish interests. You must lose your life—not control it—to become joined with God (Matthew 10:39). It's time to put down the shovel of self-effort (see Week 3, Day 4). Repent over your death grip on the need to control and now yield to the Lord totally and completely.[27] You cannot rescue yourself or turn your own life around. Embrace being a son and commit to being an obedient servant of an all powerful, yet all loving, good God. He is the One who handcrafted you in His very image, and He has prepared wonderful experiences for you.

Record any insights.

____

____

____

____

HEARTWORK

The Lord stamps men ***PROVEN*** when He is their first love. The actions of Proven Men clearly set him apart, because he is dying to self-focus and pride. You even carry your title of being stamped Proven humbly; boasting only in the Lord. You're no longer ruled by laws or burdened by commands, heavy laden with rules. You are set free! God fulfilled the law so that you could live. Therefore, stop striving in your strength to be perfect (or seen as perfect), and instead live by God's Spirit and through His power. Don't be deceived: Grace doesn't permit sin, but rather a heart shift occurs in a man broken, but not crushed, by the Lord. You start becoming so filled with His Spirit that you're now starting to desire what God desires. Your mind is renewed and transformed. You no longer act on your own. In fact, even passion for God is not obtained by striving, but by yielding. Dear friend, long to yield to the Lord, making it your highest calling.

God is calling you to yield your life so you may unite with Him.

- Will you commit to intensifying your dependency on God? It's important to realize that you will suffer setbacks during times you act independently from God, but you can trust Him to be your strength.
- Will you commit to abiding in Christ? That's how you put down the shovel!
- Will you commit to totally and completely yielding to Christ's will for your life? God doesn't force Himself on you but eagerly awaits your surrender to Him.

- Will you make a decision to believe the truth that God is good and perfect regardless of your feelings or circumstances? Ask God to give you a correct view of Him.

Make a permanent decision to live by the Spirit. Record your commitments.

PRAY

Spend five or ten minutes with the Lord. Some suggestions include:

- Confess your lack of intimacy with God and others.
- Commit to pursue and love God with all of your heart.
- Be passionate in telling God how much you love Him.
- Ponder His names (see Appendix C).
- Brag about God's might and wonders.
- Seek a broken and contrite heart.
- Ask God to break your proud spirit.
- Ask the Lord to give you a heart that loves Him.
- Pray for others. (List them as you do.)

If you are fasting instead of having lunch, consider reading the Bible at that time. Be sure to keep asking God to change you and fashion you as He sees fit. Keep telling the Lord that you have yielded completely to Him, that you are like a lump of clay for the master potter to form, and that you will accept and be content with whatever He chooses for you (even a paper weight block instead of a valuable vase).

READ THE BIBLE

Read Psalms 14, 15 and 19:12–14. Keep going to God's Word daily and applying it in your life.

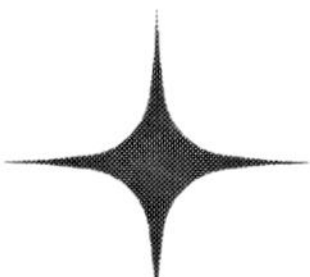

SPECIAL NOTE:

Whenever you doubt the Lord's love, return to the cross. Consider what love it took for Jesus to leave heaven and all His glory to take the form of a man like you. He was tempted in every way and experienced sufferings beyond what you could bear in order to become a perfect sacrifice and substitute for your sin. He willingly took the punishment rightfully due you in order to give you life. Do you think a God of such love wants you to remain in the misery of despair or that He will reject you? No! His perfect love, not the piercing nails, held Him to the cross. He gave you His name and has a room in heaven prepared for you. Even now, He gives you the choice to refuse His gifts. You can keep living independently from Him in agony and despair, but He longs for you to run to Him. He will not withhold forgiveness or love. Choose Him this day!

MEMORY VERSE

2 Corinthians 7:10: "Godly sorrow brings repentance that leads to salvation and leaves no regret, but worldly sorrow brings death."

DAILY READING

God designed you for relationships. Do you have a really close friend? Decide today that you'll be a friend to others. Get to know other Proven Men. The Lord uses the words and actions of other Christian men to encourage one another. Purpose to talk to other men about spiritual matters, and share with them your hopes and goals. Discuss your purposes in life. Stay connected with them.

The Lord is calling you into His service. This is the opposite of selfishness and pride, which feed worldly passions. Make a decision to live by God's standards and to forsake the world. Stop striving to gain what the world offers. To God, your life isn't measured by positions, salaries, or possessions. Real joy isn't based upon sex, fantasy, or other momentary pleasures. Take on an eternal perspective, and you'll experience fulfillment and lasting peace.

Have you taken notice how double-minded people often act? Perhaps you claim to want to bring glory to the Lord while still imagining how you can obtain something for yourself on the side. Chances are that you had no idea how much you lived a dual thought life. Now it's time to live single-mindedly for God. Be attentive to double-mindedness, and trust that you'll only be truly satisfied when you seek the Lord with all of your heart. Allow the Holy Spirit to be your guide. Test every thought. Accept and act upon only that which is holy, pure, and pleasing to God. In the end, your new eternal perspective will radically change the way you think and act. No longer will you remain focused on the moment, but you'll be living out real purpose in the reality of the presence of your Lord and Savior.

Until you understand and live by God's grace, you'll remain subject to a shame-based lifestyle. Many use shame to control others and get them to do what they want. For instance, they say, "Why did you do this?" or "You're wrong." Even failing to complete all of your daily *Heartwork* study can catch you in this self-shame trap. Do you beat yourself up or think yourself unworthy? If he's not careful, other Proven Men can resort to shaming in trying to help you overcome. He might say in a group, "Who did not finish all of the study? Raise your hand."

Each time you're shamed into acting, you place a greater emphasis on performance-based living. You think you can earn love or respect based upon your actions and not because of who you are in Christ. When you view yourself based on performance, your focus incorrectly redirects your steps or actions in your own power to overcome sin to be seen as right before God. Over time, performance-based people are unable to accept unconditional love. They are uncomfortable receiving a gift or a favor. They feel the need to repay it. They must earn love. How often have you thought, "If they only knew me, they would not like me"? Therefore, you strive all the harder to change appearances to seem worthy, but a battle rages deep in your heart because you never really measure up.

Simply put, a shame-based emotional structure emphasizes your worth based upon merit. It refuses God's grace and His healing. The problem is that you'll never be perfect. Fortunately, you can stop allowing shame to tear you down by making a choice to live by and under God's grace. It's a choice to yield to God and take on His righteousness, no longer a slave to feelings of inadequacy. Healing of a shame-based framework occurs when you see yourself as the Lord does: A wonderfully created child of God who is dearly loved.

The transformation process begins by meditating on the truth of God's perfect nature and who you are in Him. As you begin to know and experience God as He is, rather than how you once incorrectly viewed Him, a shift in your thinking and internal framework begins. You finally see that God alone is good and perfect. He truly is worthy of praise and worship. Your heart becomes refreshed, no longer needing to be perfect in the strength of your own hands. Instead, you begin by taking on Christ Himself, including His righteousness and power. You desire what He desires as you fall deeply in love with Him.

By no longer being worried about failing to measure up, you accept God's unconditional love. In your own eyes, you become humble and dependent upon the Lord to lovingly guide you and meet your needs. Through faith, you rely upon God. Real and vulnerable relationships are forged. You're free to be *open and honest* because His love is not dependent upon how good you appear to be. Rather, it's based upon a real and intimate relationship. You finally live in the freedom that there is no condemnation for those who live in and through

Christ (Romans 8:1). Who you are in Christ supplants what others think. Your life becomes stamped Proven by God, who will never reject you.

Feed upon the truths of God and experience His unconditional and unearnable love. Ask the Lord to free you from shame-based or performance-based thinking. Rejoice in the freedom of Christ and purpose to choose to be grateful and content in your new life in Christ.

Many who turn to fantasy have this shame-based emotional framework. Shame leads to broken relationships and "flight from intimacy."[28] For instance, some men are afraid to accept love, and some fear telling others about themselves—their dreams, emotions, fears, or longings—because they think that people won't like them if they really knew them. Perhaps you're horrified that someone someday might learn that you looked at pornography or masturbated. To compensate for damaged self-image, some men excel in sports or other activities to try to win approval of others. Although these outward or merit-based achievements win compliments, they never truly satisfy or replace what is missing in one's life. Compliments or praises might even be rejected because of deep feelings of unworthiness of love. How about you? Do you try to earn God's love instead of accepting that it is unconditional? Describe how these things sometimes fit you.

____

____

____

HEARTWORK

God says that no one is holy or righteous (Romans 3:10; 3:23; 6:23; Ephesians 2:8–9). You cannot earn God's love. That's where mercy and grace fit in (Romans 5:8; 10:9–13). To reject grace requires perfection, which is beyond your reach. Give up and accept God's unearned grace and His unconditional love.

Pay close attention to the process of healing from a shame-based personality. It begins with viewing God as perfect and accepting that you're not. It's who you are in Christ that really matters—an adopted and deeply cherished son who is loved unconditionally. You need not be perfect. In fact, you cannot! That's why you always remain frustrated. You're aiming at an unattainable target. Start correcting your backward thinking. What the Lord wants is a relationship with you. Healing occurs as you yield to Him and turn over all areas of your life to the Lord, including the desire to control life.

Your thought life must be brought to God, taking captive every thought on every topic and redirecting it to things pure and holy, not selfish in nature. Make time each day to spend in worship and praise. Embrace the truth that humility and dependence is the road to real freedom.

Write out any commitments you are making to overcome shame-based thinking.

____

____

____

____

PRAY

Be still. Spend five or ten minutes with the Lord.

- Meditate on how much God loves you.
- Meditate on how much Jesus gave up for you.
- Meditate on how much God has given to you.
- Keep up the fasting and heartfelt prayers, asking earnestly for God to change your heart.
- Pray for ***Passion for God.***
- Pray for ***Repentance.*** Ask for a teachable, non-judgmental heart.
- Pray for ***Open relationships*** and the ability to have feelings.
- Pray for ***Victory*** over pornography, lust, pride, and greed. Be willing to do whatever it takes.

- Pray for ***Eternal perspective.*** Stop trying to earn love or respect.
- Pray for ***Networking*** opportunities with Godly men. (List other prayer requests.)

READ THE BIBLE

Keep reading to know and love God. Read Psalm 27. (Read it out loud.)

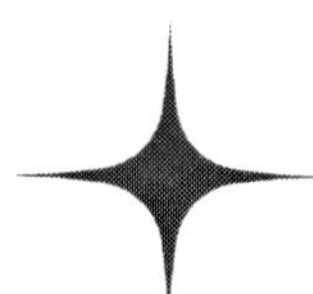

SPECIAL NOTE:

The cure to doubt and lack of faith is to immerse yourself in the Word of God. Read it to impart life. Stop reading the Bible to learn about God, but accept that it's God's living Word, written to penetrate your very bones, refresh your mind, and nourish your soul (Hebrews 4:12). When you humbly seek the Lord, the Holy Spirit lights up Scripture and opens your eyes to eternal truths. God's truth and the working of the Holy Spirit will set you free. Therefore, test everything by God's Word and seek His wisdom and understanding.

MEMORY VERSE

2 Corinthians 7:10: "Godly sorrow brings repentance that leads to salvation and leaves no regret, but worldly sorrow brings death."

DAILY READING

We stated earlier that the biggest battle you will face in life is taking the focus off yourself and putting it onto God. This is especially true for those who have subconsciously turned to sexual behaviors as substitutes for other needs. Regardless of the precise reasons you have looked to fantasy, masturbation, pornography, or other illicit sex-based activities, they all are fueled by selfishness and pride. All that seemed to matter were your circumstances and your rights.

Even your relationship with God had been selfish. God points this out by saying you don't receive what you ask for because you ask to spend it upon yourself (James 4:3). With respect to sexual healing, you once thought it noble to ask God to take away the sexual temptations so that you would not sin. In reality, you simply hated the feeling of guilt, shame, or hopelessness. You didn't truly want to live a life for God and to offer your body as a living sacrifice to Him. The Scriptures you once focused upon were the "ask and you shall receive" portions. You preferred to see God as a vending machine with no requirement to give of yourself in a mutual relationship.

Even with a wife, a selfish man focuses on the few verses that say her body is not her own and that she is to be submissive. He totally violates the letter and spirit of the law by refusing to lay down his life for her, to cherish her as Christ loves the church, to build her up, and to present her back to the Lord as a perfect gift (Ephesians 5:26).

Oh, how our thinking is so backward and self-focused! We miss out on the real meaning in life and often fight against our purpose for living. It's time to surrender your heart to the Lord.

Record any insights or decisions you are making.

___

___

___

HEARTWORK

Spend a few moments asking God to show you any areas that are blocking repentance, such as:

- What do I still get from my sin?
- Why don't I think that God's ways are better than my own?
- Do I doubt that God can really change me?

Face the truth: You're a sinner and double-minded in most everything you do. To change, you must ask God and have the faith and expectation that He will give you repentance. Ask God with a desperation and hunger for change — a change to be like Him.

Admit your utter powerlessness and inability to be renewed apart from Him and humbly ask the Lord of the universe for His undeserved mercy and grace. Then act upon the power and strength God provides.

Set your heart toward repentance. Ask God to open your heart to the need to repent as you examine His definition of repentance, which involves:

1. Recognizing all of your sins as sins against a loving God, which break you apart from Him;
2. Confessing and turning away from each sin the moment it occurs;
3. Turning to God right away, accepting His forgiveness, and answering His call to come home;
4. Allowing and trusting God to do the work to cleanse and heal you; and
5. Producing fruit by relying upon God's power and direction.

1) WILL YOU REPENT BY RECOGNIZING YOUR SINS AND NOT MAKING EXCUSES OR BLAMING OTHERS?

- "After I strayed, I repented; after I came to understand, I beat my breast. I was ashamed and humiliated because I bore the disgrace of my youth" (Jeremiah 31:19).

2) WILL YOU REPENT BY TURNING AWAY FROM YOUR SINS?

- "Repent! Turn from your idols and renounce all your detestable practices!" (Ezekiel 14:6).
- "Repent from pride—and thereby avoid God's wrath and receive His blessings" (2 Chronicles 32:26).
- "Put on sackcloth, O priests, and mourn; wail, you who minister before the altar. Come, spend the night in sackcloth" (Joel 1:13).

3) WILL YOU REPENT BY TURNING TO GOD?

- "Repent, then, and turn to God, so that your sins may be wiped out, that times of refreshing may come from the Lord" (Acts 3:19).

4) WILL YOU REPENT BY ALLOWING AND TRUSTING GOD TO DO THE WORK?

- "God's kindness leads you toward repentance" (Romans 2:4).
- "Godly sorrow brings repentance that leads to salvation and leaves no regret, but worldly sorrow brings death" (2 Corinthians 7:10).

5) WILL YOU REPENT BY PRODUCING FRUIT AND LIVING A CHANGED LIFE?

- "Produce fruit in keeping with repentance" (Matthew 3:8).
- "I preached that they should repent and turn to God and prove their repentance by their deeds" (Acts 26:20).
- "Repent and do the things you did at first. If you do not repent, I will come to you and remove your lampstand from its place" (Revelation 2:5).

READ THE BIBLE

Read Psalm 51 slowly, which is your daily Bible reading, and ask God to speak to you. Read it twice. Meditate as you do. In a moment, you'll write your own Psalm 51 to God.

PRAY

As part of your prayer today, you'll write out a prayer of repentance. Go to the Lord right now, asking Him to give you repentance.

- Confess how you have depersonalized people and lusted after them for selfish pleasure.
- Confess times you have committed adultery in your heart.
- Confess that you have not really wanted to be dependent upon God.
- Admit you cannot overcome in your own strength.
- Turn away from your attempts to live apart from an intimate relationship with God.
- Cry out to God to restore you and give you a new and intimate relationship with Jesus.

The letter *R is for Repentant in Spirit.* Will you adopt the sentiment of Psalm 51? In the space below, write your own Psalm 51 to God.

MEMORY VERSE

2 Corinthians 7:10: "Godly sorrow brings repentance that leads to salvation and leaves no regret, but worldly sorrow brings death."

WEEK 8 SATURDAY & SUNDAY

It can be difficult to fit in the *Heartwork* study on the weekends, but make it a point to spend time with the Lord. Go back over any unfinished sections of the study. In addition, select something from one of the appendices, such as the names of God, and use it to get to know the Lord. Be sure to set aside time to reflect and pray.

Spend some time examining the source of pain in your prior relationships. Don't, however, look to fix blame. Instead, ask God to uncover the source of numbness, anger, or the inability to trust. What's the Lord revealing? As you consider the pain, ask God to open your eyes to how your sexual activities are linked to a fear of vulnerable relationships. Ask Him to reveal ways in which you have responded to pain by shutting down. Ask God to help you learn to trust again.

TESTIMONY

"I enjoy Proven Men because it is an environment that is encouraging on a weekly basis. Whether I am experiencing setbacks and discouragement, or victories and joy, I know that I can share that with the other guys there and they will know what I'm talking about either way. Proven Men has been the catalyst that has turned my entire life around when it comes to purity and pornography and for that I am eternally grateful."

Passionate for God,
Repentant in spirit,
Open and honest,
Victorious in living,
Eternal in perspective, and
Networking with other ***PROVEN Men.***

WEEK NINE

TESTIMONY

"I learned that I'm not in this battle alone. There is a brotherhood. Maybe not a brotherhood that I will keep up with . . . but a silent team of men that understand one another. Men that I can turn to if there is ever a need and not get frowned on about it, but encouraged."

Passionate for God,
Repentant in spirit,
Open and honest,
Victorious in living,
Eternal in perspective, and
Networking with other ***PROVEN Men.***

MEMORY VERSE

2 Corinthians 10:5: "We demolish arguments and every pretension that sets itself up against the knowledge of God, and we take captive every thought to make it obedient to Christ."

It's been eight weeks, which, when work is done every day, is about the time it takes to begin breaking old habits or establishing new ones. Have you been consistent in doing your daily *Heartwork*? If you've been devoting yourself to the Lord, then it may be getting a bit easier for you now. If not, begin again. God grants you a new "today" to set your sail toward Him. Describe how your heart is changing and softening toward God.

____

____

____

____

Earlier in this series you asked yourself:

❑ Do I believe that God is good?

❑ Do I trust God with total control over all areas of my life?

Believing God is good means to trust Him. It doesn't mean you act perfectly. So don't rob yourself of joy by holding back. Make a choice today that God is good and to trust Him. Keep being *open and honest* in your discussions with the Lord. It's time to give up all of your so-called rights and follow the Lord with passion.

DAILY READING

One reason so many people remain in bondage to pornography is that they don't really see it as evil. As a result, it's difficult to hate or turn from it. A person doesn't truly repent of a behavior that he fails to consider wrong. How about you? Do you still refuse to see pornography as idolatry and wicked?

Sadly, our society actually condones and promotes subtle forms of pornography. Hardly any television shows or advertisements pass up the opportunity to use sex to entice. Most grocery stores have racks filled with magazines displaying scantily dressed women. In short, our entire society is given over to idolizing the human body and receiving instant gratification.

Even though you're tempted at every corner, you don't need to join the masses. The will of man doesn't prove itself right merely because others enroll. God is jealous for your love. He knows that when you lust after the ways of the world, you're left empty. Telling you to turn from the world is for your own good!

Who is the commander of your life, and which master do you want to serve? God instructs you to guard your eyes and heart and to go against the flow of the world. How about it? Are you careful about what you allow your eyes to see or your mind to dwell upon? Just as a good soldier doesn't involve himself in the affairs of the world, you must not play with sin (2 Timothy 2:4). The proof of your dedication and devotion to God is in your eyes. They are a doorway to your heart and soul. Do they scan the horizon for someone to lust after, or are they fixed upon God? Don't let your eyes master you, but be the master over them!

What will it take for you to turn from evil and cling to good? Ask God to reveal to you the evil of pornography and to cause you to hate it because it blocks you from enjoying the Lord. Hate it for the harm it causes others. Each time you use pornography, it leads someone else into sin. You're the market that lures others to exchange their self-respect for money or attention. You indirectly cause them to blind their eyes from seeing God as they uncover their bodies for the insatiable lust of others. Innocence is taken from those who want to be desired and loved when they trade it away for a lie. Even their so-called consent doesn't justify your participation in what kills their souls and leads them into an ever-degrading path of destruction.

Dear friend, repent because God warns that it's better for a huge rock to be tied around your neck and thrown into the sea than for you to participate in another person's fall (Luke

17:1–2). Hating sexual sin is not easy. When Joel first confessed to his wife that he was regularly masturbating and lusting after other women, she could see that he was not fully repentant or broken over the sin. She calmly stated, “You are only sorry you got caught.” Joel wanted to lash out at her, but she was right. He still didn’t hate his sin.

Sure, he didn’t like the shame and guilt afterward, but Joel had to admit that he secretly enjoyed the moment. Joel had to retrain his thinking and living. From then on, he kept focusing on how sin grieves God, and how he didn’t want to grieve Him any longer. Joel kept reminding himself: “Pornography and masturbation are sins, and God hates sin; therefore, I hate pornography.” He continually went to the Lord and placed himself in a position to receive true repentance in order to want to turn from pornography, masturbation, and any other things he placed ahead of his relationships with the Lord and his wife. Until you see pornography, lust, and fantasy as wrong because they damage relationships, you will only pretend at stopping. Even if you must ask God every day for weeks, don’t stop petitioning the Lord in earnest for a heart that hates chasing after pornography.

The healing path for addiction to pornography (or other forms of impurity) looks like this:

- Admitting that you have a problem.
- Understanding your root reasons for turning to pornography.
- Seeing that turning to pornography is a flight from intimacy with God and others.
- Believing that pornography (and sexual fantasy) is 100 percent wrong.
- Repenting (grieving and seeking God’s grace) the moment your mind lusts.
- Accepting God’s forgiveness and unconditional love and returning home to Him.
- Stopping self-efforts (no longer relying upon your own strength). Dying to self-interests.
- Asking and allowing God to heal your wounds and fill your heart.
- Living for a larger purpose and keeping an eternal perspective.
- Spending copious hours in praise and worship of God (i.e., passionately pursuing Christ).
- Yielding your entire life to God. Trusting Him with total control of every area of your life and living victoriously in His power.
- Purposing to live out real love and real intimacy with openness, honesty, and vulnerability.
- Staying connected (networking) with other Proven Men who are earnestly seeking the Lord.

HEARTWORK

You can serve only one master. Tonight, destroy anything in your house that's remotely pornographic, such as swimsuit editions, sports magazines, underwear advertisements, and the like. Destroy anything else you've been holding on to or things that block real intimacy with God (or your wife, such as love notes from prior girlfriends and other memorabilia). Also commit to placing a filter on your computer or cell phone, removing the Internet function from your cell phone, cutting up credit cards that you have used to buy sinful items, or even changing jobs, friends or activities that continue to lead you downward.

Are you still lusting after women in TV shows or commercials? If you still are, after eight weeks, you must now know that the TV has to go. Stop watching all TV for a season. At first, it may be hard to figure out what to do with the time. Choose to play interactive games with others and plan out relational activities to take the place of TV, such as those suggested in Appendix A. You'll get to know others better. What a great by-product. The same goes for the Internet. You don't need to be spending time on it. Don't deceive yourself: You can live without finding a good price on material things and without checking out news or sports. If you must know the daily news, buy a newspaper. Just be sure to strictly limit what sections you read and the amount of time you spend.

We need to always be on guard. Because of our past brokenness, we will always be vulnerable to attack.

PRAY

Spend time using the above-stated healing path statements as a tool for prayer.

- Ask God for His strength for replacing self-seeking with God seeking.
- Participate with the Lord in choosing to hate evil and seeing pornography as evil.
- Stay focused in prayer; keep talking to God.
- Ask God to renew your mind, and to allow you to see things through His eyes.
- Pray for others, especially other Proven Men.

READ THE BIBLE

Are you reading the Bible daily? There's no substitute for hearing from God. Romans 6:21 says: "What benefit did you reap at that time from the things you are now ashamed of? Those things result in death!" Settle in your mind that any so-called benefits from pornography, masturbation, or fantasy are short-lived, unfulfilling, sinful, and lead to the death of relationships. Right now, read and meditate on Colossians 3:1-17.

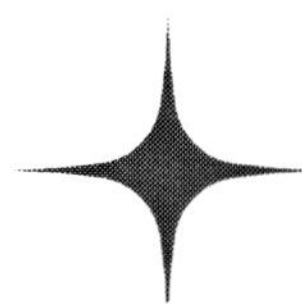

SPECIAL NOTE:

When you're living by the Spirit of God, temptations take on a new meaning. In the past, your stomach may have churned knowing that if you were not strong enough, you would end up giving in to lust. The times you fell were many. Now, however, temptations are an opportunity to grow and judge the level of your true commitment to the Lord.[29] Armed with an eternal perspective and relying upon God's power, begin to view temptations as an invitation to turn to the Lord, giving Him control. Your role is to desire absolute purity and to earnestly seek God's face. *The Lord will turn your weakness into His victory!*

MEMORY VERSE

2 Corinthians 10:5: "We demolish arguments and every pretension that sets itself up against the knowledge of God, and we take captive every thought to make it obedient to Christ."

DAILY READING

The Lord grants victory to His children as they seek Him with all of their hearts and live according to the working of the Holy Spirit in their lives (Galatians 5:16). This is especially true for those who had turned to pornography. Which master will you serve? Will you see pornography for what it is, evil? Confess that you have turned from God, hunting for some pleasure you think He was withholding. Acknowledge that your idolatry, self-centeredness, and pride have actually torn others down while you were participating in exploiting them. Your thoughts and actions were tarnishing the beauty of God's children. Now, as you receive a heart of repentance from God, accept His forgiveness. The Lord doesn't demand that you sit in isolation as payment for your sin. Instead, He immediately forgives and purifies you from the stain of sin (1 John 1:9) and wants you to enter His courts (Psalm 100:4).

The next time you're tempted, choose whom you'll serve, and meditate upon who is Lord of your life.[30] As you make the decision to live under the power of Christ, accept all of Him. Stop just pretending that He is Lord and make Him your Lord. Give up the reins of your life. He will supply the right amount of power to overcome sin. He wants you to succeed. In fact, each time you unite with a prostitute in body or heart, you drag God with you, since He permanently indwells all who believe (1 Corinthians 6:16–17, 2 Timothy 1:14). Trust that He doesn't want you to sin. The Lord will be your help. Turn to Him at the moment of temptation. Don't allow thoughts to linger.

Have you committed to set your heart against pornography? Have you made an irrevocable commitment to never turn to it again?[31] Do so now. Consider this analogy. If you committed to stop eating chocolate, would you leave a candy bar easily accessible on the counter? Would you dwell upon the pleasure you could have from it? No. Well, it's time to stop thinking and dwelling upon pornography. Unlike the candy bar, pornography is a forbidden fruit that causes tremendous harm to all who eat of it as well as their families. Don't torture yourself by constantly dwelling upon some temporary pleasure that might be found in pornography. Stop accepting the lie that no one gets harmed and giving in "just this one time." Instead, think about the love of God and consider how He alone can fill the real needs and voids in your life without your feeling empty or dirty afterward.

Constantly remind yourself of God's truths and promises. Regularly meditate upon and visualize the cross of Christ— the greatest proof of His unconditional love for you. Respond to the Lord with thanksgiving and appreciation. Married men, accept that the woman you're married to is perfect for you. Choose to value her above all others. Single men, wait upon the Lord. He has not forgotten about you. *Each should be mindful not to scorn God's gifts by wanting something else or by lusting after other things.* Purpose to have a grateful heart and a content spirit. Finally, do as God wants when He says, "Hate what is evil; cling to what is good" (Romans 12:9). God will empower you to sustain and fulfill your commitment to hate the evil of and forever forsake pornography.

Record your insights and decisions.

____

____

____

____

An idol is anything you greatly admire or pursue instead of the Lord. God tells us not to have idols—He is jealous for our attention and affection (Exodus 34:14).

Consider these verses about idolatry, allowing God to speak to you:

- "For rebellion is like the sin of divination [witchcraft], and arrogance like the evil of idolatry" (1 Samuel 15:23).
- "Put to death, therefore, whatever belongs to your earthly nature: Sexual immorality, impurity, lust, evil desires and greed, which is idolatry. Because of these, the wrath of God is coming" (Colossians 3:5–6).

Describe how looking at pornography or looking at another person with lust in your heart is the same thing as making pornography or self-gratification an idol in your life.

Given what God says about idols, how do you expect that He will react to your having an idol (pornography, greed, etc.) in your life? Seeking after idols also interferes with your prayer life. You ask the Lord for gifts and blessings, but you worship false gods! Does this help you see why, with this double-minded lifestyle, you're still in bondage to sin? Repent and turn away from evil. You must join one team and not the other. Therefore, choose to hate sin and live by the Spirit.

Explain in your own words why spending more time with God and worshiping Him are the antidotes for lust and impurity.

The next time you're tempted to lust after a person or an image of a person, turn away or close your eyes and ask God to bless that person. That's right, pray for them. Expect that you'll be tempted to focus on them in a sexual way while praying. Choose to engage in a spiritual battle. Refuse to see their body shape as you pray for them. Ask God to protect them from leering eyes (yours and others). Ask the Lord to guide them into purity and holiness. With practice and reliance upon the Lord, you'll be able to take captive every lustful thought and even view women as sisters and men as brothers. What victory you'll experience as God entrusts you to protect and bless others instead of take from them.

HEARTWORK

Have you made an irrevocable decision that you will never use pornography again? It's not enough to say "I will try" or "I will do my best." That leaves the door open for failure. Make that decision right now, that *it's not an option,* and then ask God to give you His power to carry it out. Trust that He will. Now, be *willing to do whatever it takes.* Write out your commitment here.

____

____

____

PRAY

Seek God first. Healing will follow.

- Keep asking God to show you that lust, pornography, and other sexual sins are evil and ugly.
- Ask God to open your heart to hating sin. Commit to hating pornography and ask God to empower you.
- Ask the Lord to draw near to you as you draw near to Him.
- Tell God you commit to pursuing Christ, seeking Him with all your heart.
- Reconfirm in prayer right now any commitments you have made to God.
- Ask God to break your pride and turn you into a needy, dependent servant.
- Pray for others (your family, Proven Men, co-workers, etc.).

READ THE BIBLE

Read and meditate upon 1 Peter 2:11–12 and Galatians 5:16–26. Ask God to speak to you. If you have time, read Matthew 5:27–28 and James 1:13–15.

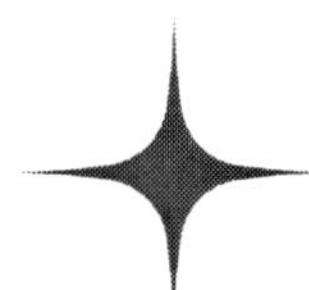

SPECIAL NOTE:

No matter how often temptations tug at you, immediately turn each and every time to God. As you faithfully tighten your grip on God, instead of seeking to control the temptation yourself, Satan will tire of battling God. Don't misunderstand, Satan doesn't want to leave you alone. However, if the more he tempts you, the more you cherish and rely upon Christ, he will see his plan backfire. He will visit you another time, hoping to find you acting in your own strength.[32]

P is for Passionate for God. The spirit and flesh wage war against each other. Sinful desires seek to capture your soul (1 Peter 2:11). God says that if you live by His Spirit, you won't gratify sinful desires (Galatians 5:16–26). Therefore, turn your passion toward God.

MEMORY VERSE

2 Corinthians 10:5: "We demolish arguments and every pretension that sets itself up against the knowledge of God, and we take captive every thought to make it obedient to Christ."

Have you set a bouncer at the door of your mind, and do you take captive every thought?[33] Throughout the day, practice rejecting all sexual thoughts immediately. Refuse to take any bit of pleasure from them. Some men follow a three-second rule to determine if they sin when looking at a woman. That's ridiculous! Don't look for three seconds and then turn away. Turn away immediately. Be aggressive in attacking such thoughts. You'll begin to experience victory when you mean business (God's business) and keep going to the Lord for His strength.

Write out in your own words what it means in this week's memory verse, 2 Corinthians 10:5, to:

1. "take captive every thought"

____

____

____

____

____

2. "make it obedient to Christ"

___

___

___

Describe what thoughts you struggle with and need to take captive (sexual and other) and think through how to take them captive.

___

___

___

___

___

A friend once told me that when he went to a restaurant for lunch he felt tempted to look at a sensually dressed woman. Although he asked God for help in fighting the temptations, during the middle of the lunch, he could stand it no more and looked at her with lust. When asked to describe the situation further, he recalled, "As I first entered the room, a faint thought entered my head: 'Sit facing the wall, not the woman.'" We both laughed. It's interesting to see that the Lord did provide him a way of escape after all; he just chose not to use it.

When prior sexual images or unclean thoughts enter your mind, make it a practice to actually think, "I take no pleasure from you." Cut off the thought mid-stream. Don't let it finish. Then confess the thought as sinful and ask for forgiveness. Keep asking God for His power, and rely on it. Repeat this same process every single time, even if it's every minute as you first get started.

We each are being challenged to change the way we see people. For instance, a proud man may think that God loves him more than others. He somehow deceives himself into thinking that he's better than others and that he deserves God's love and blessings. At the same time, however, he would treat women as objects and others as less important than himself. How about you? Do you sometimes view women as sex objects by focusing on a body part or selfishly dreaming about how they exist to please you? Do you often compare yourself to others? Are you quick to see faults in others? Do you complain when others disagree or don't go along with your ideas or desires? Take a moment to think through how you view others.

DAILY READING

Although there's not a program to purity, there is a Proven path or outline for growing with Christ, which leads to freedom from pornography and other compulsive activities. The following six principles should help clarify your new direction in life and dependency upon the Lord:

Passionately seek God. Take the focus off yourself and put it onto God. Turn your desire toward the Lord. Stop concentrating on your circumstances or your cravings for selfish pleasures. There's only one true, perfect, and holy God. He alone deserves worship and praise. It actually demands much effort to withhold what is due another. Your refusal to release your passion for God becomes a full-time job and robs you of the riches He intends for you. Run to the Lord, who loves you unconditionally and is the only source of true life and healing. During times of worship, the Lord imparts Himself to you, which burns away apathy, anger, self-pity, self-condemnation, and pride. Ask for and receive God's forgiveness and enter into a passionate and restored relationship with Him. Make time to simply praise the Lord.

Repent from your sin of turning from God. You must see pornography as evil, a sin that grieves God because it: (1) treats others as objects for degradation; (2) makes you discontent with what God provides; and (3) keeps you from seeking intimacy with the Lord. Confess your idolatry, which is acted out through pornography, lust, and fantasy. Your selfishness and pride place you on a throne above God. Without receiving true repentance from God, you'll remain at a distance from God, and all of your relationships will be shallow and unfulfilling. Nothing will satisfy an appetite for self-pleasure. Therefore, weep and mourn. Cry out to God to break your stubborn, hard heart. Practice repenting after each impure thought.

Openly communicate with God and others. End the pretense. No longer say that you hate sin while secretly enjoying it. Turn away from false intimacy and be willing to accept the pain that goes along with deep relationships. Begin with the single greatest relationship you can and must have, unity with God. Will you talk openly to the Lord? In fact, what kind of a relationship exists if you don't communicate? Stop praying at God, instead of praying with Him in a relational voice. Tell the Lord of your hurts and what troubles you. Ask questions and listen for answers. Be real. Be vulnerable. Purpose to get to know God on a personal basis. Spend time on your knees in respectful but open conversations. Ask God to expose any underlying issues in your life or sources of pain that keep you from turning to Him and instead fleeing from intimacy. Talk about your desire for absolute purity and your need for the Lord to carry out your commitments. Allow yourself to have and experience feelings rather than stuffing them away. However, don't let the feelings become your master. You need not give into anger or lust.

Victoriously live the life God has given you. God grants you a way of escape. Rely on it. As you live by His Spirit, which prompts you, you will live in victory (Galatians 5:16). It's only when you take back control that you sin. When tempted, take captive the thought and cut it to shreds. Don't take pleasure from any lustful thoughts. Each and every time you stumble, return to God immediately in confession and seek His forgiveness. You'll be restored. Reject performance-based thinking and self-condemnation. As you accept the Lord's mercy and unconditional love, you'll remain in His camp and under His wing, wearing the name of God on your sleeve. Put down the shovel of self-effort and become dependent upon Christ.

Keep an Eternal perspective. The thinking of man is futile and leads to sin. As you focus upon your circumstances, you become consumed with yourself. What rights do you so desperately protect that you would rather live apart from God than be a needy, dependent servant? Fifty years from now, what will matter? Read and dwell on God's promises in Scripture. Ask God to give you His perspective. Begin seeing trials as opportunities to grow. Accept that God won't give you more than you can bear and that He provides a way of escape, then look for and rely upon it. Keep your center of gravity based upon your home and citizenship in heaven. Set out to be grateful and content in all circumstances.

Network with other Proven Men. The Lord sent out His disciples two by two. Don't go it alone. Because you were created for relationships, you won't have rest in your soul by holing yourself up in a room reading a self-help book or by allowing others to see only the exterior of your life. As iron sharpens iron, so do two Godly men sharpen each other (Proverbs 27:17). Engage with other men in open and vulnerable relationships (see Appendix P). Attend church because you want to obey the Lord and fill your innate need to engage in corporate worship. Join a men's Bible study or group in order to encourage and be encouraged in living a Christian life. Purpose to connect with *Network Partners* for the rest of your life.

Memorize the PROVEN acronym, testing your life daily by each letter.

HEARTWORK

Today, settle in your heart that pornography and unbridled lust are evil. Recognize that they will destroy your relationships or any hope of real intimacy and that they will keep you distanced from God. Ask the Lord to reveal the truth about pornography and fantasy to you. *Did you irrevocably commit that pornography and sexual immorality are no longer options in your life?* Restate your commitments here. Ask God to honor your commitment and then rely upon His strength to carry it out.

____

____

____

PRAY

Spend five or ten minutes praying for others. Be earnest in asking God to bless them. Some suggestions include praying for your family, missionaries, other men in your church, co-workers, and neighbors.

READ THE BIBLE

Be sure to fill your mind daily with God's Word. You have a lot of backward thinking to undo. Read 1 Corinthians 13:4–13 and Romans 12:9–21.

MEMORY VERSE

2 Corinthians 10:5: "We demolish arguments and every pretension that sets itself up against the knowledge of God, and we take captive every thought to make it obedient to Christ."

Masturbation (and a fantasy life) is something you try to keep a secret and private thing, and it's something you do by yourself for yourself. Many men make vows to go to the grave never admitting to someone that they masturbated. This sexual sin is like a noose around their necks, and Satan wants them to try to keep it a hidden sin so that they feel alone. *The letter O in PROVEN is for Open and Honest.* God wants you to walk in the light and not to keep things hidden in darkness.

Describe how you feel after you masturbate (see *"Feelings Chart"* in Appendix F)?

____

____

____

____

God wants to free you from guilt, shame, and self-condemnation (Romans 4:7–8). Decide now to accept His love and forgiveness and to rely on His power to stop the downward cycle.

DAILY READING

Even in a world where self-indulgence is flaunted, there remains one thing that is secret and shameful: Masturbation. For many, it's the single greatest source of self-condemnation. Although some advocate that it's always a harmless activity, inside we know otherwise.

Those gripped in bondage feel the pain and aren't easily consoled when others claim that it's not harmful. For most of us, the only way to continue masturbating is to shut off our conscience and lock out God, both of which are destructive.

Despite the fact that the word doesn't appear in the Bible, we know that masturbation is almost always sinful. Jesus told us that to even look at a woman with sexual lust is the same as adultery (Matthew 5:28). It's hard to imagine not having lustful thoughts as a prelude to or an instrument of masturbation. In any event, anything that turns you inward and self-focused opposes God. Masturbation is mostly an inward activity which tends to block out real intimacy with God and others.

Why does God want to keep you from lusting or turning to masturbation? As an initial matter, it feeds a self-centered lifestyle. Intimacy with God is about the furthest thing from your mind when you are hunting for sex or escaping into a fantasy world culminating in masturbation. Please note, the Lord wants you to be fulfilled, not left empty. He knows how lonely masturbation is and how it cannot bring peace or lasting joy. Only true intimacy with God feeds and frees your soul. In addition, masturbation ushers in many other problems beyond guilt and shame. It fosters treating others as objects and idolizes sex over intimacy.

Years of masturbating can actually so fine-tune your response to sexual stimulus that you may experience difficulties in permissive sexual relations with a spouse. For example, a spouse cannot measure up to a fantasy, thereby causing frustration and discontentment. You may also develop premature ejaculation or you may lose the desire for normal sexual relations with a spouse. Masturbation can feed a lustful fire that cannot be extinguished. You'll end up charting a course of seeking new and increased thrills to make up for the fulfillment lacking in masturbation. Eventually, you may add pornography to your rituals. The door often opens to practices that you could never imagine, such as the use of animals, voyeurism, exhibitionism, sadism, and even rape.

What's the solution? It isn't getting married. A wedding ring doesn't quench the fire you stoke. You'll carry over rituals and selfish practices into your marriage. Although you might seek alternative solutions, such as expecting or even demanding sex daily from your wife, the root problems and dysfunctions don't just disappear.

You won't find lasting healing through self-help because human efforts always fail. The good news is that the Lord can and will heal you and change your improper desires. *The letter V in PROVEN stands for Victorious in Living.* God wants you to live a holy and pure life, but it's so much more than just living a good life free from masturbation or another sin. It revolves around living out a relationship in holiness because our God is holy. The Lord has the power to change you into His likeness to foster that relationship in order to stamp you Proven. Each moment you allow the Holy Spirit to be your guide, you'll live in victory (Galatians 5:16).

What keeps a person locked into rituals of self-sex? The root that feeds such a desire is pride and the accompanying selfishness. Self-focus naturally turns to self-pleasure. Ask the Lord to reveal your pride. It exists no matter how much you have condemned or belittled yourself. Your pride either minimizes the problem or wants you to rely upon self-effort to overcome masturbation. Pride also keeps you from talking about masturbation because you're worried what others may think of you. A good question to ask yourself is whether the main reason you want to end masturbation is because you hate the consequences. That reason never produces change. A proud heart pays less attention to the fact that you made masturbation an idol in place of intimacy with God. Pride also blocks you from deeply worshiping and praising the Lord or humbly considering others more important than yourself. Pride acts to stop you from freely giving of yourself to others. It also prevents you from yielding control to God and becoming dependent upon Him.

Although the reasons people turn to masturbation are many, the cure is the same: A deep abiding relationship with the Lord. *The bondage of masturbation can be broken only when you are broken over your flight from intimacy with God.* You must develop a daily, dependent relationship with the Lord. As you earnestly seek Him, the Lord opens your eyes to the pain of missing things in your life that cause you to keep going back to destructive practices. God will provide healing and give you an appetite for things holy and pure. No longer will you foolishly repeat your folly as a dog returns to its vomit (Proverbs 26:11).

Record insights and commitments.

____

____

____

____

HEARTWORK

Are you ready to receive God's healing? Do you want purity more than instant pleasure? Will you love the Lord more than you love your own life? As long as you keep the focus upon yourself or your circumstances and rights, you'll never fully yield your life to God. You'll remain a fringe Christian or perhaps a polished cup on the outside but still be filled with greed and lust on the inside.

The way out of masturbation is to pursue that which:

- Nourishes your soul instead of staining it.
- Fosters relationships instead of weakening them.
- Encourages you to give of yourself to others instead of taking for yourself.

Although there clearly is a struggle between your old and new natures, did you know that the internal magnet of your soul is attracted to God, not toward the world? This means that you must fight against your true needs such as intimacy with the Lord in order to pursue pornography and other sinful practices.

Meditate for a moment upon James 1:13–15: "When tempted, no one should say, 'God is tempting me.' For God cannot be tempted by evil, nor does he tempt anyone; but each one is tempted when, by his own evil desire, he is dragged away and enticed. Then, after desire has conceived, it gives birth to sin; and sin, when it is full-grown, gives birth to death."

Do you see that temptations arise out of your own selfish desires, and that when you are enticed by the world, you literally have to drag yourself away from God? Once you're away from God, your own desires grow until you can stand it no more and give in to sin. Because sin never satisfies you seek even more self-love, allowing masturbation to be your idol. In the end, you squeeze God out. That's why you must always wear the armor of God and take captive every thought before being enticed to sneak out of God's camp. Adultery or other sexual sins don't just happen. You are first enticed by your selfish desires, and over time, you put aside God.

PRAY

Spend five or ten minutes with the Lord in prayer.

- Tell God you really want to be free from self-love, lust and masturbation and to be hooked on Him.
- Tell God you will not secretly enjoy fantasies or sexual sins anymore.
- Tell God you now believe and trust that He is good and able and willing to set you free as you yield to Him.
- Commit to getting to know and love God as the top priority in your life.
- Be real and *open and honest* with God. If you are hurting, cry in prayer as you talk to Him; if you are filled with joy, sing Him a song; if you have sinned, repent and accept His forgiveness.
- Pray for others. (List them as you do.)

____

____

____

____

READ THE BIBLE

Keep reading the living and active Word of God. If you read it to get to know God, it will change you. However, if you read the Bible just to acquire knowledge about God or to check off homework, you'll be a legalistic Pharisee, and God will spit you out of His mouth. Right now, read Psalm 51 with a desire to live for the Lord.

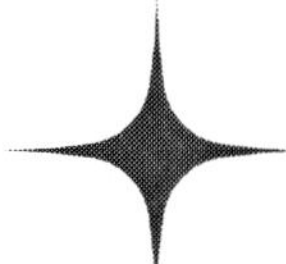

SPECIAL NOTE:

Often self-pity or self-condemnation keep you in bondage. Maybe you think you need an escape from pain or drudgery in life. Some have a deathly fear of closeness to others. Whatever the lure, masturbation can be as addictive as drugs. In fact, just like a runner's high, the body produces certain chemicals in the brain during ejaculation.[34] No doubt it psychologically deadens the pain for the moment. Rituals also have an addictive, habit-forming quality. In short, you can be chemically or psychologically programmed to "need" the relief of masturbation. However, the relief is temporary and unfulfilling. Masturbation can never meet the actual needs you have for real relationships with God and others.

MEMORY VERSE

2 Corinthians 10:5: "We demolish arguments and every pretension that sets itself up against the knowledge of God, and we take captive every thought to make it obedient to Christ."

WEEK 9 DAY 5 (FRIDAY)

What are your plans for Friday night? Keep it a holy night dedicated to praise and worship of God.

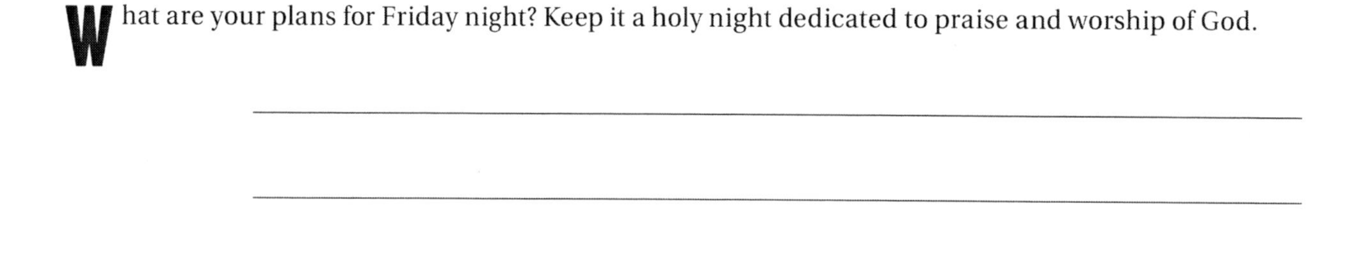

DAILY READING

Do you want victory over masturbation or another sexual sin? Begin disciplining your mind and body as instruments of holiness. This includes fiercely attacking every evil or impure thought. It also means putting an end to the rituals you once followed as a prelude to masturbation or other sexual sin. Next, solidify your decision that masturbation is not an option in your life. Make that decision now. In addition, make a covenant with your own eyes not to look with lust upon others (Job 31:1) or to view people as sexual objects.

Don't be in a hurry—it's your pride and selfishness that make demands for a quick fix. The Lord isn't in a hurry, and He speaks in a gentle, soft tone. To hear Him, you must slow down and wait upon Him. You won't find God by racing through portions of Scripture or rushing through your daily *Heartwork* study. In all things, purpose to meet with the Lord and to hear from Him.

At times, sit still in a room, quietly asking God to open your heart to Him. Don't present a list of requests but ask what He wants you to know. As the Holy Spirit speaks to you, carefully weigh His words. When He moves you to act, immediately obey. If God reveals sin, admit it without excuse and repent. If you don't understand something, tell Him. The Lord permits *open and honest* communication—even to ask why. For instance, if the Holy Spirit prompts you to forgive an abuser, you might be angry because you don't want to release this person. Tell God of your hurts, but do so respectfully. In time, your heart will open and change as you want to experience the fullness of God instead of retreating to your self-protected world where sin abounds and you harbor hatred.

Keep passionately turning to the Lord and obeying His commands. It's during times of worship and praise that He heals and renews your heart. Have you truly repented over masturbation and other selfish sexual acts? Guard against confusing self-pity or self-condemnation with repentance. Even tears are not proof of repentance (Matthew 27:3–5), which requires real humility. Godly sorrow is a recognition that you have grieved God by turning away from Him and living independently. Beating yourself up because you disappointed God is nothing more than pride-driven self-scolding because you failed to measure up. Real repentance, on the other hand, involves desiring intimacy with God more than self-efforts to fix what's broken in your life. Learn to recognize when you engage in the false humility of shame-based self-condemnation or self-efforts. Admit that it's pride that fuels selfish thoughts which block out the Lord and thwart real repentance. In fact, without true repentance over sin, you won't experience complete reconciliation and restoration. True humility is the doorway to divine intimacy and the healing of wounds. The humble won't fall because they're carried by the Lord.

In addition, your prayers and communication with the Lord must be open and honest. Allow the Lord to reveal and then heal the deep roots of your emotional pain. Reject the sinful response you have taken of simply blocking out relationships and intimacy. Trust that God is good and that He can and will heal you as you turn to Him. Then act upon God's strength and promises.

- What struck you from this reading?

____

____

List anything you need to change in your life and state how you intend to make that change. Be sure that your plan is in God's strength and not your own.

HEARTWORK

To have victory, you must set your heart against masturbation or any other sin in your life. If you haven't done this, you won't permanently stop. Will you make a commitment now that masturbation is *not an option*? Will you do *whatever it takes* to stop? Write out any commitments or prayers.

Expect a battle. On which side do you want to be? Satan and his deceptiveness and false intimacy, or God and His unconditional love, unlimited strength, and the gifts of peace, joy, love, and eternal life? Victory is guaranteed as long as you choose to stay in God's camp and not sneak off here and there to make friends with the enemy.

O is for Open and Honest. Give up secret sins (pornography, masturbation, and all fantasies) and turn to God. He will never leave you or forsake you (Hebrews 13:5). Because God already knows what sins you commit, there's no need for pretending. *God forgives you for imperfection, but He won't tolerate deception.* Be *open and honest* with Him and yourself. The Lord is pleased by a heart that seeks after Him with passion. He will reward you with His righteousness.

ADDRESSING LUSTFUL DREAMS:

What about sexual dreams? Are they sinful or beyond your control? When you make a decision for purity, you can expect increased temptations and even lustful dreams. What can you do about them? No part of your life should be off-limits to God. Even your dream life must be under His control. During the midst of healing from masturbation or pornography, you may find that sexual dreams pop up on occasion. This is an area you should not ignore or brush off as something that just happens. When the Lord brings healing, it's to all areas of your life, including your dreams.

Although dreams are in the realm of the subconscious, Satan has no control over any aspect of your life that you don't somehow open to him. Perhaps sensual dreams indicate that you're secretly holding onto some aspect of sexual sin.[35] Maybe you haven't given God control of every small area of your life. It may be the last stronghold Satan has left to try to turn your attention back onto yourself by enticing you with some fantasy. Whatever the reason, you're not helpless.

Consider Galatians 2:20: "I have been crucified with Christ and I no longer live, but Christ lives in me. The life I live in the body, I live by faith in the Son of God, who loved me and gave himself for me." Give Christ total control and authority over your life, which He desires. He will guide you to a victorious life. When you wake up and realize that you had a sexual dream, immediately confess it as sinful. Don't simply accept that dreams are beyond your control. Repent over illicit dreams. They likely are a product of your secret desire to hold onto the fantasy life that you still welcome while awake. Forcefully remove all evil and impurity from every part of your mind. The key is not to accept even a moment of pleasure from a sexual dream. In other words, don't keep replaying it in your mind. Rather, take it captive, rejecting any pleasure from it. The same is true for any sexual thought during the day. Destroy and ruin the moment. Condition your dream life, as you do your daily thought life, to consider all impure thoughts as something to ruthlessly exterminate. Keep turning your entire life over to Christ and give Him authority to evict the intruder. Bend your will more completely to die to self and reject fantasy and all impure thoughts so that you may live through Christ. Cling even harder to God in living out a Proven life.

PRAY

Ask God to reveal to you and cause you to accept that lust, pornography, and other sexual sins are evil and ugly. Ask God to fulfill your desire to hate all sin. *Do you see a pattern here?* It cannot be overemphasized that change comes from God and that God answers prayer. So pray.

- Ask God for the things that He delights in giving.
- Spend time meeting with God in heartfelt petitions for others.
- Pray for other men striving for purity.
- Pray for your family.
- Make a list of other things you need God to do in your life and the lives of others, then earnestly pray.

____

____

____

READ THE BIBLE

Read 1 Corinthians 6:12–20. Read these verses several times, asking the Lord to open new depth to these words He has written for your benefit.

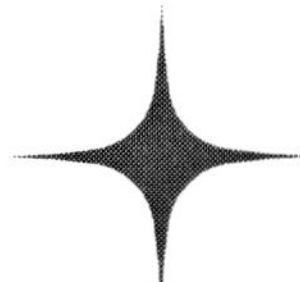

SPECIAL NOTE:

Do you truly want to end the charade and pretense? Are you willing to do whatever it takes to stop seeking selfish sex and other sins that flow from pride? What blocks you from experiencing complete freedom from masturbation, pornography, or lustful fantasies? It may be that your pride is so thick that if you were healed, you would take all the credit for overcoming it. God knows that such pride will only lead you to another selfish activity. Perhaps you don't really want to stop. You prefer scratching out any bits of pleasure you can instead of admitting your need for others or depending on God. Maybe you doubt that God can give you real strength to overcome pride and certain sexually addictive behaviors. You cannot see God-sized power because you still see yourself as the source of life or strength. It's time to yield your entire life to the Lord and allow Him to renew you.

Become a Proven Men partner. Is your heart changing? Do you want to see other men break free and live out sexual integrity? You can help by joining the brotherhood of Proven Men by praying for the ministry, making a tax deductible donation, and volunteering to lead other men. Visit our website to learn more about how you can become a partner: www.ProvenMen.org.

MEMORY VERSE

2 Corinthians 10:5: "We demolish arguments and every pretension that sets itself up against the knowledge of God, and we take captive every thought to make it obedient to Christ."

Pray with your family or a friend on Saturday night and pray again on Sunday morning before church. Spend a few minutes this weekend sharing with others the exciting things you have learned and how God is moving in your heart. At some point this weekend, read Proverbs 19. Finish any remaining parts of the *Heartwork* study and go to bed early each night to begin fresh new days with the Lord.

Have you given up all TV for a season? Think about making such a bold decision for the Lord. Also, eliminate or greatly reduce your time and locations on the Internet. *Are you praying five or ten minutes a day? Are you reading the Bible daily to get to know God?* Keep developing disciplines of meeting with God, but be sure it's not fake. You must give of yourself to have an intimate relationship with the Lord.

WEEK TEN

A WIFE'S TESTIMONY

"Four years ago a marriage of 19 years was under so much destruction from sexual sin that lives were being torn in two. (We have 3 boys.) I came across your website after looking everywhere for help. Finally one day he came home from work at an early hour, he was so distraught that I feared for his mental state. He confessed all. I mean all, for the last 20 some years. As I stood and listened to him account for all he had done I began to thank God that I wasn't crazy and my husband was seeking God and professional help. He went through a year of weekly counseling with a pastor, and your 12-week study, which he did faithfully. It has been 4 years and I know there are days that he still struggles but God is first in his life and he has reread the study and passed it on to others. I just wanted to thank you for offering this to individuals and for the support you have given, we were married 22 years this month and I know that God is working in and though us daily. Continue to pray for strength. And yes the question I always get from other wives is 'Did you forgive him?' The answer: 'Yes because God forgave me!'"

Passionate for God,
Repentant in spirit,
Open and honest,
Victorious in living,
Eternal in perspective, and
Networking with other ***PROVEN Men.***

MEMORY VERSE

Hebrews 13:5: "Keep your lives free from the love of money and be content with what you have, because God has said, 'Never will I leave you; never will I forsake you.'"

The primary lesson for you this week is reviewing why people remain in sexual bondage and then making a decision that "knowing God will be the greatest pursuit of my life."[36]

DAILY READING

What are you willing to do to receive God's healing? Most people claim that they want to be delivered from sin but really only want to be free from its consequences. Of course, no one really says to himself, "I'll just pretend to want to be made well and keep on sinning." Instead, he subconsciously believes that he must have this one little escape. He is afraid of what life will be like without it or what God may ask him to do. Our hearts are capable of such deceit that we actually think we are cooperating with God when we are really choosing to ignore His prompting and the ways of escape that He offers.

One reason people remain trapped in bondage to sexual sin is that they have never truly made a decision for absolute purity or holiness. Please understand that God isn't moved into action by selfish requests to remove temptations, because: (1) He is not a vending machine, and (2) He isn't pleased by His children living an independent life, merely free from a certain sin. The Lord wants a personal and complete relationship with you, His adopted son. In fact, God already fused Himself to you. The moment you trusted Jesus as Lord of your life and asked Him into your heart, He entered, and the Holy Spirit permanently indwells your soul. It's time to give God total control.

Why must you choose absolute purity? Because God is absolutely holy, you must be holy too. Another reason to be pure is because it grieves God for you to have idols. When you choose to go your own way without regard to Christ, you're telling the Lord that you've found something you consider more precious than Him, an idol to worship. Your self-actions and self-interests grieve and repress the Holy Spirit living inside of you. In the end, you refuse to look to or enjoy intimacy with God. Take note: Choosing the world (pornography, greed, etc.) is choosing to reject the Lord. It's little wonder that you don't find things of God to be fulfilling—you have trampled them underfoot. How can you say with your lips, "God, free me from masturbation," when written on your heart is, "But I don't really want to meet with you personally or daily"? What pride it takes to say, "Heal me of pornography," but then keep God at bay because you think you can provide for yourself in other areas.

Your arrogance and double-mindedness don't end there. You claim you don't want to look at pornography because it grieves God, yet you hold onto other sins such as bitterness, greed, and indulgence. Understand this: The Lord wants you to live in intimacy with Him and experience holiness across the board. Every sin you harbor grieves the Lord and signifies your self-reliant and prideful spirit. A real relationship with God is 24/7. It's an all-out unity of two becoming one.

Recall once again this familiar verse: "I have been crucified with Christ and I no longer live, but Christ lives in me. The life I live in the body, I live by faith in the Son of God, who loved me and gave himself for me" (Galatians 2:20).

Don't gloss over this passage. Each time you read this verse ask God to melt your heart. Is it your cry to live by faith in Christ and be fully yielded to Him, or are you still too proud and believe you should be the one making the decisions for your life despite the Holy Spirit's permanently indwelling you as a deposit, guaranteeing your place in heaven with the Lord? Confess to God that you've wanted to live a selectively Christian life. Confess how you've wanted heaven on earth, on your terms, where you become the object of praise. Admit that you didn't want a full-fledged relationship with God but rather for Him to make your life easy and soft. Ask the Lord to open your eyes to your pride and selfishness. Drop to your knees in sorrow for acting in pride, the same pride as the devil himself.

Right now, tell the Lord that starting today you want to know Him for who He is, not how you've wanted Him to be. Search for Him like a hidden treasure so that you'll see His beautiful, wonderful, and perfect nature. Ask God to give you passion to live for and through Him with a soft and repentant heart that openly communicates with the Lord as a true and loyal friend. Commit to becoming a needy and dependent servant of the only true and worthy God. Desire to seek sexual integrity as a way of giving glory to the Lord in real worship and to be holy in all areas of your life, because He is holy and because you never want to leave His side again.

Did you pray these things? Have you made an irrevocable commitment to live for God? The Lord will supply your ability to carry out a desire for absolute purity and across-the-board holiness as you earnestly seek His face. Accept His power. Passionately pursue God and then trust completely in Him. Stop doubting that He can handle your problems. Try to see things from God's eternal perspective. Otherwise, you'll fail to see that God has your best interests at heart, and you won't accept His leading, power, or strength. You'll be fooling yourself.

HEARTWORK

Here's a helpful question to determine whether and why a person is still in bondage to sexual sins: "Am I willing to do whatever it takes to receive God's healing?" *Can you honestly say, "No matter what the cost, Lord, I am willing"?* Notice that you're asking to receive God's healing instead of to stopping to lust. Do you understand the difference? Until you do, real freedom may escape you. Make sure that you're willing to do whatever it takes to live a holy and pure life in a relationship with God and not merely looking to God for help in ending habits you find distasteful.

Are you asking the Lord to take control of every single area of your life, without holding back anything? Your *open and honest* answer says a lot about who you say God is and whether you really want Him to heal you. If you cannot say absolutely yes, you are blocking God from fully using His healing power in your life. You'll keep struggling because you're still using your own strength and power.

List any non-sexual sins in your life, such as exaggerating the truth, gossip, comparison to others, boasting, gambling, anger, pride, or greed.

____

____

____

Have you allowed non-sexual sins to stay in your life because they were just not important enough to address (selective living), or did you think you could handle these little sins on your own (self-reliant living)? God wants you to be holy in all things, which results only from depending upon Him in everything. Consider what God means in His Word when He says that those who are faithful with a few things will be put in charge of many things (Matthew 25:21). If you're not faithful in using God's power to eradicate gossip or other so-called lesser sins from your life, why expect to be given power to overcome sexual sins?

Do you think God only wants His children to be free from sexual sins but not to be free from lies or other unfaithful acts? *Similarly, if you seek to use your own strength to overcome small sins, why would you turn to God for overcoming larger sins? Do you see the big picture now?* Be dependent upon God in all things and seek to really know Him intimately; be His friend and His obedient child.

God doesn't want you to just live a life free of sexual sins; He wants a relationship with you. He is absolutely holy in all areas, and He wants you to be like Him. Friends share things in common. Consider this familiar verse: "Be holy, because I am holy" (1 Peter 1:16). Even if you once overlooked this command or merely dismissed it as an impossible statement, try to view it in a new way as you view God differently. Close your eyes and imagine God gently calling your name, whispering to you, inviting you to enter His court: *My son, My son, be holy as I am holy; draw near to me so we can be close* (see 1 Peter 1:16; James 4:8). This invitation is largely about how you must give up sin and turn to Him so you can enter His pure and holy temple. God's commands are designed to lead you to His holy mountain to be with Him.

PRAY

Answer God's calling by meeting with Him in intimacy right now.

- Seek holiness and purity across the board.
- Dedicate your entire life (in all areas) to the Lord.
- Yield your life completely to God and give Him total control. Make the decision permanent.
- Pray for holiness and purity in the lives of other Proven Men.
- Pray for your family. (List them.)

____

____

____

____

READ THE BIBLE

Read Psalm 34. Let your heart sing as you absorb God's Word.

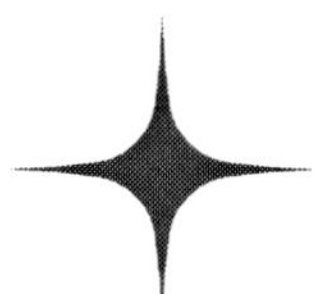

SPECIAL NOTE:

Meeting with the Lord in times of praise and earnest prayer is perhaps the greatest moment of receiving God Himself into your life (and thus His healing, wisdom, and strength). It's then that you are lifted to His courts and enter His presence. The world and its lusts become purged and burned away, replaced by passion for more of Him. The gifts of repentance and humility are poured into you during times when you long to be with Him. Your purity grows in direct proportion to the time you spend with the Lord in earnest prayer and devotion. During such times of intimacy, God imparts truth, life, and healing to you. That's the operating room of the Great Physician. You'll live out a Proven life as you commit to living out absolute purity in total dependence upon and gratitude to God.

MEMORY VERSE

Hebrews 13:5: "Keep your lives free from the love of money and be content with what you have, because God has said, 'Never will I leave you; never will I forsake you.'"

Why is it vital to keep free from the love of money? One reason is that by dwelling on material things, you don't earnestly pray or seek after God; you forget His promises, and you forget about Him. The Lord knows that the love of money (greed or pursuing material things) keeps you from being content with what He knows is best for you. Your desire for temporary selfish pleasures will only drag you outside of God's camp and breed discontentment.

Being content with what you have means not seeking more pleasures, more wealth, or more of anything of this world. Explain why God's promise, "Never will I leave you; never will I forsake you" (Hebrews 13:5), leads to contentment.

____

____

____

____

____

Will you commit to trusting in the strength of the Lord alone? Ask God to reveal to you that what He does give you is sufficient and in your best interest for a joyful and peaceful life.

DAILY READING

One of the biggest reasons people remain trapped in bondage to sexual sin is that they haven't fully embraced the true nature of God and their relation to Him. This plays itself out in many ways. For instance, some refuse to turn completely to God because they love themselves and their sins too much. They remain ignorant of the fullness and beauty of God and how He offers Himself freely to us. Others incorrectly believe they are unworthy of God's love or grace and see their sins as too great to be wiped clean. Many merely want temptations to be taken away. They ask God to spare them of all trials and temptations and to grant them happy lives without the necessary aspects of intimacy or dependency. They lose sight of the fact that trials develop perseverance and aid in making you whole and complete. Do you want to be changed by God and live out a pure life? If anyone purposefully positions himself to see and meet with God, he will be changed. He will find a completely loving God who eagerly desires to hold and protect him. He will know a God who so freely and perfectly forgives that it's as though each day he becomes a new creation.

To grow in Christ, you must humbly seek the Lord with all of your heart in order to passionately and openly worship the King of the universe, your Father and friend. You must transition from wanting to control your own life to wanting what the Lord wants. His desires will become your desires when you see God as good and therefore trust Him. It's that simple.

Consider how you choose to trust people. How would you react if someone invited you to go with him on an unspecified vacation, asking you to meet him at the airport? If you didn't know the person very well, you might be a bit anxious, but as each day seemed better than the day before, you would trust him with the rest of the vacation.

Well, God has a perfect life planned for you. However, you keep lagging behind and taking side trips because you don't trust Him. Even though some of the days He has planned will be hard, He has all of the right equipment for the venture. As you get in shape, you're able to handle difficulties with ease. The trials merely perfect you for tomorrow. Your growing fitness enables you to go to higher levels and more places. What a journey God has for you, to travel with Him as your personal guide! Don't you want to be conditioned by Him so that you can go where He leads?

God changes you by drawing you to Himself through the outpouring of His unconditional love. No whip is needed because His beauty and perfect nature are irresistible if you permit yourself to experience Him. As you yield control to and trust in God, He imparts perseverance, which must grow so that you can withstand the temptations and evil forces of the world and journey with Him to special places. Your obedience reflects your love for God and permits further refinement of your spirit and will. You become more than a worshiper of God: You unite as one with Him (1 Corinthians 6:17), experiencing His perfect holiness and righteousness. Your old nature of pride and self-focus is put away. Victorious living naturally follows.

- Do you love a certain sin that seems too much to give up? What is it, and why do you cherish it?

____

____

____

____

If you spend time with Jesus with the goal of getting to know Him, you'll fall in love with Him. Then you'll want what Christ wants more than you'll want sexually immoral activities. Your desires will change. You'll experience lasting freedom. Start the process now by meditating on the proof of God's love for you, beginning with the cross. Christ's willingness to take your punishment is proof positive.

Is the healing process going too slowly for you? It won't be if you're too busy seeking after God to worry about how much time has gone by. Don't get me wrong. At first, it's normal to be mindful of how many days since you last committed a sexual sin. For some, counting a few days provides a glimmer of hope. However, you cannot place your worth on length of time or seek to rush the process. Otherwise you'll put more emphasis on behavior modification techniques than upon purposing to daily living out each element of a Proven life as part of the process of turning to the Lord.

Those living in lasting freedom no longer base their worth on how many days they have not masturbated or looked at pornography. Many are often too busy fighting in a battle to check the score. Ultimately, Proven Men finally sees that true freedom is living each day for Christ. You see, victory is not based upon or measured by how much less a certain sin is present, but how you respond to setbacks. I rejoice each time a man shares what he learned after he stumbled.

Joel's battle was so fierce that it was three months before he popped his head out of the foxhole to count the days. Taking a quick look around, he noticed the battle line had moved farther away, but he quickly hunkered back down. Even after long periods, Joel did not constantly count the months or the years since he last masturbated. His treasure became "today," and he uses each "today" in seeking the Lord's face. The same freedom is waiting for you.

When we move into the truth that our worth (our value, our significance) is not determined by what we do or don't do, but by the unconditional love and acceptance of Jesus Christ, such wisdom renews us beyond our greatest expectations. I received an email from a fellow Proven Men teammate that clarifies that wonderful point:

> As I am starting to see into the heart of Jesus—the source of pure love—I am finally beginning to understand that our sexual dysfunctions and the inordinate time we spend thinking about it take up only a very tiny corner of His heart. Indeed, there is so much light there that our little darkness is wiped totally clean. This shouts the great truth: Jesus is far more interested in having a progressively intimate relationship with us rather than emptying us of our inappropriate choices. It helps to know that Jesus is saying: "I'm crazy-nuts about you. I want all of you, brokenness, fears, failures, and all the rest." It is when we inevitably return that love that nothing else will matter except pursuing Jesus.

This type of eternal perspective helps create passion toward and openness with Christ that frees us from dwelling on setbacks instead of focusing on our relationship with God that leads to appropriate repentance and lasting victory.

Be patient. God often heals slowly in the area of sexual impurity on purpose and for good reason. It requires time for you to get to know God intimately and to fall completely in love with Jesus. Once you do, you'll fulfill your purpose in life: To love God with all of your heart and to love others as yourself (Matthew 22:36–39). Peace is assured, and holiness follows.

HEARTWORK

The by-product of an intimate relationship with God is the loosening of the grip of sexual sins. Read this sentence again, contemplating its meaning and application in your life. The greater goal of knowing Jesus intimately is what brings about the holiness and purity you desire.[37] That's why you must not make it the goal to stop masturbating. Don't misunderstand. A short-term goal can be to immediately stop masturbating while you are pursuing God. But the greater goal of knowing Jesus is the way to absolute purity.

R is for Repentant in Spirit. Have you recognized yet that you have made pornography, lust, or masturbation idols in your life? If you refuse to see this, how will you repent? Without repentance, how will you obtain forgiveness and be right with God? What good would be served if God just delivered you from something bad that you cannot even see as evil? If you make seeking selfish pleasures your passion in life, what difference is made if one item (e.g., masturbation) is removed? Are you not still an idolater when you have greed or other selfishness in your life? God wants to give you permanent freedom across the board. Repent from your selfish desire to be instantly healed of one sin without the benefit of becoming a needy dependent servant of the Lord, and without living a holy life across the board. Right now, surrender your will.

PRAY

In true humility, talk to the Lord and spend five or ten minutes being with Him.

- Repent from any idols of greed, selfish practices, pride, self-sufficiency, etc.
- Repent for not making getting to know and love God the number one priority of your life.
- Ask God to be your real and only source of power and strength.
- Write out any prayers or decisions God prompts you to make.

___

___

___

___

READ THE BIBLE

Are you reading Scripture daily? Keep it up. Right now read Hebrews 11:1–40.

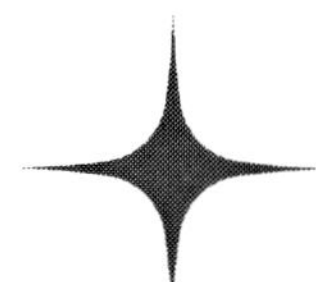

SPECIAL NOTE:

Earlier, the term "truth therapy" was introduced. Basically, it means immersing yourself in God's truth to counteract the lies of Satan and any incorrect thinking you have formed about yourself, about God, or about whether you will be healed. Because God is perfect and all-knowing, He is always right. He has given you a book that is totally reliable. The Bible is your book of promises and truths. When you read it to know God, you are changed.

MEMORY VERSE

Hebrews 13:5: "Keep your lives free from the love of money and be content with what you have, because God has said, 'Never will I leave you; never will I forsake you.'"

DAILY READING

You were created to experience and enjoy intimacy, first with God, and then with others. However, many tend to shy away from true intimacy due to the deep pain associated with prior relationships. They turn to false forms of intimacy that they think they can control and keep safe. Pornography, masturbation, and fantasy seem to be about the safest forms of "intimacy," especially when sex is incorrectly equated as a replacement for love. But, they are false forms of intimacy, which cannot bring lasting fulfillment. Worse yet, they block real intimacy.

- Do you fear aspects of intimacy, i.e., letting your guard down or being completely open? Explain how and why.

Have you ever considered why pornography is the largest moneymaker on the Internet? The reason people end up spending billions of dollars a year to buy Internet pornography is because it doesn't and cannot supply the real needs that are missing in life. In other words, people keep trying to force it to work by buying more and more. In fact, many websites offer free sneak previews or thumbnail pictures because they know that people won't be satisfied and will only crave greater thrills. Eventually, some turn to harder core and more costly pictures in the vain hope that these more expensive fantasies will satisfy.

If you struggle with pornography, fantasy, or masturbation, chances are that you've closed off areas of your heart to God and others. For instance, a married man may have sexual contact with his wife but withholds his innermost self. Similarly, single men often look to forms of sexual pleasure in place of intimate (non-sexual), open, and vulnerable relationships. Those turning to sexual activities to fill their lives are actually running away from real intimacy. Not so surprising, then, the key ingredient to sexual healing is intimacy with God.

Because many of us had poor success with some prior relationships, we doubt that intimacy with God or others is possible. We are afraid because we view it as giving control to someone who might hurt us. Chances are you have many barriers against trusting God. Perhaps you blame Him for your circumstances or you don't think He heard your cries for help in the past. Some would rather be in charge of their life at any cost, than risk being hurt again. The reasons are numerous, but the cure is the same: To see God as good and to trust Him.

What would occur if you really viewed God as totally good and having your best interest in mind? What if you felt His great and rich love? Suppose you thought His peace could totally soothe your wounds. Well, these things are the true nature of God. No matter how painful your past relationships with others have been or how blurred your view of God, you simply must allow God to join with you in spiritual intimacy. You might think, *"But how can I? I don't really know God enough to turn to or trust Him with my whole life."* This concern is real to many, and yet the solution quite simple. Open your eyes to see the Lord as He really is: Perfect. Purpose to find God. To all who seek, they find; to all who knock, the door will be opened; and to all who thirst for righteousness, they will be filled (see Matthew 5:6; 7:7). Don't shrink away. Besides, where else can you go to receive healing? Deeper inward? The truth is that only God can mend your wounds. Only He can rescue you. Openly tell God of your fears and concerns. He won't reject you. He will never leave your side (Hebrews 13:5). He has proven His love on the cross. Let Him carry your burden now.

Intimacy with God is available to you. God wants you to meet with Him. You were bought at a very high price by the Lord in order that you could live in freedom from sin and shame. You're of great value to God. It's now time for you to see God as good. It's time to appreciate the love of the Lord. It's time to live out your purpose in life of worshiping a worthy God and experiencing Him in intimacy.

Yes, intimacy with God is waiting for you. It's born through a lifestyle of worshiping the Lord from your heart and praising Him with your lips.[38] Expressing passion for God releases your soul and tears down walls around your heart because you are drawn into the very presence of a holy, loving, and merciful God. While with the Lord, you no longer hold onto anything else. You're set free.

The key to developing intimacy with God is focusing on Christ, not your circumstances. Begin by thanking the Lord throughout each day and set out to become His best friend. There's no other way to know your God than to spend time with Him. Reading books about God is not the same as being with Him. Won't you go to Him now? Open your heart to Him. Thank Him for each blessing during the day. Sing love songs and write letters. Read the Bible as though it was written to you—it was. Talk to God in prayer, not asking for selfish requests or babbling on with memorized words. Pour out your heart in open and vulnerable discussions and communications.

Without a growing, intimate relationship with your Father God, you won't know and experience His deep abiding love, which heals past wounds and imparts great faith. Spending long periods of time in worship and open communication forges a mighty friendship that can be relied upon. You'll experience the character and nature of the Holy One as you meet with Him. Your mind and soul will be transformed and heart renewed. He promises that all who hunger and thirst after Him shall be satisfied (Matthew 5:6). It's time to hunger and thirst for God instead of the world.

V is for Victorious in Living. Are you walking in victory? If you're regularly experiencing setbacks and defeats, you likely haven't yet fallen deeply in love with Jesus and agreed to give Him total control of your entire life. The remedy is to make a decision to love God with passion by spending lots of time meeting with Him. Give up TV and Internet time and replace it with praying, reading Psalms, singing hymns, and writing love letters to Christ. Your family may think you're crazy to sing praise songs at home, but why not be sold out for God? In the end, they would rather have that than your continuing to live a double life and having a restricted heart. You would too.

- Will you commit to establishing and maintaining a lifestyle of worship and praise? Explain how you will put this into practice.

____

____

____

____

Pride is a major stumbling block to being dependent upon anyone, even God, because it leads to some of the following thoughts:

- "I can do it myself."
- "I don't need help."
- "My sins aren't that bad."
- "I don't need God."

Describe how you struggle with any of these types of self-sufficient thinking.

____

____

____

Does pride still make you think things such as these:

- "I can change my heart."
- "I can overcome a sinful action."
- "I can be kind, good, and faithful."
- "I only need a bit of help from God to overcome."

HEARTWORK

Do you see yourself as absolutely dependent upon God? If not, why not? Be *open and honest.* Confess any such pride to God. Cry out to God for forgiveness, and then admit your powerlessness over sin.

PRAY

Begin by asking God to humble you, to soften your heart, and to make you a needy, dependent servant. Next, tell God you accept His unconditional love and trust Him with total control of your life. Seek Christ with all of your heart. Be sure to include heartfelt prayers for others. In fact, keep the focus off yourself and circumstances. The antidote to selfish prayer is to pray for others. Spend five or ten minutes doing so now.

READ THE BIBLE

Keep reading Scripture and asking God to reveal truth. Read Psalm 16.

SPECIAL NOTE:

Despite the truth that apart from God we cannot be healed, many still refuse to turn to the Lord because their pride won't bend. For them, being dependent upon anyone—including God—is not an option. Sadly, this same pride blocks them from seeing God as good and worthy of praise. Pride can also create a form of jealousy that limits their praise of others, even of a perfect God. Next, it leads to doubt whether they really need God. In their minds, the sun always rises and they seem quite capable of supplying most of their own needs. In effect, they treat themselves as gods. Okay, few may consciously consider themselves to be a god, but consider the fruit of pride in their lives. Consider the result of pride in your own life. It's not a pretty picture. Your prideful actions are the complete opposite of—and stand opposed to—God. It's time to surrender your will to the Lord.

MEMORY VERSE

Hebrews 13:5: "Keep your lives free from the love of money and be content with what you have, because God has said, 'Never will I leave you; never will I forsake you.'"

DAILY READING

A young man grew up in a distant land where football was a national sport. Because he was a very skilled athlete, he was invited to join a game after school. He arrived wearing short pants and a light shirt. All the other men, however, were wearing pads and helmets. This man would face serious risk if he were put on the field not knowing the rules of American football instead of soccer and lacking the special equipment to compete.

If you don't know the rules or don't have the special equipment for spiritual warfare, what disaster awaits! Satan is a real spiritual being, described by God as a roaring lion seeking to devour the spirit of man (1 Peter 5:8). Would you enter a lion's den unarmed and unprepared? Of course not! How, then, do you explain your ignorance of spiritual warfare? Just as a lion won't pass up an ostrich with its head buried in the sand, the devil won't pass you up simply because you didn't know he was harmful. An easy target is not overlooked.

Certainly, you know that there are spiritual forces that affect your life. You're quick to admit that your spirit is damaged by harsh words of a friend. How much more harm, however, is inflicted by a powerful spiritual being that considers you an enemy. The tactics or weapons aren't as obvious as a knife, but they cut just the same. Satan is pleased when you become a slave to lustful, judgmental, or self-centered thoughts. He is pleased by your ignorance and refusal to put on God's armor. You die a slow death without knowing that you're under attack.

Consider these descriptions of Satan:

- devil (Matthew 4:1)
- murderer (John 8:44)
- liar (John 8:44)
- lord of darkness (Ephesians 6:12)
- evil one (Matthew 13:19)
- ruler of the earth (John 12:31)
- tempter (Matthew 4:3)

Do you know who Satan is and why he wants to tempt, deceive, and devour you? Briefly, the story of the rise and fall of the devil goes like this: Before creating the earth and man, God made angels. The most beautiful and powerful angel was Lucifer. Sadly, Lucifer began focusing on himself, noting his own beauty. He became puffed up and proud. In rebellion against God, he began seeking praise from other angels. Therefore, his name was changed to Satan, and God cast him out of heaven, together with one-third of the angels who also rebelled. On earth, Satan set out to pervert man, who was made in God's image and designed to worship God and enjoy God's fellowship. It pleases Satan when man refuses to praise and acknowledge God. Satan and the other fallen angels (called demons) want to destroy all that God considers precious, including you.

Although we don't understand why God cast Satan to earth and permits him to rule the world until the end of this age, we do know that Satan is real. Scripture says he holds the power of death (Hebrews 2:14–15). Despite his great power, however, Satan cannot defeat God. He has no ability to live inside a Christian because God already has made each adopted son His temple. Nor can Satan ruin the work of the Lord. In fact, God has given man authority over Satan when acting through Christ (1 John 3:8; Luke 10:18–19). You'll always fail, however, when you act in your own strength. Also, you grant Satan a foothold into your life when you allow anger, pride, greed, lust, or other sins to fester and go unconfessed to God (Ephesians 4:27). The good news is that by the strength of Jesus Christ, you can repent and resist Satan (James 4:7). God has spiritual armor for you to wear and spiritual weapons to fight with against the forces of evil (Ephesians 6).

Don't be deceived; a spiritual battle takes place around and over you. Make a decision to take a stand for the kingdom of God and wear His armor. Join with Proven Men in the army of God, taking your position as a loyal soldier who willingly obeys the Lord's commands.

Record your insights.

HEARTWORK

Right now, commit to getting to know Jesus as the top priority in your life. Open your eyes and heart to His glory and grace. Seek Him with all of your heart. Indicate your decision below.

If you aren't accustomed to wearing and using God's armor daily, you won't know how to use it when Satan does attack—and he carefully plots his attacks! As you're becoming more proficient using the armor of God, you'll be able to rely upon God's strength when Satan attacks (i.e., when you're tempted to lust).

Read Ephesians 6:10–18.

- Why wear God's armor? (See verses 10–11.) Describe where and how the real struggle takes place in overcoming sexual sins. (See verse 12.)

____

____

____

- Read Appendix K. Describe how to put on and use each piece of the armor:

HELMET OF SALVATION:

____

____

____

BREASTPLATE OF RIGHTEOUSNESS:

____

____

____

SHIELD OF FAITH:

____

____

____

SWORD OF THE SPIRIT (WORD OF GOD):

BELT OF TRUTH:

PRAYER:

GOSPEL OF PEACE:

PRAY

P is for Passionate for God. Spend five or ten minutes meeting with God. Keep the focus off yourself and circumstances and practice praying for others.

- Ask God to change your heart so that you are passionate for Him.
- Ask God to show you how to wear His armor and how to live under His protection.
- Make a commitment to wear His armor daily.
- Commit to praying in the Spirit on all occasions and with all kinds of unselfish requests.
- Ask God to make you alert to spiritual warfare and the source of temptations.
- Pray for other Proven Men.

READ THE BIBLE

Meditate again on Ephesians 6:10–18. Immerse yourself in His Word—the only place where you will obtain eternal truth! Be sure to keep asking God to reveal truth to you.

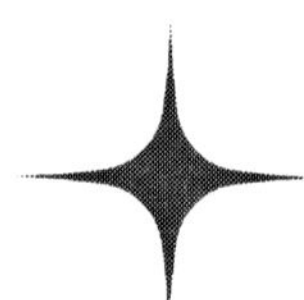

SPECIAL NOTE:

After this series is over, consider using the book *Lord, Is It Warfare? Teach Me to Stand* by Kay Arthur (WaterBrook Press) as one of your next morning study aids. It's not too early to plan your next study. Don't drop the shield at the end of twelve weeks. Go to Appendix M and plan to follow the suggestions for your next studies. Purchase the materials now so you can begin right away.

Will you embrace and wear the whole armor of God daily? Just like weapons of this world, using God's armor requires practice to be proficient.

MEMORY VERSE

Hebrews 13:5: "Keep your lives free from the love of money and be content with what you have, because God has said, 'Never will I leave you; never will I forsake you.'"

DAILY READING

Today's Daily Reading is largely a time of reflection and meditation. Use it to reaffirm your total dedication to the Lord. Go slowly through each reflection, making decisions and yielding to the Lord. Ask God to speak to you and listen to what He has to say.

- Commit to living holiness in all areas of your life. What sins have you overlooked? Spend a moment listening to God. Confess each sin that the Holy Spirit brings to your mind.
- Turn complete control of your life over to Christ. Put down the shovel of self-effort and ask Jesus to take it up. Pray this verse as your own: I have been crucified with Christ and I no longer live, but Christ lives in me. The life I live in the body, I live by faith in the Son of God, who loved me and gave himself for me. (Based on Galatians 2:20.)
- Meditate upon how you will turn to and rely upon Christ to resist temptations that you face each day.
- Be still and ask God to reveal to you anything that you're still holding onto or that's blocking you from becoming passionate for Him and living out a lifestyle of worship and praise.
- Tell the Lord about any struggle you're facing, whether it is sexual temptation, greed, anger, jealousy, or something else.
- Ask God to reveal to you in greater depth who He is, how much He loves you, and who you are in Him. Ask God to make His unconditional love real to you and to use His unconditional love to draw you close and to heal your wounds. Picture this in your mind.
- Ask God to mend your broken relationships with parents, siblings, friends, or a spouse. Ask the Lord to show you ways in which you block out others, withhold love

or forgiveness, or are selfish. Ask the Lord to open the door and show you what to do to seek and pursue reconciliation with others.

- Ask God for passion, including a burning desire to read the Bible daily, pray, and praise Him.
- Ask the Lord to tell you what things He wants you to know. Be still and anticipate Him. Stay focused upon hearing from God without making any petitions or allowing your mind to wander.

God designed you to rejoice and delight in Him. Meditate upon the following verses:

> "Let the righteous rejoice in the Lord and take refuge in him; let all the upright in heart praise him!" (Psalm 64:10).
>
> "Once more the humble will rejoice in the Lord; the needy will rejoice in the Holy One of Israel" (Isaiah 29:19).
>
> "May my meditation be pleasing to Him, as I rejoice in the Lord" (Psalm 104:34).
>
> "Blessed is the man who does not walk in the counsel of the wicked... But his delight is in the law of the Lord, and on His law he meditates day and night" (Psalm 1:1–2).
>
> ". . . my soul will rejoice in the Lord and delight in His salvation" (Psalm 35:9).
>
> "Delight yourself in the Lord and He will give you the desires of your heart. Commit your way to the Lord; trust in Him and He will do this: He will make your righteousness shine like the dawn, the justice of your cause like the noonday sun. Be still before the Lord and wait patiently for Him; do not fret when men succeed in their ways, when they carry out their wicked schemes" (Psalm 37:4–7).
>
> "Great are the works of the Lord; they are pondered by all who delight in them" (Psalm 111:2).

"They that wait upon the Lord shall renew their strength; they shall mount up with wings as eagles; they shall run, and not be weary; and they shall walk, and not faint" (Isaiah 40:31).

HEARTWORK

- State how you will rejoice and delight in Christ and write down the exact times of the day you will dedicate to worship and prayer.

____

____

____

____

- Have you made knowing God the greatest pursuit of your life? *If not, will you do so now?* Write out your prayers and commitments to do just that.

____

____

____

____

- Have you given up control of all areas of your life to God? List any area of your heart still off limits to God. Ask the Lord to reveal anything you have not turned over to Him, such as your thought life, finances, occupation, or choice of entertainment.

____

____

____

____

PRAY

Spend five or ten minutes meeting with God the Father. Pray to get to know Him as a living being. Seek to become intimate with God in times of prayer.

- Commit to turning over all areas of your heart to Him.
- Praise the Lord with all of your heart.
- Tell God of your love for Him.
- Sing or hum a melody to Him, perhaps a favorite verse of a song or of Scripture.
- Ask God to give you His power and strength to carry out the commitments you make.
- Ask the Lord to make you a needy, dependent servant.
- Ask God to break all remaining pride in your heart.
- Pray for others, including church leaders, the country's leaders, and your family.

The fifth letter in a PROVEN life is E, which means Eternal in Perspective. Do you believe the Word of God, and do you want to apply it in your life? The things of today will all perish, and they don't satisfy. The Word of God, however, will never pass away (see Matthew 24:35).

READ THE BIBLE

Read 2 Chronicles 6:12–39. Read God's Word so that you can love God. Guard against being just an information gatherer. Soften your heart and do what God's Word says (see James 1:22).

What are your plans for tonight or Saturday night? Be sure your plans are based upon something in the *"Relational Exercises"* in Appendix A. You are creating a new Proven lifestyle. Therefore, do so with purpose. Consider writing a psalm or love note to the Lord tonight.

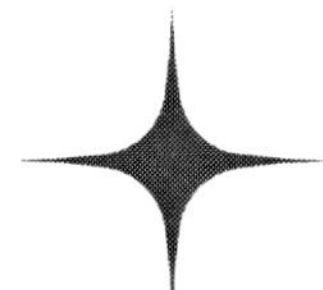

SPECIAL NOTE:

Develop a game plan for turning your weakness into strength. By turning to and relying upon God's power, you'll experience victory. Record your plan of eliminating certain practices, confessing sins as they occur, and devoting yourself to the Lord.

Become a Proven Men partner. If this Study been a blessing to you, then start becoming a blessing to others. As you are getting close to completing the Study, you are nearly ready to be used by the Lord in the life of another man. Plan now to become a volunteer. Visit our website to learn more about opportunities to help other men. Consider also making a generous financial contribution so that we can keep restoring families one man at a time by helping people embrace a proven way of life that produces lasting victory from strongholds of pornography and sexual addiction. We can't do this without you. Visit our website: www.ProvenMen.org.

MEMORY VERSE

Hebrews 13:5: "Keep your lives free from the love of money and be content with what you have, because God has said, 'Never will I leave you; never will I forsake you.'"

It's time to do business with pride. Pride not only prevents you from passionately worshiping the Lord but also blocks you from seeing your sins as wicked and keeps you from being repentant in spirit. Pride causes you to think you deserve all that you have and more. A proud man is fixated upon his rights and considers himself better than others. He fails to recognize masturbation, lust, fantasy, and all forms of pornography as idols. A proud heart sees no great need to be utterly dependent upon God and fails to grasp that repentance is a precious gift of God. What little passion, repentance, and openness you'll experience with such a worldly perspective.

The only cure for pride is humility. God Himself modeled humility in that Jesus Christ, who was and is God and created the world, chose to take the form of a man. What could be more humble than that? Christ didn't stop there. He allowed men to ridicule and scorn Him. He was beaten beyond recognition and hung on a wooden cross with nails pounded into His flesh while being jeered. A crown of thorns was thrust upon His head to ridicule His claim to be the King of Kings. At any time, Jesus could have said, "Enough. I will not suffer or die for people. They can all be damned and destroyed." But His perfect love won out, just as it wins us over to Him. If the Lord is humble and meek, on what basis do you strut about in pride? Dear friend, seek humility, or your pride will swallow you whole, leaving no room for God or His healing. Go to the Lord now. Ask for repentance and humility.

Read Galatians 5:16–23, which compares the effects of living by your own power versus living by God's power. Ask God to meet with you and reveal truth to you.

Break out of your old patterns. For instance, use relational building tools to deepen your intimacy with family and friends (see Appendix A). In addition, what ministries are you involved in at church? Part of loving God and others is serving them. Be mindful not to replace serving them with loving them. Choose something that's low profile. Stay behind the scenes. Pride is a major factor in seeking selfish pleasures, and you can get puffed up even in your service to the Lord. How about mowing the lawn, sweeping floors, moving furniture, or taking out the garbage? Do the thankless jobs and don't seek to be noticed.

WEEK ELEVEN

TESTIMONY

"I was a Christian, yet I was still immersed deeply in sin (sexual or otherwise). Over the years, I would find a church, attend for while, meet some great people, and then leave. It all came back to, 'How can I go to church, yet be spending so much time sinning?' Shame was never the reason for my leaving, but I didn't want to be the person that talked passionately about God one minute and the next be lusting. The two just couldn't exist for me, yet I knew no practical way to eliminate this sin from my life. I had to find a way to 'fix' this sin, *before* I could truly turn to God. I failed. It's sad that I believed this fallacy for so long.

"On one, all alone, I realized my life was CRAP! It was the moment that I call 'bottom.' In that moment, I knew that my life was worthless, and I started browsing around on the Internet, not for porn, but rather, some insight into how Christians find their way out of deep pits. I stumbled across a snippet of a site that describes men struggling with sexual integrity and recovery, and it sounded promising. It was only a snippet though, and I kept poking around and I found your study.

"In that 12 weeks, I discovered some things, beautiful things: God's Truth and Grace. For the first time in my life, I was on a path to freedom, freedom from sin that I had been enslaved to for my *entire* adult life. I learned that I wasn't 'abnormal' and that hiding my sin from people is what leads me right back to sin! I learned that I cannot fix my sin on my own, and if I wait to talk to God until I can, I will never truly live.

"Lord, thank you for your Truth, even when it hurts, and thank you for your endless Grace."

Passionate for God,
Repentant in spirit,
Open and honest,
Victorious in living,
Eternal in perspective, and
Networking with other ***PROVEN Men.***

MEMORY VERSE

Ephesians 4:2: "Be completely humble and gentle; be patient, bearing with one another in love."

The primary lesson for you this week is to develop a humble heart of worship. You have just two more weeks left in this series. Do you have your next study picked out and the book(s) on order? (See Appendix M for suggestions.) Consider repeating this twelve-week study. When going over it a second time, ask God to give you fresh eyes to see His character in deeper revelation. Many Proven Men have repeated this *Heartwork* study several times and grown closer to God as a result.

Do you still have an insatiable hunger for earthly pleasures such as pornography, masturbation, fantasy, or greed? God says that to love the world or anything in the world is hatred toward Him (see 1 John 2:15–17). These are very strong words. How do you react?

____

____

____

____

What keeps you from turning to God and trusting Him? Are you afraid He will hold back something good from you? God wants you to be filled (see Matthew 5:6). He wants to satisfy your real needs, deep in your soul. In fact, the Lord created you for real intimacy. Fantasy, however, is make-believe and robs you. It doesn't satisfy. The solution is found in seeking real intimacy with the Lord and others. As far as sexual intimacy, God didn't hold back on you. He purposefully created you as a sexual being, capable of enjoying real and fulfilling intimacy, including sexual intimacy, but He knows that true sexual fulfillment without guilt and shame is available only in a loving marriage based on real intimacy.

HEARTWORK

Hear the Word of God:

"As for you, you were dead in your transgressions and sins, in which you used to live when you followed the ways of this world and of the ruler of the kingdom of the air, the spirit who is now at work in those who are disobedient. All of us also lived among them at one time gratifying the cravings of our sinful nature and following its desires and thoughts. Like the rest, we were by nature objects of wrath" (Ephesians 2:1–3).

Let those verses speak to you. By being trapped in slavery to prideful and self-centered actions, you're living as though you are spiritually dead, just as the devil before you. Perhaps you're numb already.

Read the good news of the next verses:

> "But because of his great love for us, God, who is rich in mercy, made us alive with Christ even when we were dead in transgressions—it is by grace you have been saved. And God raised us up with Christ and seated us with him in the heavenly realms in Christ Jesus, in order that in the coming ages he might show the incomparable riches of his grace, expressed in kindness to us in Christ Jesus. For it is by grace you have been saved, through faith—and this not from yourselves, it is the gift of God—not by works, so that no one can boast. For we are God's workmanship, created in Christ Jesus to do good works, which God prepared in advance for us to do" (Ephesians 2:4–10).

Allow God to speak to your heart right now. Trust in the One who created you and loves you deeply.

DAILY READING

Last week, you began addressing the reality of spiritual forces and battles. Having an *eternal perspective* is a large part of the PROVEN Model for living in purity and holiness. You're living in a time of battle between good and evil.[39] Your permanent home is not on earth but in heaven (see Philippians 3:20). The world is a temporary war zone. As in all wars, there will be periods of great struggle and even injury, but you already know that God is the victor. The Lord created Satan, and God cannot be defeated. As a child of God, you surely will taste of His victory and share in the fruit of His kingdom. Why then do you still cling to the notion that life in this world should be without difficulties? Instead, choose to endure hardships and other costs of being a Christian (2 Timothy 2:3). The Lord uses your trials to make you fit for His kingdom (James 1:2–4). Allow the Lord to lead the battle charge until the day of redemption, when you'll finally be at rest and apart from all evil. The Commander-in-Chief tells you that in this world, the only safe place for His servants is under His care and control. Meanwhile, the enemy awaits for those who wander off or chart their own course.

God warns you in advance that you'll be tempted to leave His camp. Don't be deceived. Satan wants to rob you of peace. Therefore, stay on the Lord's path. Be mindful, however, of God's advance notice that you'll experience sufferings—even persecution (John 15:20). God uses these difficulties to fashion you into an even better servant, more equipped and prepared to do battle (James 1:2–4). Follow His instructions to *network* with other Godly men, as iron sharpens iron (Proverbs 27:17). Think about it, who do you want beside you in times of war: Someone not interested in conditioning, training, or following orders, or a fully trained, loyal, obedient, hard-working soldier that is proficient with the weapons of war? Won't you join the spiritual brotherhood of Proven Men? Keep striving up the holy mountain, encouraging one another along the way, but never allow the journey to distract you from who it is you are seeking and living for.

During battles and resulting victories, you'll gain perseverance and an unshakable faith in the Commander. When the next trials come, you'll realize and utilize the power of God as you gladly yield control to Him. You're stamped tested and approved for use by God, and you carry the attributes of a good servant: Faithful, loyal, and obedient.

Never forget, that you're a created being;[40] you're designed to live for and in communion with God. If you refuse to accept your position in God's family, how will you fully live? How will you prevail against the evil one? It's pride that strives to accomplish that which you cannot and were not meant to do! Oh, how a proud heart refuses God and sees humility as weak! True humility turns to and relies upon the greatest power in the universe. The Lord says the lowly can move mountains because they look to the One who is able (Matthew 21:21), yet the proud man will wear himself out digging a hole that keeps filling in.

- What are the key points of today's Daily Reading? Write them down.

____

____

____

____

Rely upon the power and strength of your Master, Jesus Christ, to overcome sin. Remember, when you fall in love with Jesus, you'll want to do His will. You'll want holiness more than you wanted pornography, greed, or other forms of self-will. Therefore, be passionate in your pursuit of God.

PRAY

Are you praying for five or ten minutes a day? God doesn't want you punching clocks, but He desires your first fruits. He wants you to talk to Him. Ask God to give you His perspective on prayer and to protect time spent alone meeting with Him. Again, keep the focus off yourself or circumstances while praying; begin a lifestyle of praying for others.

- Ask God to show you what a passionate pursuit of Him looks like. (Discuss this pursuit with your Proven Men leader and others next time you see them.)
- Draw near to God right now. According to James 4:8, He will draw near to you.
- Tell the Lord you're renouncing all sin, not just sin in general. But specifically tell Him the sins in your life—everything that separates you from intimacy with God and healthy relationships or intimacy with others.

- Tell God that you're rejecting false intimacy (pornography, chat rooms, fantasy, etc.) and pursuing *open and honest* relationships with Him and others.
- Keep praying for other Proven Men.
- Pray for others. (List them.)

____

____

____

____

READ THE BIBLE

Be sure to read the Scriptures daily, and be ready to meet with God. Right now meditate on 1 Peter 2:11–17. Read slowly, asking God to open your heart and mind to Him. Ask God to reveal truth to you. If you have time, follow the same principle while reading 1 Peter 3:8 through 1 Peter 4:19. Don't rush.

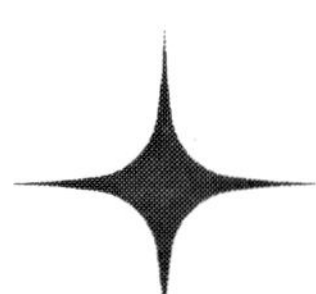

SPECIAL NOTE:

In Ephesians 2:10, you are told: "For we are God's workmanship, created in Christ Jesus to do good works, which God prepared in advance for us to do." Do you see that the good works are not your own, but they are from God? God tells you that all of your "righteous acts are like filthy rags" (Isaiah 64:6). When you fall in love with Christ, you want what He wants. Only then are you able to do "good works" through Jesus and according to His purpose and plan (Ephesians 2:10; Philippians 2:13). In just the same way that you cannot earn God's love or salvation by your good works (Ephesians 2:8–9), you cannot do good works to overcome sexual sins.

MEMORY VERSE

Ephesians 4:2: "Be completely humble and gentle; be patient, bearing with one another in love."

DAILY READING

The first letter of a PROVEN life stands for Passionately pursuing God with your full heart by lifting praise, offering worship, and entering into relational prayer. Won't you turn to the Lord and break free from your old ways and prideful spirit that don't look outside of yourself. Falling in love with God is a matter of looking to and seeing God as He is: Perfect, holy, and almighty. God, and God alone, truly deserves praise. Give the Lord what is due. Declare the truth of God and His goodness.

The by-product of a heart that freely worships God is a unity of spirit with Him. You actually become closer to God, experiencing His character during such times of true praise. How remarkable! When you give God glory, your own heart expands. The Lord is released to fill even more of you. The more you humbly yield in passionate praise and pursuit of God, the more whole and complete you become. During times of open and vulnerable communication with God, old wounds are healed, and the fruit of the Holy Spirit grows in your life. For instance, there will no longer be room in your heart for bitterness because you now relationally experience the Lord and receive His joy, peace, and contentment. When your deepest relational need is met (intimacy with God), you won't feel compelled to turn to false forms of intimacy or to medicate yourself with self-pity in chasing after the temporary pleasure or numbing aspects of illicit sexual activities.

Turn to Appendix N, which is an outline for using your heart, mind, and hands as a way of developing intimacy with God. Don't just read it to learn information, but determine to put these things into practice. Return to the study after dwelling on the outline.

HEARTWORK

The key to developing a heart and lifestyle of worship and praise is spending copious amounts of time doing it. Don't cut corners here. Worshiping and praising God will transform you. Record any commitments to falling in love with the Lord and using your heart, mind, and hands for His service. Write Him a love note below.

____

____

____

____

PRAY

It's time to adopt a new prayer life. God wants you to wrestle before Him and to be passionate about the things you pray about. If you don't care about a response, why ask for it? If it's really important, however, then ask like it is. As your intimacy and dependence upon God grow, you'll pray in a pleasing manner that moves the Lord to action. Pray for your family and others. Be specific in your requests, asking for things in God's will and then being persistent. Also, thank Him now for the answers to your prayers that He will do in His perfect way and timing. Plan to spend five or ten minutes in prayer. If you make a list of names of people to pray for, you'll soon find that it won't be long enough.

____

____

____

____

READ THE BIBLE

Trust that the Bible is what God says it is, His Word. It's living and active. Read it to get to know God and not to learn about Him in your head. Read and meditate on John 15:1–17; Hebrews 4:16; James 1:5–8; and 1 John 5:13–15.

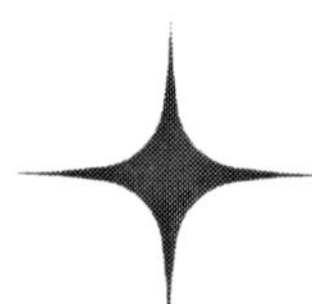

SPECIAL NOTE:

One of the largest walls that blocks out God from your life is pride and accompanying selfishness. Unfortunately, we often are too proud to see our own pride! "For in his own eyes he flatters himself too much to detect or hate his sin" (Psalm 36:2). Therefore, earnestly ask God to search you constantly and reveal areas of pride. Similarly, if you are in active sin, you must repent in order to be right with the Lord. The Lord wants to bless you and accomplish His purposes and plans through you. You simply cannot have unrepentant sin in your life.

Become a Proven Men partner. Don't let pride or fear stop you from helping other men. One way you can help men is to make a financial contribution to our ministry so that we can keep creating new resources. You should also consider volunteering to lead other men. Our website shows you how you can make a difference in the lives of others. Visit our website: www.ProvenMen.org.

MEMORY VERSE

Ephesians 4:2: "Be completely humble and gentle; be patient, bearing with one another in love."

WEEK 11 DAY 3 (WEDNESDAY)

DAILY READING

Prayer releases God to act in and through your life. In fact, the entire power of God is available to Proven Men during prayer. *Have you learned how to pray?* It may seem like a silly question to ask, but most people don't truly pray at all. Instead, they repeat words over and over again, string together eloquent sounding words, or make long lists of things they want. Putting God's name at the beginning and end and saying "amen" doesn't turn these things into prayer. Prayer isn't simply asking God for favors. Prayer is a form of relating to and communicating with God. It also involves asking God to accomplish His will through you. True prayer begins to conform your desires to His.

Do you want to learn how to pray? The disciples asked Jesus to teach them to pray (Luke 11:1). They certainly had heard Jesus pray many times before, so we can trust that they were not asking for specific words to repeat. Although meditating on the aspects of the prayer often referred to as "The Lord's Prayer" (Luke 11:2–4) can be a wonderful experience, you should guard against simply repeating these same words over and over. The Lord tells you not to go on babbling in prayer (Matthew 6:7), but to engage in relational communication with a living being. The model Jesus taught was that in all things and at all times you're to communicate with your heavenly Father. Purpose to engage your heart and soul when you pray.

Turn to Appendix O, an outline of the purpose, practice, and power of prayer. Return here after you dwell on that outline. Keep asking God to teach you how to engage in real heart-felt, relational praying. Record your insights.

____

____

____

____

Periodically, refer to the outline in Appendix O to realign your prayer life, keeping God in the center.

Recognize areas where your prayers were not prayers at all but were selfish requests, not based upon meeting with God. Right now, confess how you've merely asked for things from God, not to know Him or to do His will but to get something from Him.

HEARTWORK

E is for Eternal Perspective. Praying for others is a wonderful way of putting into practice a Proven life. Therefore, ask the Lord to instill in you a desire to pray for others like you really want God to bless them as dearly loved ones.

PRAY

When you pray, ask God to meet with you. Seek to become empty of yourself and put to death selfish desires. Allow the Lord to transform and renew your heart and mind such that the Holy Spirit guides your petitions to and communications with God. Right now, spend time with the King of Kings. Keep the focus upon the Lord and His will and off yourself and your circumstances.

- Repent over pride and for seeking praise for yourself.
- Ask God to change you from the inside out.

- Ask the Lord for His perspective, one not dependent on your emotions.
- Consider others more important than yourself, and ask God to give you real love for others.[41]
- Spend five minutes lifting others up to God. List them here as you do. It will help you stay focused.

____

____

____

____

READ THE BIBLE

Read 1 Peter 5:5–11 and Luke 6:37–42.

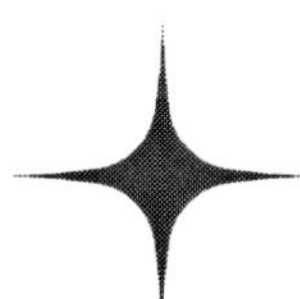

SPECIAL NOTE:

The more you fix your eyes upon the Lord and live as a needy, dependent servant, the more you'll understand that God wants you to pray. You'll discover that God answers true prayers, where you communicate intimately with God to seek Him and His will. In short, relational prayers move God to action because they are based upon a PROVEN Model of living and communicating passionately, repentantly, openly, victoriously, eternally, and networkingly (together with Him).

MEMORY VERSE

Ephesians 4:2: "Be completely humble and gentle; be patient, bearing with one another in love."

DAILY READING

You are asked to wait upon and listen for God. How can you hear a spirit being who normally doesn't speak in words audible to your ears? Although this is a fair question, guard against doubting that God speaks to you.

First of all, don't be so proud to think that God must speak for your ears to hear. Is it not your heart that is the center of love? Is it not your heart that the Lord wants fully devoted to Him? Why not, then, expect the Lord to speak to your heart instead of to your ears? You may have heard other say they hear a still small voice in their hearts when God is speaking to them. The Lord wants you to hear Him this way too. Is your heart soft and open to God? Are you being still, waiting and expecting to hear from Him?

God also speaks to you while you are meditating upon His words in the Bible. At times when you read Scripture, your heart can melt as wax and even burn with unquenchable fire (Luke 24:32). Let your heart open up to God. It's time to put away pride and take on a humble heart that's fully dependent upon the Lord.

Want to see God? He's all around, waiting to reveal Himself to the humble, those thirsty for living water. Practice looking for Him. As you purpose to find God, you'll see the Lord's handiwork all around you. Look for and then thank the Lord throughout the day. You'll soon find that your praise can never cease. You could shout "Holy, holy, holy Lord!" for millions of years and still not run out of reasons to praise Him for His flawless perfection in all that He is and does.

Turn to Appendix D and take time to read God's attributes, then return here.

- Did you meditate upon His attributes? The Lord is perfect in every single one of the attributes on that list. Therefore, your praise should never end.
- Do you see not only how humility toward God is appropriate but also that it actually takes effort to suppress praise? Shout out your praise! Allow your worship for God to passionately flow from your heart, lips, and hands.

HUMILITY

If you were on a team that included a trained 500-pound sumo wrestler, it wouldn't be weak to admit his strength or to select him in a wrestling competition against another team. You would clearly see the wisdom. When it comes to spiritual matters, however, are you too proud to turn to God? Do you choose to fight Satan alone?

Humility appropriately recognizes your limitations. It also properly acknowledges good qualities in others and offers appropriate praises. We congratulate students on good grades, athletes on good performances, and chefs for good meals, yet we tend to withhold praise from God, who doesn't have a single flaw and performs works of might and wonder far beyond human abilities. It's time to re-evaluate the virtue of being humble before a mighty God and then submit, yield and obey.

Pride is one of the largest obstacles to effective prayer. It blocks out God's healing and keeps you from living according to His plan. Humility, on the other hand, is the antidote for pride. It moves God to action.

Humility is seeing yourself as your loving God sees you. Jot down notes describing how you've incorrectly viewed yourself (e.g., puffed up or self-righteous) and how you will now correctly see yourself through the lens of God (e.g., dearly loved, but a needy dependent servant). Note, however, that humility is not about bashing yourself, but is all about being dependent upon God.

____

____

____

____

Jesus tells us this about being humble: "Take my yoke upon you and learn from me, for I am gentle and humble in heart, and you will find rest for your souls. For my yoke is easy and my burden light" (Matthew 11:29–30). Jesus Christ can tell you about humility because He set the perfect example for it. Jesus, who is God and created the world, chose to humble Himself by taking the form of a man so that you might live. Jesus didn't use His power to save Himself from persecution or His earthly body from death but was humble to the point of being crucified as a sacrifice for you. Jesus endured scorn and ridicule and a death He didn't deserve, yet He didn't open His mouth in defense against false accusations (Acts 8:32). If He hadn't willingly been crucified for sins He didn't commit, you wouldn't have a Savior. Jesus humbly gave His life freely for you!

Read these verses on humility and record any insights:

> "Humble yourselves, therefore, under God's mighty hand, that he may lift you up in due time" (1 Peter 5:6).

____

____

____

____

> "Be completely humble and gentle; be patient, bearing with one another in love..." (Ephesians 4:2).

____

____

____

____

"Do everything without complaining or arguing..." (Philippians 2:14).

"Each of you should look not only to your own interests, but also to the interests of others. Your attitude should be the same as that of Christ Jesus: Who, being in very nature God, did not consider equality with God something to be grasped, but made himself nothing, taking the very nature of a servant, being made in human likeness. And being found in appearance as a man, he humbled himself and became obedient to death—even death on a cross!" (Philippians 2:4–8).

"God opposes the proud but gives grace to the humble" (James 4:6).

Are you afraid to ask God to humble you because you're more concerned about being seen as a fool in the eyes of men rather than desiring to be a needy, dependent servant of the Lord? You may have the wrong view of God.

The Lord doesn't sit in heaven waiting to whack anyone who asks for humility. True, sometimes God knocks us down a peg, and yes, it hurts at the moment, but it's not done with evil motives or just to flatten us. Rather, it's out of love, because "He guides the humble in what is right and teaches them His way..." (Psalm 25:9).

God seeks to build you up for use in His service. The Lord wants to perfect you. In fact, you're not usable for God's work when you're puffed up, running around barking out orders as though you were the Commander-in-Chief, or developing your own plans apart from Him. Proven Men admit that God's ways are right, and they're glad God humbles them. They continually ask for humility. We want God to lift us up more than we want to look good in the eyes of men. It's only when we are humble that God can work through us. Start viewing humility as a gift instead of a punishment. It's an opportunity for blessings!

HEARTWORK

Spend a few minutes right now asking God to humble you. Don't hold back.

PRAY

God created a way for you to relate to Him. Go to Him right now in relational prayer.

- Ask the Lord to put real love (His love) in you.
- Express your love for God.
- Commit to being grateful, thankful, and content.
- Listen for God. Ask Him to open your heart to Him; ask Him to reveal His will to you.
- Pray for others, including those who have hurt you.
- Ask God to enable other Proven Men to forgive and unconditionally love their parents, spouses, and anyone who has hurt them deeply.

- Pray for anyone else the Lord places on your heart. (List them.)

___

___

___

READ THE BIBLE

Is the Bible becoming your spiritual food as Christ said it should be (see Matthew 4:4)? If not, perhaps you aren't preparing your heart before you read, or maybe you're not reading to get to know and experience God versus reading the Bible because that's what Christians are supposed to do. Ask God to meet with you as you read 1 Corinthians 13:3–6: "If I give all I possess to the poor and surrender my body to the flames, but have not love, I gain nothing. Love is patient, love is kind. It does not envy, it does not boast, it is not proud. It is not rude, it is not self-seeking, it is not easily angered, it keeps no record of wrongs. Love does not delight in evil but rejoices with the truth."

Read this passage again, but turn it into a heartfelt prayer by inserting your name as you read (e.g., If I give away all I possess but have not love, I gain nothing. Lord, please grant me love. Love is patient; God, please make me patient; Love is kind; Lord, please change my heart so that I am kind). Repeat the prayer, now inserting the names of others.

If you have time now or over the next several days, read through Psalm 27. Allow each verse to speak to your heart. Ask the Lord to open your heart to His love, perfection, and mercy. Commit every day to falling deeply in love with God.

MEMORY VERSE

Ephesians 4:2: "Be completely humble and gentle; be patient, bearing with one another in love."

Spend a few minutes reviewing each of the eleven memory verses in Appendix R.

DAILY READING

Do you view the command to pick up your cross daily and follow Christ as harsh? Perhaps you liken it to a contest to see who can withstand the most pain in trying to earn love. When Jesus says, "Take my yoke upon you," His desire is to lighten your load, not increase the burden (Matthew 11:30). When you take up the cross, it's Jesus Himself who carries it. He invites you to join your life with His. You take up the cross not by carrying it but by yielding to Jesus. You allow the Lord to supply the power. He provides the direction and carries the burden. You do, however, need to die to lust for the world and replace it with a longing for the Lord. You must stay in His camp to enjoy His protection and peace. Your will must bend to His, because only one can lead at a time. Start following the Lord and letting Him carry the load.

Chances are great that you have recently experienced, or are presently going through, a trial. List what you commonly do when facing a trial. For instance, do you rejoice, go numb, escape into fantasy, curse God, weep bitterly, engage in self-protection, or enlist others to defend you?

____

____

____

You should expect trials, which have a divine purpose. Open your heart to what God says about trials: "Consider it pure joy, my brothers, whenever you face trials of many kinds, because you know that the testing of your faith develops perseverance. Perseverance must finish its work so that you may be mature and complete, not lacking anything. If any of you lacks wisdom, he should ask God, who gives generously to all without finding fault, and it will be given to him" (James 1:2–5).

It seems strange to expect joy during trials. This notion must truly come from God, yet you should not confuse joy with happiness. The world seeks happiness and quick fixes. Joy, on the other hand, comes from an eternal perspective and by intimately experiencing God. Joy is not dependent upon circumstances, whether good or bad. Joy is finding contentment in all circumstances because you have yielded to the Lord and are no longer frantically trying to protect your so-called rights.

An example of joy not being dependent upon good circumstances includes the time when Jesus sent out some seventy people to go before Him in nearby towns. He had given them power to perform miracles. An interesting interplay occurs when they return. Read carefully what transpires in Luke 10:17–20. They return with joy and say to Jesus, "Lord, even the demons submit to us in your name." In response, Jesus says, "Do not rejoice that the spirits submit to you, but rejoice that your names are written in heaven." Contemplate this response, and then state why you think Christ spoke of this eternal perspective.

An example of joy not being rebuffed by bad circumstances is the life of Paul, who said while in chains in prison, "I will continue to rejoice, for I know that through our prayers and the help given by the Spirit of Jesus Christ, what has happened to me will turn out for my deliverance" (Philippians 1:18–19). Paul also exhorted from his cell: "Rejoice in the Lord always" (Philippians 4:4). Therefore, you can and should choose joy at all times in your life. You are responsible for your attitude and perspective. Rely on the Lord and keep an eternal focus. Choose to be joyful always. It's a decision you can make, provided you are acting in the strength of the Lord.

HEARTWORK

Chances are that you've had some moments of victory in your life, perhaps even months at a time, yet the same sin or a similar one usually makes its way back home. Why? It's never enough to empty a house of temptation or evil. The Lord warns that a house swept clean is waiting, almost begging, to be filled with something (Matthew 12:43–45). If you throw out all pornography and make every effort to rid your life of things that were used in the rituals of sexual sins, you're an empty house. Unless you fill your heart, mind, and soul with the Lord, evil will return in even greater force than before. Therefore, fill your house daily with worship and praise. Read the Bible to meet with God. The Bible is active and alive, so let it penetrate your soul. Prepare your body for God by treating it as a temple where God resides. Prepare your mind by inviting and including the Lord in all you do, think, or say. Learn to pray continually by openly talking to God and dwelling upon Him throughout the day. Also, tell Him about everything in your life. In short, choose the one master you will serve. Then live wholeheartedly for Him! Don't merely seek to rid yourself of temptation, but passionately pursue a real and active relationship with the living God.

READ THE BIBLE

Read Romans 5:1–11. Sing out to the Lord in your heart.

As part of a plan of praying continually, make time today or tonight to pray-read the names of God (Appendix C). Speak each of His names to Him in a loving and longing manner. Give Him glory. Right now, make a decision to fall in love with God the Father and Jesus His Son. Then put it into practice by spending time meeting with and experiencing God.

PRAY

Rejoice in the Lord. Be thankful and give praise to God.

- Ask for God's strength and power to carry out your goals and commitments to Him.
- Ask God to make you a humble, needy, dependent servant.
- Ask the Lord to open your eyes to the self-focused way you have viewed life and God.
- Pray for the gift of repentance. Ask God for humility.
- Commit to putting down the shovel of self-effort and giving Christ total control of your life.
- Spend time praying for others who are in bondage to sin and for other Proven Men.
- List others to pray for and spend the remaining time asking God to pour out grace upon them.

____

____

____

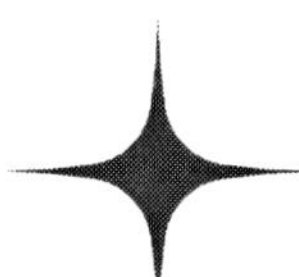

SPECIAL NOTE:

O is for Open and Honest. If you say you want to love God and want to give up sexual sins, can you also say that you want holiness across the board? In other words, do you just want to stop masturbating because you don't like the consequences of that particular sin or because you want to live a holy life? To be holy means to be holy in all areas. Being holy and pure means loving and forgiving others as well as not striving for wealth or power. Proven Men desire to be totally faithful, truthful, and single-minded for Christ.

MEMORY VERSE

Ephesians 4:2: "Be completely humble and gentle; be patient, bearing with one another in love."

This is your last weekend in this Proven Men study. Make it special with your family and with the Lord. Do you have your next daily study ready to go (see Appendix M)? If you don't have it planned out, you probably won't begin it. Don't stop now! The discipline you've developed will quickly wither away if you take a vacation from God. Besides, healing is not a one-time event. It's a by-product of a growing love relationship with the Lord. Allow God to stamp you Proven by making pursuing Him the greatest joy and priority of your life.

This weekend, set aside couch time to chart out a new family course. Read James 4:1–12. Put down the shovel of self-effort, and God will take up your cause! The future looks bright because of the hope God gives you. He loves you dearly and wants to bless you richly. Don't rush it. Use the space below to write a note to the Lord.

WEEK TWELVE

TESTIMONY

"We have corresponded in the past and I just want to say thanks from a pastor and man of God who found your program to be of great value to me in the ministry. I went through the program some years ago when you all were first up and operational. From that point to now, we have continued to be men of 'Proven' stock.

"I have one of my men going through the program now and he is 6 weeks 'sober' so to speak although we are talking about sexual bondage. He reported to me this morning, 'Pastor, it's been six weeks now.' I am excited for him as I remember how it feels to overcome addictions. Sadly, there will be others who don't mind staying in their messy situation. For me, it is encouraging to see this program work in the lives of so many and then here in front of my eyes. The beautiful thing about it all is that he feels comfortable talking to me about it now. At some point and I pray, he becomes one of those leaders who will take this program to new levels in our church, community, and state.

"Thanks for a job well done!"

Passionate for God,
Repentant in spirit,
Open and honest,
Victorious in living,
Eternal in perspective, and
Networking with other ***PROVEN Men.***

MEMORY VERSE

Ephesians 5:3: "But among you there must not be even a hint of sexual immorality, or of any kind of impurity, or of greed, because these are improper for God's holy people."

DAILY READING

You're nearing the end of this Proven Men study. Do you see that your heart is changing? Keep asking the Lord to renew your mind and transform your will to conform it to His.

The primary lesson for you this week is to be prepared to keep "doing" for the rest of your life what you've learned in this study (James 1:22). The second is to be committed to *networking* with other Proven Men and ministering to others (see Appendix P regarding *network partnerships*).

Do you have a burden for others? As you begin taking the focus off yourself, you'll see great pain in the lives of others. You'll also start seeing people as dearly loved children of God and not as objects for your pleasure. The more you yield to God, the more you experience His divine nature, including His compassion.

Meditate upon the following passage: "Praise be to the God and Father of our Lord Jesus Christ, the Father of compassion and the God of all comfort, who comforts us in all our troubles, so that we can comfort those in any trouble with the comfort we ourselves have received from God. For just as the sufferings of Christ flow into our lives, so also through Christ our comfort overflows" (2 Corinthians 1:3–5).

List what God does for you in times of trouble and state how He uses your troubles for good.

____

____

____

____

Did you notice that as a Christian, you're not exempt from suffering? God warns you in advance that you'll suffer. God likens your difficulties to Christ's sufferings, which He says flow into your life. As the sufferings keep flowing into you, they need to be released or you'll grow bitter as you hold in all of your pain. God has a perfect plan for refreshing you by washing out your sufferings and any bitterness or anger as you extend comfort and compassion to others.

God tells you that you must comfort others with the same comfort He granted to you. As you do, this extension of outward comfort to others washes out the pain of your underlying trials and sufferings. If you don't extend yourself to others, you bottle up the pain inside.

Consider the analogy of the Dead Sea. It's a tremendous body of water that has all of the elements for sustaining abundant life; yet it's dead because, unlike other seas, it's fed by many inlets but has no outlets feeding other waterways. By permitting incoming water and having no outflowing tributaries, the Dead Sea retains heavy quantities of salt and other impurities that kill life.

How about you? Do you merely want to hold inside of you all the blessings the Lord bestows upon you? Your refusal to look to the interests of others and extend heartfelt comfort and compassion is a restriction of the outflow, thus causing bitter waters and contaminants to remain inside your soul. How is this true for you? State any prayers or commitments for releasing His blessing through your life into others. Talk to God right now.

HELPING OTHERS

As a person is healed from a trouble, he generally longs to see others saved from the same thing. For instance, when people first become Christians, they are excited to share their faith with others. They want their friends to know the great depth of God's love for them as well as the truth about the one and only way to Him: Trusting in Jesus alone—not good deeds—for forgiveness of sin and reconciliation to God. Sadly, regardless of the level of your excitement, not everyone wants to hear about the Lord. What seems so clear to a believer remains hidden to non-Christians. For example, even though the Gospel of John states several times that a person must trust in Jesus alone by God's Spirit in order to be saved (John 3:3–16; 6:53; 11:25–27; 14:6), not all who read it can see it.

The same is true for those trapped in sexual sins. Many aren't open to seeing their sin. They refuse to accept that the healing path requires total surrender over all aspects of their lives to the Lord. They simply aren't willing to do whatever it takes to experience lasting freedom. Even reading this twelve-week study won't change a man who doesn't want God to change him. Just as you can lead a horse to water but cannot make it drink, you can present the cool stream of living water to people trapped in sexual bondage but cannot force them to repent and turn to God.

Although your heart can be grieved over a dear friend who refuses God's mercy, grace, and healing, you shouldn't and cannot judge them. Don't forget that many of us have spent nearly a lifetime of self-centered living, including years of pornography, masturbation, lust, or fantasy. You must not force healing upon them. They need to be ready to repent and replace their selfish life with a Proven life.

That doesn't mean there's nothing you can do for those still too proud and stubborn to yield to God. First and foremost, you can and should pray. As you're learning, only the Lord can change a heart. The good news is that prayer moves God to act. The perseverance you are developing through trials and by working through this *Heartwork* study will greatly benefit you now. It may take many hours, or even years, of praying to see fruit in another's life. Don't give up!

Second, continue living out a Proven life. Often the only thing that others accept as proof of God's ability to change them is seeing another changed life. Let the light of God shine through yours. As you yield control to God, you'll be changed from the inside out. Where once you were arrogant and seeking praise, you're now becoming kind, gentle, compassionate, and caring. The change will be obvious to other proud men. They'll wonder what's the source of the peace (and even joy) you have in your new position of humility. And you'll be watched. After hearing your testimony, some will sit back and watch for several months before believing that your faith and new Proven life are real. Only when they are satisfied that you're changed and won't judge them will they take the risk of accepting help. Expect that many will still remain guarded as they share portions of their lives with you. They'll give some details and wait to test your reaction. The good news is that the unconditional love and non-judgmental heart that the Lord is forming in you can cut through some of the hardest defenses in those finally ready to do business with God.

Do you want to see others healed? As you tilt the mirror upward toward God and off yourself, you'll want to love and serve others. The reflection they'll see is that of Christ, not you. The Lord wants to use you as His arms to hold and comfort the hurting. If you want to be used by God in the healing process of others, pray specifically for the Lord to humble you and to work in other men. Your greatest need is not education or training, but to be filled by and to follow the leading of the Holy Spirit. To be used by God, you must know Him and live a life punctuated by prayer and praise. Therefore, *make it your purpose to seek God with all of your heart, to yield total control, and to live by His Spirit.* As you do, you're becoming more complete, stamped by God and ready to serve. What a privilege awaits!

N is for Networking with Other Proven Men. You have a role in *networking* with and encouraging others to become Proven Men. God will use your pain and struggles to help other men trapped in sexual bondage. Your life will be a shining example and a ray of hope. That's right. God will use your story to guide and encourage others just as He is using mine. Be sure that you're an encourager and a source of strength to others, rather than someone who complains, tears down or destroys. Finally, stay connected with other Proven Men. Don't cut the cord and seek to strike out on your own. Remain part of the team. Keep a mountain climbing team image fresh in your mind. Be sure to encourage and strengthen other Proven Men; we all need continuing encouragement.

PRAY

Open your heart to the Lord. Keep communicating with Him for five or ten minutes.

- Ask God to make His will and plan for your life clear to you.
- Pray for His leading and direction.
- Commit to waiting upon the Lord.
- Keep this goal always before you: To make loving and pursuing after God your number one priority for the rest of your life. Then you will recognize His voice and calling.
- Keep praying for others with a heart of compassion. (List them to help you remain focused.)

____

____

READ THE BIBLE

Read until you hear God speaking to you. Then meditate upon what He reveals. Ask Him to talk to you. Begin with Romans 1:18 through 2:16. Be willing to slow down or stop when God presses something on your heart. It's communion with the Lord that counts, not the number of verses you read.

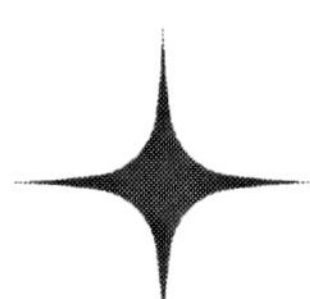

SPECIAL NOTE:

You'll always make mistakes and offend people when you minister to others, but when you lead with your heart and minister in the Lord's strength, you'll be able to win many of your brothers. Set the example of saying, "I was wrong; please forgive me." Don't wait for a brother to be more mature than you. Even if he was 90 percent at fault, always be the peacemaker and the one seeking reconciliation. "If it is possible, as far as it depends upon you, live at peace with everyone" (Romans 12:18).

Give back. You are in your last week of the Study. It's time to start planning on how to give back. Millions of men are dying for a helping hand, and we can't reach them without you! Please consider volunteering to guide other men. Visit our website: www.ProvenMen.org.

MEMORY VERSE

Ephesians 5:3: "But among you there must not be even a hint of sexual immorality, or of any kind of impurity, or of greed, because these are improper for God's holy people."

Yesterday, you read the good news that God intends on using your victory through failures and struggles to help others (2 Corinthians 1:3–5). However, the Lord works through you only when you are living out a Proven life. This is because a proud man will stumble and lead others astray (Matthew 15:14). A humble, needy, and dependent servant, on the other hand, is the mightiest of men in God's service. Today you'll learn more about your role in helping others.

DAILY READING

As you minister to others facing struggles with sexual temptations, be on guard against all forms of pride. Here are some common traps:

- Comparing yourself to others.
- Wanting to be seen as an expert.
- Seeking praise from men.
- Overlooking your own sins.
- Becoming so busy working for God that you stop meeting with Him.

Never forget that healing and spiritual maturity are lifetime processes. Your battle against sin is not over and will never end. Victory lasts only while you stay under God's wing, so expect a fight. Expect that as you hear the stories of men, you'll be exposed to sexual topics that can tempt you to fantasize and leave God's camp. Satan doesn't want another soldier helping the wounded. The devil wants to distract you and make you fall. The Bible cautions us to be especially careful when seeking to restore a fallen brother because you might be tempted in the same way (Galatians 6:1).

If you get puffed up, God will allow you to deal with temptation in your own strength and stumble. The Lord didn't spare many a Godly man, and He won't spare you if you wear a banner of pride; yet the Lord is faithful and true to forgive a repentant man. God wants you to prosper. Therefore, don't throw in the towel if you have a setback. Rather, take on an *eternal perspective* that the goal is living intimately with God and receiving His righteousness. A setback should not deflate but motivate you further in putting down the shovel of self-effort and becoming even more repentant, needy, and dependent upon the Lord. Consider these practical points for ministering to others:

1. Don't wait until you are perfect. It's your pride that says that you must be perfect in the eyes of others. Don't hold back from ministering to others or even leading a small group because you don't have formal training or a degree. The Holy Spirit is your best guide. If you're humble and demonstrate true love for others, you'll make a good and Godly leader. Be willing to say that you're not an expert but rather a dependent servant of God looking to link up with other men who want to seek God with all of their hearts. Being co-equal can break down barriers for some. No one really wants to be lectured by someone who never struggles or who merely points out their flaws. It's unconditional love and kindness that leads men to repentance and draws them to the one place where healing occurs. Show that type of love to others, and they'll want to have the same Proven life that's being formed in you. (If you are thinking of hosting a small recovery group, obtain a copy of the *Leader's Guide* to this study, available through online bookstores or at www.ProvenMen.org.)

2. Be open and honest, vulnerable, and real. This example is so important for others to see and follow. Most men who struggle with sexual impurity are running from intimacy. They don't know how to be vulnerable. If you're not open and transparent, don't expect them to be. The healing process will be thwarted in both of you. In addition, love covers a multitude of sins (1 Peter 4:8). If you're speaking the truth in love (Ephesians 4:15) and others know you really want them to succeed, they can overlook some miscues you'll make. At the same time, you should be repentant. For instance, if you use a shaming technique or judge them at any point, confess it and seek their forgiveness. Similarly, regularly confess to them your struggles, sins, and setbacks. Practice and model real repentance, such as being truly sorrowful for turning away from God and then racing back to Him.

3. Lead with your heart, not your head. Many seek to serve the Lord, but a man of God is one who seeks Him with all of his heart. Your heart matters most to God. That's the

place where He meets you. The same applies for times you're asked to speak or teach: Do so with your heart. Don't memorize speeches, but talk from your heart. Teach others about the heart of God and how to possess a passionate, repentant, and open heart. In all you do, do it from a soft heart.

4. Practice and teach James 1:22, which says: "Do not merely listen to the word, and so deceive yourselves. Do what is says." How often do we say to others: "I encourage you to read the Bible and pray?" And yet, how little do we do such things each day? Let's become doers of the Word. The *Heartwork* study is filled with many truths about the healing path, but it requires action in addition to desire. As for you, a fellow servant, you must act and carry out the commands of God as you encourage others to follow the same path. Never forget that head knowledge won't heal but will deceive. Love others well by practicing what you teach.

5. Teach others what it means to live a Proven life. We connect to God and receive Him into our lives through *passionate* praise and worship. A *repentant* spirit kills the pride that feeds on the selfishness that gives birth to sexual sin. *Openness* and honesty foster relationships that bring healing and replace the false intimacy we used as substitutes for the void in our lives. *Victory* is not won by a program but by yielding a life to a perfect and good God. Share the *eternal perspective* that we were created for a relationship with God and others. Make it your goal to point men to a real, deep, intimate relationship with God. There's no other way to have continuous healing from the wounds of life or to be free to experience God. Knowing God, which is far different from knowing about Him, is life (John 17:3). Finally, for the rest of your life keep *networking* and connecting with other men.

6. Pray for others. This will be one of your most treasured duties, because only the Lord can change and heal a man. Therefore, spend time petitioning God on behalf of others. Be devoted to prayer! Along the same lines, be sure to communicate with the men during the week.

Be sure that when you talk to others, it's with a message that Jesus loves them unconditionally and is the only true source of healing. Explain to others: With Christ, hope is a promise and transformation His delight. God will change anyone who yields to the Spirit of God and makes pursuing the love of the Lord his top priority in life. Make these things true in your life!

Ephesians 5:19–20 teaches ways to be an encourager: "Speak to one another with psalms, hymns and spiritual songs. Sing and make music in your heart to the Lord, always giving thanks to God the Father for everything, in the name of our Lord Jesus Christ." If you're writing and singing psalms and hymns from your heart and you're constantly giving thanks to God, you'll be a joyful person and a joy to be around. People will want to follow your example. Right now, commit to being an encouraging person. Your responsibilities include wearing compassion, kindness, humility, gentleness, and patience; to bear with and forgive one another; and to be self-controlled (Colossians 3:12–14; Ephesians 4:2.) Will you put on such things? Write out your commitment to pursuing God with all your heart and mind.

____

____

____

____

____

____

PRAY

Engage in true relational prayers with your Lord.

- Ask God to make you a needy, dependent servant that relies on His power and His wisdom.
- Ask Him to show you when you're relying upon your own strength.
- Ask God to open your heart to what love really is instead of false intimacy.
- Honestly evaluate your life compared to the scriptures you read today.
- Confess ways you have not been patient or kind and how you have not protected others.
- Ask God to open your eyes and heart to how you've been proud and a self-seeker.
- Ask God to exchange your ways for the ways of Christ.
- Ask God to give you His power to put to death your selfishness and pride.
- Ask God to change you into a servant of righteousness and a willing agent of the Lord.
- Pray for family and friends. Pray for other Proven Men.

READ THE BIBLE

Read James 4:1–16. Agree to fully submit to God. Meditate on the memory verse.

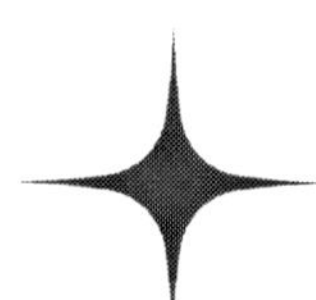

SPECIAL NOTE:

Pride will always be a sin issue that you face. God calls you to be humble, but your sinful nature wants to elevate you. Therefore, follow this command: "Test everything. Hold on to the good. Avoid every kind of evil" (1 Thessalonians 5:21–22). In other words, constantly test your own motives. This action applies even to work done at church. Is it for His glory or for your recognition? When you discover pride as a factor, go to the Lord; confess your sin and seek forgiveness. Ask God to remove pride and to give you brokenness and humility.

MEMORY VERSE

Ephesians 5:3: "But among you there must not be even a hint of sexual immorality, or of any kind of impurity, or of greed, because these are improper for God's holy people."

HEARTWORK

Do you have a heart that is passionate toward God? Right now, read *"Developing a Heart of Worship"* in Appendix G.

In the space below, prepare your own game plan for developing a heart of worship for God.

____

____

____

____

____

____

DAILY READING

ARE YOU LIVING OUT A REPENTANT SPIRIT WITH YOUR FAMILY?

- Be the first to say, "I was wrong, please forgive me."

- Admit wrongs that you've committed at work and other places and tell your family how you responded (e.g., when you raised your voice at a co-worker, you went back and sought forgiveness).
- Read Psalm 51 as a family and teach about repentance.
- Are you being open and honest with your family?
- Have talks with your children about the proper role of sex. (Consider using a weekend away kit developed by Family Life Ministries (http://www.PassportToPurity.com/).
- Regularly hug and tell each of your family members and friends that you love them.
- Permit and encourage displays of emotions and feelings (and be an example in this area).
- Talk about feelings and emotions with your family and others.
- Be vulnerable, open, and honest.

ARE YOU LIVING A VICTORIOUS LIFE?

- If you're not walking in victory, what role model is there to follow?
- The prayer of a righteous man is powerful and effective because it's heard by God (James 5:16).
- Seek God's righteousness by pursuing Him faithfully.
- To live by the Spirit is to walk in victory (Galatians 5:16). Don't walk, run to God! He never turns you away.

DO YOU HAVE AN ETERNAL PERSPECTIVE?

- Dwell on the fact that your home is in heaven. Put aside greed and the worries of this world.
- Do you truly know that God is good, and do you trust Him with all of your life?
- What is the primary purpose for your life? Have you shared with others your life goals?
- Are you investing your life in the lives of others with both quality and quantity time?
- Married men, are you the primary person responsible for disciplining your children, including teaching them about right from wrong according to God's standards and teaching them about the knowledge and fear of God? Church youth groups support but don't replace your role or responsibility.

ARE YOU NETWORKING WITH OTHER PROVEN MEN?

- Does your family see you investing your life in the lives of other men?
- Do you have close and intimate men friends?
- Are you vulnerable and even transparent with an accountability *(network)* partner?

Twelve-weeks is nearly over; so commit to repeating this *Heartwork* study or list your next study below (for ideas see Appendix M):

____

____

____

____

Will you commit to passing on a heart of worship to others, including children? The second of the Ten Commandments states: "You shall not make for yourself an idol... You shall not bow down to them or worship them; for I, the Lord your God, am a jealous God, punishing the children for the sin of the fathers to the third and fourth generation of those who hate me, but showing love to a thousand generations of those who love me and keep my commandments" (Exodus 20:4–6).

God tells us that if we are idolaters, we will pass our sins down to our children and their children. Many found their dad's pornography under his bed or on his computer, and that's where he likely found his dad's pornography. If a father never hugged or told his son that he loved him, the son likely won't do these things with his children. The good news is that if we turn to God, giving up our idols and loving the Lord with all of our hearts, then God will show such great love and mercy to us that our children and their children will be blessed.

PRAY

Spend five or ten minutes talking to God. Ask Him to reveal any generational sins such as pride, greed or lust. Ask Him to break them. Give total control to God and hold nothing back. Be committed to being stamped Proven.

- Pray for your children (or future children) and your spiritual children.
- Pray for your spouse (or future spouse).
- Pray for other Proven Men.
- Pray for your pastor.
- Pray for missionaries.
- Pray for others. (List them here.)

____

____

____

READ THE BIBLE

Use the Bible as a way of getting to know and love God. Read Hebrews 12:28–29 and Matthew 6:19–24.

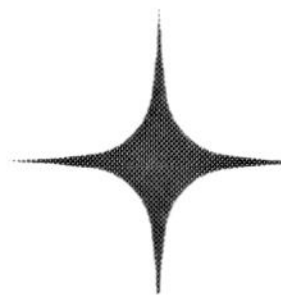

SPECIAL NOTE:

If you're a self-seeker, you'll pass down to your children and others the ways of the world and a life of discontentment and God's wrath. If you die to yourself and are living by the Spirit, however, you'll pass on to them blessings upon blessings. It's really your choice. How selfish are you going to be? There are several things you can do for your children and others. First, live out the love of Christ. People, including children, know the difference between preaching and teaching. They know when you're real. How about it, are your faith and actions real?

Are you setting boundaries for your children or others you influence to keep them safe? These include:

- Knowing their friends.
- Installing Internet blocks on all home computers and cell phones.
- Setting and enforcing curfews.

Be sure that you don't rely upon boundaries alone to protect your children or other people you influence. Just as setting boundaries doesn't turn away your own sensual desires for sin, neither will it for them (Colossians 2:20–23). If you set rules such as no R-rated movies but then swear and become enraged at home, what have you taught them? If you require them to go to church, but you don't love God with all of your heart, won't they see church as something people just have to do?

Two of the best examples you can set for children are: (1) gently loving your children's mother (if children know that their father loves their mother, then they feel safe, secure, and loved), and (2) showing sincere interest in their activities and achievements.

A few other ways of instilling in others a heart of worship include:

- Praying with them daily.
- Helping them select a daily devotional.
- Allowing them to see you in prayer and study.
- Monitoring your inputs and theirs, including movies, TV, Internet, magazines, and music.
- Attending church with your children. It's okay to make it a rule that children will attend church, but also look for ways to make the experience real, meaningful, and enjoyable.

Part of training is explaining. Be ready to tell others why you do the above things. People need to understand the "why" before they can embrace these things themselves. Also, explain why we need to be humble, gentle, kind, patient, etc. Write out your reasons to some of these items and then set aside couch time to discuss them as a family.

MEMORY VERSE

Ephesians 5:3: "But among you there must not be even a hint of sexual immorality, or of any kind of impurity, or of greed, because these are improper for God's holy people."

It's time to tear down and remove all idols in your life. With respect to the memory verse, what will you do to remove any hints of sexual immorality? For example, use an Internet block, don't watch certain movies, stop coarse joking, and be wholly devoted to your wife if married. Removing hints of sexual sin also includes not being alone with women other than your spouse, not flirting, not taking second looks. What other things will you remove or decide not to do to live this out as a pleasing sacrifice to the Lord? Don't be fooled. Where your mind or eyes wander reveals which master you're serving. List other ways and then make a game plan to carry out your goals.

DAILY READING

Let's review the big picture. Go back and read *"Freedom from Sexual Bondage"* (in Appendix J).

- What do you understand better now than you did twelve weeks ago?

____

____

____

____

____

What will you do to remove any hints of the idolatry of greed from in your life? Greed could show up in your life as day trading of stocks, fretting over bills, fantasizing about winning the lottery, or engaging in get-rich-quick schemes. Choose to be content. Make it a firm decision.

____

____

____

____

____

We hope this series has consistently pointed you toward your real home in heaven and that you are experiencing new freedom. Always remember that healing is a work of God and that you must keep turning to and pursuing Him with all of your heart.

Plan to follow one of the suggested studies in Appendix M. Turn there now. Record your next study here:

____

____

____

____

HEARTWORK

Make a covenant similar to this: Each new day the Lord gives me I will die to selfishness and pride and live out each element of a Proven life.

Each day for the rest of your life test yourself by the PROVEN acronym so that you'll live out a life in which you are:

Passionate for God.
Repentant in spirit.
Open and honest.
Victorious in living.
Eternal in perspective.
Networked with other PROVEN MEN.

By living such a Proven life, although you may be tempted daily, you'll be an approved workman who passes the test (2 Timothy 2:15). You can do this!

PRAY

Pray for your family and other Proven Men. Consider using Psalm 119:1–16 as a model. Talk to God about the new course of your life.

READ THE BIBLE

Read 1 Corinthians 6:12–20 and Romans 1:18–32; 2:1–16. Record any insights.

MEMORY VERSE

Ephesians 5:3: "But among you there must not be even a hint of sexual immorality, or of any kind of impurity, or of greed, because these are improper for God's holy people."

WEEK 12 DAY 5 (FRIDAY)

Review all of your memory verses, which are listed in Appendix R. Do you have all twelve memorized? If so, you'll be like the psalmist: "I have hidden your word in my heart that I might not sin against you" (Psalm 119:11). Keep referring to them so they become powerful friends.

DAILY READING

One theme verse for Proven Men Ministries is 2 Timothy 2:15: "Do your best to present yourself to God as one approved, a workman who does not need to be ashamed and who correctly handles the word of truth." You're now part of the Proven Men team, stamped approved by God. There's no need to be ashamed. You correctly handle the word of truth because you are living it out; you're doing what it says. God is becoming a real and intimate friend. You have been and are continuing to be transformed.

A gentle reminder: If you don't feel like a spiritual giant just yet, that's okay. At this point in Joel's life (after twelve weeks of study and counsel), he was just beginning to stop staring at the ground while walking through the subway on his busy commute to work so that he would not lust after women. Joel was scared about going on to a general daily Bible study and was afraid that he didn't have enough spiritual training to overcome without a purity support group; yet Joel knew that he truly committed to never turning back to his former selfish way of living. Pornography and masturbation were no longer options. He put into place accountability, and he knew he would keep striving because Jesus would supply the strength. Jesus was his one and only hope, and Joel would fully trust in Him.

Just like Joel and other Proven Men, you can and must count on God's promises. They must and will come to pass. Be still and rest in the Lord. Spiritual maturity is an ongoing and lifelong process. You will grow. Don't be impatient with yourself. Keep staying the course. Victory is assured!

If you experience a setback, don't quit. Instead, use it as a wake-up call that you took the focus off the Lord and put it back on yourself or your circumstances. Renew your heart and mind by going back to the source of life each time you sin. Consider also revisiting Week 4, Days 4 and 5 after times you fail. Remember, God is interested in a relationship with you, not merely knowing that you don't commit a particular sin. When you get complacent or live in your own strength, you're ripe for a fall; but don't throw in the towel. Accept discipline from the One who loves you and is seeking to draw you back (Hebrews 12:5–6). Keep growing in a deeper dependent relationship with the Lord.

Recall the two reasons God created you: (1) to worship and glorify God, and (2) to be His child and friend (Matthew 4:10; James 2:23; John 1:12; and 1 John 3:1). Consider again how knowing this purpose for living gives you freedom and meaning in life. When you fight against such purpose, you fight against God. Always remember that the Lord wants you to turn to Him in love and fellowship and that He is patient and forgiving. The process of putting away idols and passionately seeking the Lord is what makes you whole and complete, bearing spiritual fruit instead of turning to selfish actions.

Don't ever lose sight of what it means to be ***PROVEN***: Passionately pursuing God; Repenting when you fail; being Open and honest with your feelings and communications; walking in His Victory; keeping an Eternal perspective; and loving and serving, i.e. Networking with others. This model is not just for those desiring sexual purity; it's what all children of God are called to be. Live a Proven life. Test your life regularly against each letter of the PROVEN acronym, using it as a way to check the condition of your heart and a reminder to embrace each element.

HEARTWORK

Take a stand. Tell Satan, "No more ground!" Make an irrevocable commitment that pornography, masturbation, and sexual immorality of any kind are not an option in your life. Make absolute purity your spiritual act of worship (Romans 12:1–2).

Spend the last bit of time in this study worshiping God. Be in awe of Him. Read the names of God with passion and pleasure (see Appendix C) and get to know His perfect attributes (see Appendix D).

Use the space below to make a game plan, write a note to God, and chart a course for your life.

____

____

____

____

READ THE BIBLE

Read Matthew 6:24–34. Trust in God for your future. You are now part of the Proven Men team and are His forever.

Final Remarks and Personal Salutation from the Founder of Proven Men Ministries, Ltd.

- Enjoy God, minister to your family, and do the things you've learned and will learn.
- Keep praying for and having fellowship with your brothers in Christ.
- Know that you're dearly loved and are God's most treasured possession!
- Keep finding meaningful and pleasing ways to worship your precious Lord.
- Continue each day in study, in God's Word, and in prayer. Make sure you begin your next study immediately!

I have no greater joy than to hear that fellow Proven Men are walking victoriously in the truth! Please make my joy complete by being like-minded, having the same love and passion for the Lord and each other, and becoming one in spirit and purpose. I look forward to reading letters and testimonies from you and witnessing the work of the Lord through your life and in the lives of those you touch.

Go forth. Live a holy and pure life embracing the Proven Men Latin battle cry, Coram Deo, "Before the eyes of the Lord!" By presenting yourself to God as an approved workman, you will no longer need to be ashamed but will correctly handle the word of truth, which God entrusts to you, His friend (see 2 Timothy 2:15).

Keep referring to the PROVEN acronym to remind yourself how to live and whom to live for!

Passionate for God.

Repentant in spirit.

Open and honest.

Victorious in living.

Eternal in perspective.

Networked with other PROVEN MEN.

SPECIAL NOTE:

Congratulation! You finished the Study. Plan to go through it again. But this time, consider going through it with another man. If you have a person in mind, use our free guide for two men located in our Bookstore on our website. Also, plan to support our ministry with a generous tax deductible donation and by volunteering. Visit our website: www.ProvenMen.org.

Endnotes

1. One of the foundational principles in the book *Sexual Healing: God's Plan for the Sanctification of Broken Lives* by Dr. David Kyle Foster, p. 19, is the notion "as you begin your quest for sexual healing, don't forget who does the healing (God does), and where the ability to achieve results comes from (it comes from God)."
2. See *Sexual Healing,* p. 304, "There is no one single part of the Christian life that is more important than spending copious hours praising and worshiping God, for it's in that time of truth and intimacy that He imparts His life and character to us, and we are made to be like Him."
3. The concept of false intimacy is thoroughly discussed in the exceptional book *False Intimacy: Understanding the Struggle of Sexual Addiction* by Dr. Harry Schaumburg (NavPress, 1992). The concept is also stated in *Sexual Healing* on p. 187: "The sex addict is in a flight from intimacy with humanity. He is deathly afraid of it. He has been deeply hurt by it in the past or has been raised in a family environment that punished attempts at relational intimacy. Intimacy, for one reason or another, is a chance not worth taking. For him, it's better to live in a world of fantasy sex rather than risk the hurt of rejection in attempts at true intimacy."
4. *Sexual Healing,* p. 29: "We are a Gift of the Father to Christ" (based on John 6:37, 39).
5. *Sexual Healing,* p. 38, discusses the world's view of love, which is "an earned commodity" and equates love with sex, and explains God's definition of love, which is unconditional.
6. *Sexual Healing,* p. 319, devotes an entire section to "Living by Grace Rather Than Performance Orientation". In addition, it states, "Stop all of your attempts to earn God's love and approval. It cannot be earned. It's freely given. It is unconditional."
7. This bicycle riding analogy is adapted from one used in *Sexual Healing,* p. 289.
8. According to *Sexual Healing,* p. 291, "Sexual healing is a life-long process, punctuated with significant healings, awakenings and deliverances—all wrought through an increasing dependence on, and devotion to, the Lord." The book goes on to state that the "Failure to see Healing as a Process with a Purpose" is one of the major mistakes made by those seeking freedom. *id.* p. 271.
9. This spiral was adapted from *Sexual Healing,* p. 292, which explains the downward cycle as follows: "After setting us up for a fall through weakening us spiritually in our dealings with unrelated sins, Satan then hits us with the more obvious transgression: • Sexual temptation • Fall • Guilt • Shame • Condemnation • Hopelessness • Temptation • Fall."
10. The term "Truth Therapy" stems from *Sexual Healing,* p. 268, which defines it as involving "regular meditation on the truths of scripture...that contradict what we are feeling and experiencing in our battle with sin."
11. *Sexual Healing,* p. 65.
12. *Sexual Healing,* p. 71, "Be careful to center your actions in knowing Him, responding in love to Him out of His already demonstrated love for you on the Cross. When you catch yourself going to God with the primary purpose of getting something, then stop, reorient your priorities and approach Him again."
13. *Sexual Healing,* pp. 309–310, "It's important to see that the anger, bitterness, resentment or unforgiveness that you've nourished over the years as a result of your pain has actually made things worse. It has created an emotional block that secretly opposes all attempts at healing and reconciliation. It is harming you rather than the person against whom you hold it."

14. *Sexual Healing,* p. 73, contains an exercise of writing a short paper answering the question, "When I think of God as my father, I feel..."
15. *Sexual Healing,* pp. 76, 90.
16. *Sexual Healing,* p. 85, suggests: "Meditate on the idea of God (Father, Son & Holy Spirit) being your sole hero in life and ask Him to make it so."
17. *Sexual Healing* describes this process slightly differently (pp. 95, 314). It states that after you begin an intimate relationship with God, He'll begin speaking to you "through inner impressions and even sometimes through a still small voice that seems to go directly into your mind and heart without the benefit of the ears." It also discusses how Bible passages and circumstances are also ways God will get His message across to you. God also "orchestrates events and inputs around us in such a way as to repeatedly drive home an idea."
18. A book, *The Wounded Heart,* by Dr. Dan Allender (NavPress), uses the term "firelighters" and applies it to adult survivors of sexual abuse from childhood. Those concepts helped shape this discussion. If you or a loved one has suffered childhood abuse, consider reading it after the conclusion of this study.
19. *Sexual Healing,* p. 202, "We do not look back into our past in order to fix blame on others, but so as to discover where we have already fixed blame, so that those vows and judgments can be repented of and the people forgiven and released."
20. Consider the way it is stated in *Sexual Healing,* p. 285, "Make an across-the-board commitment to holiness, forsaking all to live for Jesus. Turn your heart toward correction and the humility of unquestioned obedience to God. Allow Him to enter into every area of your life."
21. According to *Sexual Healing,* p. 184, "The behavior that they choose (or that sometimes seems to choose them), never brings about the desired result. In desperation, the addict increases their participation in the behavior in a subconscious attempt to force it to work, and are left feeling like some crazed animal—the antithesis of what they wanted."
22. *Sexual Healing* states, p. 186, "Oddly enough, in order for the sex addict to be healed, he (or she) must discover the source of his pain (with the help of the Holy Spirit), and resolve the issues that he finds. He must confront the very things that hurt him—in essence, embracing the pain in order to heal it. He has to stop hiding from the things that hurt him and he must stop concealing them from those who can help him."
23. *Sexual Healing,* p. 186.
24. See *Sexual Healing,* p. 194, "Their biggest battle is turning from a focus on 'self' to a focus on God."
25. *Sexual Healing,* p. 191, describes it slightly differently: "The sex addict will depersonalize the object of their lust and use sex in a flight from intimacy rather than as a means of intimacy."
26. See *Sexual Healing,* p. 201, "Yield!!! totally and completely, with full and absolute dependence on the power of God (which is brought forth through intimacy with Him), to overcome your addiction by healing the inner emotional damage that you have suffered throughout your life, and in particular, your childhood."
27. See endnote 3 above.
28. See *Sexual Healing,* p. 223, "See temptation as an opportunity for righteousness and growth in spiritual maturity."
29. See *Sexual Healing,* p. 223, "If, however, you turn to God with a heart committed to being made holy every time Satan tempts you, he will eventually realize that by tempting you, he is actually causing you to turn to God, which is the last thing he wants to do. He will then withdraw until a more opportune time when your resolve has weakened or with a new approach of strategy."
30. See *Sexual Healing,* p. 219, "When the temptation comes, stop and ask yourself: 'Who is Lord of my life? Who do I love more?'"
31. *Sexual Healing,* p. 219, states it this way: "Set your heart against pornography by making an irrevocable decision that using it will never again be an option in your life."
32. *Sexual Healing,* p. 222, lists this as a practical component to overcoming sexual addiction: "Set a guard (bouncer) at the door of your mind" and "aggressively attack every impure thought the minute it enters your mind. Do not give it time to dwell. The more time it dwells, the more power it gains to remain."
33. See *Sexual Healing,* pp. 183, 193.
34. See *Sexual Healing,* pp. 243–44, "[Many] who achieve sobriety from masturbation, experience a continued demonic assault in their dream life.... You must not leave this ground of the unconscious mind left open to the enemy. As abstract as it may seem, you must pray that God take the ground of your subconscious mind." It also suggests that you "attack the stronghold immediately. Don't rest for even a moment in the afterglow of your dream. Ruin the pleasure of it so that your mind has nothing to look forward to at the specter of a repeat episode."

35. This model is adapted from one used in *Sexual Healing,* p. 239.

36. See *Sexual Healing,* p. 285, "Make knowing Him the greatest pursuit of your life. If you do this, you will not remain in sin."

37. See *Sexual Healing,* p. 272, "The greater goal of knowing Him intimately, is what brings about the goal of holiness."

38. See *Sexual Healing,* p. 273, "Intimacy then is established through a life-style of worship and praise—singing love songs to our Lord and gazing upon His glory in the Spirit—practicing His presence with the same persistence and regularity as we would anything else that is necessary for life."

39. See *Sexual Healing,* p. 300, "We must always remember that we have been born into a battle—the battle of evil against good (Satan against God), and that as members of Christ's body, the Church, we will suffer wounds from the battle."

40. See *Sexual Healing,* p. 301, "A second component to the 'eternal perspective' is who we are in relation to God—that we are created beings who are incapable of doing anything truly and perfectly good without the redemption, the restoration, the equipping, and the work of God in and through us to accomplish it."

41. The book *Sexual Healing,* p. 319, forcefully makes this point: "Before you do anything else, stop and ask the Lord to put real love into you—love for both God and your fellow man. For it is God who pours out His love into our hearts by the Holy Spirit (Rom. 5:5)."

Appendix A: Relational Exercises

Open and honest relationships don't just happen; they're formed. Make a decision to nurture relationships with family and friends. Plan out daily activities to foster openness and vulnerability. Consider the following ideas:

DAILY FAMILY DEVOTIONALS

My Utmost for His Highest by Oswald Chambers is an excellent daily devotional for the whole family. The updated edition in today's language is recommended. Each day's reading takes only a few minutes. Other devotional suggestions include *Jesus Calling* by Sarah Young, *Jesus Freaks* by DC Talk (which compiles short stories about martyrs in church history), and *The Prayer of Jabez* by Bruce Wilkinson. Take the lead and initiate daily devotionals with your family.

Develop family traditions that you and others can look forward to at certain times of the year, such as taking a hay ride every Halloween, going to a B&B for your anniversary, telling the Christmas story each Christmas Eve, attending a ball game annually, decorating the house for birthdays, scheduling annual trips to the zoo, or watching the Christmas light show.

FOR SINGLES

Single men should engage in prayers and devotionals with other men. For right now, you may need to avoid acting as a spiritual leader with a girlfriend because of the intimacy involved.

OTHER PRAYER IDEAS

Pray as each issue, decision, or problem arises. Don't wait until meals or morning prayer times. Pray right away. God is interested in your situation and in your relationship. Go to Him often.

Pray with others. It can be hard to pray out loud, but work through discomfort. When you pray, don't try sounding eloquent or using someone else's words. God wants your heart, thoughts, and words.

Consider popcorn prayers, i.e., taking turns saying short prayers. Each person in the group should pray. Keep each prayer short (i.e., 15 seconds and only one topic) and from the heart. Keep jumping in and pray what God places on your heart.

Develop special prayer events or times, such as turning off the lights and praying by candlelight.

Pick out a favorite Bible story such as the parting of the Red Sea, and tell it in your own words. Describe how awesome that must have been. Get the family to engage and be a part of the story.

OTHER FAMILY MATTERS (CONVERSATION IDEAS)

Learn the love language of family and friends and then start doing daily things that speak to it. The five major love languages are:

- Time spent (just being together)
- Gifts (even inexpensive items, such as flowers, candy, or trinkets, make this person feel loved)
- Words of affirmation (some thrive on being told compliments and reassuring words;

you cannot say too many times things like "I love you," "You look great," "That was really neat the way you did that," or "Supper was delicious")

- Acts of service (drying dishes, putting clothes away, vacuuming, and doing other chores speak volumes to this person)
- Touch (hugs, a gentle hand on a shoulder, holding hands on walks) (See *The Five Love Languages* by Gary Chapman.)

Often family members, especially husbands and wives, have different love languages. If you are "gifts" and your wife is "acts of service," for example, no matter how many gifts you give (because that is what makes you feel loved), she still needs to see you do acts to feel your love. Find out the love language of others in your family and do it, especially if it's different from the one you wish they had!

Couch time. If you're married, schedule weekly or monthly couch time when just you and your wife (no kids or company) talk about family matters and set personal and group goals. Be truly interested in your wife's goals. Listen, listen, listen. Affirm, affirm, affirm. If you have children, discuss each child, setting specific goals and how to accomplish them. Be sure to talk about their good qualities and thank your wife for doing a great job raising them.

If you don't have children, you still need couch time for open communication and a deepening relationship. If you are single, set aside time to talk to other men about the direction of your life and your desire to follow God. Get feedback from other men who love the Lord. Be sure to put couch time on the calendar and guard its time.

Keep a journal and use it as a way of remembering goals and events.

Practice talking about feelings by asking others how they are feeling. Never remark, "Oh!" or "Really?" or "Why do you feel that way about that?" Comments like these signal that feelings are taboo. Allow others (and yourself) to have feelings and to be able to share them. Listen and don't try to fix things. Practice listening and affirming. Acknowledge and accept others' feelings.

Keep trying out new family hobbies that everyone can participate in, such as puzzles, rock collecting, walks, or games. Discuss what each liked about the activity.

Ask your family what fears or concerns they face. Ask your men friends about their dreams. Encourage them to dream and to accomplish their dreams by relying upon God's strength.

Talk about childhood memories. Even if your childhood was difficult, God is sovereign. Use your past and your memories for the Lord. Others long to hear personal stories. Don't stuff past events or downplay your life. Be open and communicative. Also, ask others about their childhood and memories.

If you're married, ask your wife what things you can do to make her feel more secure and loved. Singles, ask other men what things you should be preparing to do when you're married. Don't lament that you're not married. Enjoy God and engage in training as a good soldier for Christ.

Listen, listen, listen. Practice listening. Put the newspaper down, get off the computer, turn off the TV, and then lean forward and listen. Don't offer advice. Repeat back some of the things your wife or friend says so you both know that you're hearing correctly. If your wife says how hard the day was because the vacuum cleaner broke or the laundry was piled up, tell her, "It sounds like it was a frustrating day." Let her keep venting if needed. Keep listening. You'll be surprised to see how listening will build a relationship!

SPOKEN WORDS AND TOUCH

Married men, tell your wife of her beauty and how your love is more infinite than the stars. Each spouse must work on keeping open lines of communication.

If you're single, don't be discouraged. A God that numbers the stars knows what is best for you and the right timing. Make your relationship with the Lord the number one priority in your life. Don't be consumed with finding a spouse. Keep in mind that God knows your needs and promises to provide for them. Focus on becoming the person that God wants you to be. He will provide a spouse in due time. Keep your attention on pleasing God and serving others. The more actively you love and serve others with pure motives, the less you'll be consumed with your circumstances. Run as hard as you can after Christ. God can surely provide a mate running as fast toward Him. How blessed you'll be!

Compliment family and friends on things you notice, such as their gentle spirit, good attitudes, or politeness. Use words that build up others. Practice listening and replace complaining with praising. Look for the good in others, not their faults.

Give many hugs a day to family members. Hug and listen to your children. Get on their level and be interested in them. By your actions, teach good forms of communication with them. Single men, learn to hug other men; don't practice on women. Remember, you must flee from temptation and avoid even the appearance of impropriety. Married men, honor your wives in this way, too!

Communicate your feelings. Don't pretend you're happy when you're worried. From time to time, review the *"Feelings Chart"* in Appendix F. Get acquainted with your feelings and talk about them. Similarly, tell your family many times a day that you love them.

TELEVISION

Television is one of the biggest time killers, and it fosters selfish thinking. Even if you make watching television a family activity, it doesn't build the relationships your soul desires. Exercise great control and discretion when deciding whether or what to watch. Some alternatives include scheduling a family or friend night with no TV and instead playing games without being competitive or complaining, engaging in other fun activities that require teamwork, or inviting others over for pizza and a good movie that stimulates discussion about God, the Bible, and moral behavior. (For movie recommendations, check out movieguide.org, or pluggedinonline.com.)

MEAL TIME

Establish family meal times. Turn off the TV and require all family members to attend. Keep each person involved in the conversation, creating ways to make it pertinent and enjoyable for everyone.

Buy a special plate to use as your family's "plate of honor" at meal times. Rotate it among those in the family. For the person with the special plate, everyone should say something nice or encouraging. When dining alone, set a plate for the Lord and talk to Him. He longs to listen!

Start a practice of going around the table taking turns saying something for which you're thankful.

Be creative and introduce new elements to meal time. You might keep old Christmas cards from friends and family. Read them occasionally and pray for that family. Discuss the good character qualities they display in their lives. The next time you see them, tell them!

OUTSIDE ACTIVITIES/EVENTS

Get out of the house. Go on a picnic, to the zoo, or simply walk outside to look at the stars. Make a habit of spending time praising God and thanking Him for His creation. Look for things around you for ways to praise God, e.g., the trees and grass providing oxygen and cleaning the air for you. Share these things with the person you're with. You can't exhaust ways to be thankful to God.

MISCELLANEOUS IDEAS

For the Married

Find a photograph of you and your wife and hang it on a wall. Tell your wife you are glad you married her. Consider framing your marriage certificate. When others notice it, tell them it is an important covenant!

Plant a tree or bush in the yard to signify your renewed dedication to your mate. Then regularly tend to it and watch it grow. Use that as a reminder to tend to your wife's needs and tell of your love.

Go for a walk or bike ride (consider weekly or daily walks).

Write love notes and hide them in places she will find them, e.g., the refrigerator, the coffee container, or under her pillow. Decorate the house for special events with streamers and balloons.

Notice things around the house, for example, that the house was vacuumed. Be sure to thank her for it! Call daily from work just to say you love her. Make sure you are not distracted or doing work while you talk. It's okay to keep the conversation to just a minute or two, but make sure you give your wife your undivided attention.

For Singles

Plant a tree or bush in the yard to signify your renewed dedication to the Lord. Then regularly tend to it and watch it grow. Use that as a reminder to grow spiritually.

Plan a barbecue or a movie night. Invite men friends and include a time of prayer.

Volunteer at a soup kitchen, the local jail, or a nursing home. Ask the pastor of your church for ways to meet the needs of others. There likely are many shut-ins that would love your company. There are also undesirable tasks that no one is willing to do. Ask to do what no one else wants to do.

Develop a hobby, such as rock collecting or biking. Dedicate the activity to the Lord. Don't allow yourself to be consumed with pity or loneliness. Your life is not dependent upon being married, and marriage will not automatically create openness in you or bring you peace. Use the time being single to be single-minded in heart in a pursuit of intimacy with the Lord.

SEX AND INTIMACY TOPICS

Men, don't flirt with anyone except your wife or become a confidant of women. When a man shares intimate details with a woman who is not his wife, the result is often hurt feelings for one or both. Don't fool yourself into thinking that your relationship with a certain woman is somehow different or that you won't reap the harm God warns against.

Break out of your old ways and spend energy developing iron-sharpens-iron relationships with men.

For the Married

Practice "affection period," not "affection comma" where you expect sex each time you have any connection. Rub her shoulders while she's standing near the counter, and when she sighs or says that feels good, don't think about or ask for sex. Rub her feet with lotion or give her a back rub, but then don't have sex that day.

Ask your spouse if there's something you can do or stop doing during love making that would be more pleasing or honoring to her. Be genuinely interested in hearing her answer. Don't fool yourself into thinking you're perfect or a mind reader. Expect that she'll have suggestions. If you argue or make her feel that what she said was wrong, she will not feel safe or trust you with intimacy. Humbly and gladly accept her answers. After all, don't you really want her to experience what she finds most pleasing? Then, next time, do what she enjoys without waiting for her to ask.

For Singles

Be totally committed to waiting until marriage to have sexual relations. Begin anew if you have been sexually impure.

Don't dwell on sexual thoughts or longings for sexual relationships. This will only lead to false intimacy and fantasy. Put into practice what you've learned: Don't look with lust for any length of time and avoid magazines, TV, and Internet items that lead to false intimacy or fantasy. Replace a wandering mind with activities centered on real relationships with God and others.

If you're not dating right now, consider setting aside an amount of time devoted to the Lord to become spiritually ready before you date. In other words, perhaps hold off on dating while taking your first steps toward real intimacy with God. Only when you are walking with the Lord should you begin to date. Remember, God has the right person chosen for you. Don't rush into dating or marriage. Wait upon the Lord.

Be absolutely pure in dating. This includes honoring God and your date by avoiding even the appearance of impropriety. Be a leader. It will pay great dividends.

Appendix B: Sample Life Goals

Passionate for God

- I will read from the Bible daily with the attitude of getting to know God.
- I will pray for others and use prayer as a time to meet with God.
- I will replace secular music with Christian music, and I will often sing praise songs.
- I will write letters to the Lord.

Repentant in Spirit

- I will immediately confess and turn from each sin, including every lustful thought, anger, and greed.
- I won't justify my sins.
- I renounce fantasies, masturbation, and pornography.

Open and Honest

- I will allow myself to have feelings and will make it a point to know them.
- I will move toward intimate and vulnerable relationships.
- I won't say just what others want to hear to try to win their approval.
- I will make it a point to get to know others on a deeper level.

Victorious in Living

- I will develop a game plan to trust in God and live for Him.
- I will prepare for tempting circumstances and always wear the armor of God.
- I will rely upon God's strength, not my own.

Eternal in Perspective

- I will live by the Holy Spirit and yield my life completely to Christ.
- I will trust that God is good and turn over all areas of my life to Him.
- I will contemplate the things of God.
- I won't allow the pursuit of money to be my master.
- I will accept God's standards for holiness and sexual purity.

Networked with Other Proven Men

- I will do the *Heartwork* study each day.
- I will pray for other Proven Men.
- I will be interested in the lives of others, sharing in their joys and struggles.
- I will join men's groups at church.
- I will seek to be a friend to others.
- I will be accountable to a male friend.

SAMPLE COMMITMENT

My Life Goals

- To trust that God really is good and is in complete control of every aspect of my life.
- To live obediently and wholeheartedly submissive to God's will.
- To desire purity and holiness.
- To be humble, grateful, and content.

The evidence of my sincerity is that my thoughts and actions will be Proven in my life such that I am Passionate for God, Repentant in Spirit, Open and Honest, Victorious in Living, Eternal in Perspective, and Networking with other Proven Men who share similar life goals.

To accomplish these life goals, I will be totally committed to Christ through a heart of prayer, study, and worship and by reverent submission to my wife (or future wife) by total commitment to her and with unconditional love; to my church through a desire to build it up as though it were Christ Himself; and to my neighbors by seeing them as people made in God's image. I also agree to give up my rights. Whenever I become frustrated, disappointed, or angry, I will stop and test whether the feeling results from a hidden goal being blocked or whether it is inconsistent with the above-stated life goals. Then I will act to make my conduct conform to my non-negotiable life goals.

____

Signed this day in witness of God the loving Father, Jesus Christ my Lord and Savior, and the Holy Spirit as my teacher and guide.

Appendix C: Names of God

GOD THE FATHER

Abba Father (Romans 8:15)
Ancient of Days (Daniel 7:9, 13)
Creator (Isaiah 27:11)
Father (Luke 11:2)
Father of the Heavenly Lights (James 1:17)
God Almighty (Genesis 17:1–2)
God Most High (Genesis 14:18–22)
God of Abraham, Isaac, and Jacob (Exodus 3:6)
God of Heaven and Earth (Ezra 1:2; 5:11)
God of Hope (Romans 15:13)
God Our Father (Ephesians 1:2)
Holy One (Isaiah 43:15)
Judge of the Earth (Psalm 94:2)
King (Isaiah 43:15)
King of Glory (Psalm 24:7–10)
King of Heaven (Daniel 4:37)
Living God (Romans 9:26)
Lord of All the Earth (Joshua 3:11)
Righteous Father (John 17:25)
The God of All Comfort (2 Corinthians 1:3)
The Great and Awesome God (Nehemiah 1:5)
The Lord Is My Banner (Exodus 17:15)
The Lord Our Maker (Psalm 95:6)
The Lord Who Heals (Exodus 15:26)

GOD THE SON

Advocate (Job 16:19; 1 John 2:1)
Alpha and Omega (Revelation 1:8)
Author and Perfecter (Hebrews 12:2)
Blessed and Only Ruler (Hebrews 2:10)
Bread of God (John 6:33)
Bread of Life (John 6:35)
Bridegroom (Matthew 25:1–10)
Chosen One (Isaiah 41:1)
Christ Jesus Our Lord (2 Timothy 1:2)
Cornerstone (1 Peter 2:6)
Deliverer (Romans 11:26)
Faithful and True (Revelation 19:11)
Foundation (1 Corinthians 3:11)
Fountain (Zechariah 13:1)
Friend (Matthew 11:19)
Gate (John 10:7–9)
Good Shepherd (John 10:11, 14)
High Priest (Hebrews 3:1)
Holy One (Acts 2:27)
Horn of Salvation (Luke 1:69)
I Am (John 8:58)
Immanuel (Matthew 1:23)
King of Kings (1 Timothy 6:14)
Lamb of God (John 1:36)
Light of the World (John 8:12)
Lord of Lords (1 Timothy 6:15)
Master (Matthew 23:8)
Mediator (1 Timothy 2:5)
Messiah (John 1:41)
Mighty God (Isaiah 9:6)
One and Only (John 1:14)
Our Righteousness (1 Corinthians 1:30)
Prince of Peace (Isaiah 9:6)
Redeemer (Isaiah 44:24)
Rock (1 Corinthians 10:4)
Ruler (Matthew 2:6)
Savior (Luke 2:11)
Son of Man (Matthew 8:20)
Sure Foundation (Isaiah 28:16)
Teacher (John 13:14)
The Almighty (Revelation 1:8)
The Beginning (Colossians 1:18)
The Way (John 14:6)

True God (1 John 5:20)
Truth (John 14:6)
Wonderful Counselor (Isaiah 9:6)
Word of God (Revelation 19:13)

GOD THE HOLY SPIRIT

Breath of the Almighty (Job 32:8)
Counselor (John 14:16)
Deposit (Ephesians 1:13–14)
Eternal Spirit (Hebrews 9:14)
Holy Spirit of God (Ephesians 4:30)
Living Water (John 7:38–39)
Promise of the Father (Acts 1:4)
Seal (Ephesians 4:30)
Spirit of Faith (1 Corinthians 12:9)
Spirit of Fire (Isaiah 4:4)
Spirit of God (Genesis 1:2)
Spirit of Judgment (Isaiah 4:4)
Spirit of Knowledge (Isaiah 11:2)
Spirit of Life (Romans 8:2)
Spirit of Power (Isaiah 11:2)
Spirit of Promise (Ephesians 1:13)
Spirit of Truth (John 14:17)
Spirit of Understanding (Isaiah 11:2)
Spirit of Wisdom (Isaiah 11:2)
Spirit Who Intercedes for Us (Romans 8:26–27)
Spirit Who Searches All Things (1 Corinthians 2:10)

Appendix D: Attributes of God

GOD IS:

Love (unfailing love)
(Exod 15:13; Psa 13:5–6; 52:8; 1 John 4:7–16; Rom 8:38–39; Eph 3:17–19; 5:1–2)

Good
(2 Chron 7:3; Psa 119:68; 135:3; 145:9; Mark 10:18)

Faithful
(Deut 7:9; Psa 18:25; 33:4; 111:7; 145:13; 1 John 1:9; Heb 10:23; 1 Pet 4:19; 1 Cor 1:9; 1 Thes 5:24; 2 Thes 3:3)

Merciful
(Deut 4:31; Jer 3:12; 2 Sam 24:14; Neh 9:31; Dan 9:9; 2 Cor 4:1; Rom 11:31; 212:1; Eph 2:4; Luke 6:36)

Kind
(2 Sam 22:51; Isa 54:8; Jer 9:24; Psa 18:50; Luke 6:25; Rom 2:4; 11:22)

Patient (forbearing/long-suffering)
(Jer 15:15; Neh 9:17; Psa 145:8; 1 Tim 1:16; Rom 3:25; 2 Pet 3:15)

Compassionate
(Exod 22:27; 34:6; Neh 9:17; Psa 86:15; 103:8; 111:4; Joel 2:13)

Just
(Deut 32:4; Job 37:23; Psa 99:4; Luke 18:7–8; 2 Thes 1:5; Rev 16:7)

Righteous
(Isa 51:6; Jer 9:24; 23:6; Judges 5:11; Ezra 9:15; Neh 9:8; Psa 4:1; 7:9; 89:14; 97:12; 116:6; 119:137; 129:4; 145:17)

Jealous (jealous for our love)
(Exod 34:14; Deut 4:24; Zech 8:2; 2 Cor 11:2)

Gracious (grace)
(Josh 24:19; Isa 26:10; Neh 9:17; Exod 34:6–7; Psa 86:15; 108:8; 111:4; 116:5; 145:8; Titus 3:5–7; Eph 2:8)

Holy
(Isa 6:3; 57:15; Psa 30:4; 77:13; 99:3, 9; Matt 1:35; John 17:11; Rom 7:12; 1 Pet 1:15–16; Rev 4:8)

Wise (wisdom)
(Isa 28:29; Jer 10:12; 1 Cor 1:30; Col 2:2–3)

Truthful (veracity/truth)
(Num 23:19; Isa 45:19; Psa 31:5; John 3:33; 14:6)

Almighty
(Gen 17:1; 35:11; Psa 24:10; 46:7; 68:14; 80:7, 14; 84:1; 89:9; 2 Cor 6:18; James 5:4)

Pure
(2 Sam 22:27; Psa 18:26; 1 John 3:3)

Perfect/Blameless
(2 Sam 22:26, 31; Psa 18:25, 30; 19:7; Deut 32:4; Matt 5:48)

Gentle
(Matt 11:29; 21:5)

Forgiving
(Neh 9:17; Num 14:18; Psa 86:5; 99:8)

Wrathful (avenging evil)
(Nahum 1:2; Psa 7:11; Rom 1:18; 5:9; 9:22)

Independent (self-existing/self-sufficient)
(Psa 115:3; John 5:26; Rom 11:35–36)

Infinite (from everlasting to everlasting/beyond measure)
(Psa 33:11; 41:13; 90:1–2; Heb 1:8–12)

Eternal
(Gen 21:33; Neh 9:5–6; Deut 33:27; Psa 93:2; John 8:58; Rev 1:8)

Supreme (pre-eminent)
(Exod 15:1, 11, 18; Psa 115:3; Col 1:15–19)

Incomprehensible (beyond full description or understanding)
(Job 36:26; Psa 104:1–4; Isa 36:26; 40:18–26; Rom 11:33–34; 1 Tim 6:15)

Majestic
(Exod 15:6–7, 11; 1 Chron 29:11; Job 37:22; Psa 8:1, 9; 93:1; Jude 25)

Sovereign
(Isa 46:10; Dan 4:35; Psa 135:6; Eph1:11; Acts 4:24)

Immutable (unchanging)
(Malachi 3:6; Psa 102:27; James 1:17; Heb 6:17; 13:8)

Omnipotent (all-powerful/infinite power)
(Gen 18:14; 1 Sam 2:6–7; Psa 18:13–15; Matt 19:26)

Omnipresent (everywhere)
(Jer 23:23–24; 2 Chron 2:6; Psa 139:7–16; Acts 17:27–28)

Omniscient (all-knowing/infinite knowledge)
(1 Kings 8:39; Psa 139:1–6; Prov 3:19–20; 1 Cor 2:10)

Immortal (not created, but ever existing)
(Rom 1:23; 1 Tim 1:17; 6:15)

Appendix E: Why Jesus?

If all you want is to stop a sexual sin you hate, then you don't need this book. If you want to stay in complete control of your life, try behavioral modification techniques. Take a secular psychology class or read self-help books that tell you how to pull yourself up by your own bootstraps and fix everything that's wrong with your life.

The premise of this book is that those techniques will fail. My book exists to humbly share with you exactly what you need. From my own experience and the experience of hundreds of other Proven Men, I can tell you: If you want to live a purposeful and Proven life, you need Jesus.

You'll remain trapped in sexual addiction unless you do two things:

1. Ask Jesus to be your Savior.
2. Give Him permission to be Lord of your entire life.

JESUS AS SAVIOR

Allow me to explain Jesus in a way you might not have heard.

Many believe that Jesus came to earth to show us how to live a good life. That's not why Jesus came to earth. Yes, Jesus surely did provide the greatest example. But He didn't come here to show you how to live, but to die on the cross and rise again as your Savior.

Jesus was and is God. He is the one who created the world. About 2,000 years ago Jesus left heaven to take the form of a man. Why?

When the Lord created man, He had a divine purpose for an eternal relationship with each one of us. However, the heavenly dwelling of God is absolutely perfect. God says that nothing impure can enter into heaven (Revelation 21:27). That's a huge problem because every one of us has sinned. A single sin makes us imperfect and ineligible to be in heaven. In fact, the Bible is crystal clear that the penalty for a single sin is eternal separation from God (Romans 6:23).

It's like we are all on death row waiting to be executed. I am sure your mother or father would gladly step in your place to pay your death sentence. But they cannot because they too have sinned and are on death row.

What we all desperately need is for someone not on death row to be willing to take the punishment for us. Of course, that means they would have to live a sinless life. Do you see where this is going? Only God could live a sinless life on earth. That's why Jesus took on flesh 2,000 years ago. Being man and God at the same time, Jesus did not commit a single sin (1 Peter 2:22; Hebrews 4:15; 2 Corinthians 5:21). The good news is that Jesus was willing to lay down His life for yours.

Jesus personally paid the penalty of your sin when He died on the cross. John 3:16 is perhaps the best known verse in the Bible: "For God so loved the world that he gave his one and only Son, that whoever believes in him shall not perish but have eternal life." If you were the only person to have ever lived, Jesus would still have come to earth to die for you. It had to be that way. He loves you and doesn't want you to perish or to go on living without

Him as part of your life. In fact, Christ offers you His name and His righteousness to replace your sin-soiled life.

By living a perfect life, Jesus became an acceptable sacrifice and substitute for your sin. Then he conquered death by rising from the grave and returned to heaven. Now, when the death sentence is handed down for your sins, Jesus stands in your place—provided you have accepted His free gift of forgiveness occurring when you ask the Lord to permanently dwell in your heart. That way, when you die and the punishment of death must be paid, Jesus who lives in you, has already paid. The penalty is paid in full.

What do you need to do to ask Jesus to be your Savior? The Bible says, "If we confess our sins, He is faithful and just and will forgive us our sins and purify us from all unrighteousness" (1 John 1:12). He won't reject you. Everyone who turns to Jesus and believes in Him become children of God and therefore inherit eternal life in heaven (John 1:12). This includes you and me, but you must personally ask for and accept the free gift of forgiveness.

If you turn to Jesus and accept His shed blood as the perfect sacrifice and substitute for your penalty, you're no longer considered impure no matter what bad things you've done or will do. God the Father will not reject you because His Son, who now lives in you, already paid the full penalty of death for all your sins.

Right now, go to God with a surrendered heart. You'll be asking Jesus, who paid the death penalty that was due to you, to forgive you and to enter your heart. Ask Him for His grace and mercy. He wants to give it to you.

SALVATION

To ask Jesus into your heart and accept God's righteousness, pray something like this:

God, I know that I am a sinner and deserve death. I know that Jesus is God and that He died on the cross to rescue me from the penalty of my sin. Please forgive me. I receive the free gift of eternal life, which comes solely from the perfect sacrifice of Jesus Christ for my sin. I pray and ask you, Jesus, to come into my heart right now and to make it your permanent home. Take total control of my life. I choose to follow you and turn away from sin, including my former lifestyle. Thank you for loving me and forgiving me. I commit to following you forever. In your precious name, Jesus, I pray these things. Amen.

If you prayed this prayer with your heart, then congratulations! You're my eternal brother in Christ. You're free from the power of death. Jesus now permanently lives in you, and you're God's child.

JESUS AS LORD

It's now time to daily make Jesus Lord of your life. That's the key to sexual integrity.

You've taken a very important step. You've realized that you can't win the battle on your own. You've probably tried many times and failed, but you're finally on the right track. You see, your battle is not about using more of your own power or even about overcoming bad influences. Instead, it's a spiritual battle. In fact, the Bible teaches that "our struggle is not against flesh and blood, but against the rulers, against the authorities, against the powers of this dark world and against the spiritual forces of evil in the heavenly realms" (Ephesians 6:12).

The only way to stop being a slave to sin, such as pornography, is to rely on Jesus Christ. These are more than just words. When you need forgiveness, power, and strength, you go to the source of forgiveness, power, and strength: Jesus. His power is available to you, so turn to and yield your entire life to Him.

Now the journey begins, but you never travel alone! A wonderful by-product of having an intimate relationship with God is victory over sins, including sexual immorality. Jesus desires to take control of your life and lead you in His holy and pure ways. The power of the Holy Spirit is ready, willing, and more than able to lead you victoriously if you let Him, but you must want to love and serve God more than your former selfish and prideful ways. You need to start hating sin because it blocks your relationship with Jesus Christ.

Making Jesus Lord over your daily life is what being on the Proven Men team is all about. Each day you wake up you give control to the Lord. Throughout the day, you test your thoughts and actions against the six PROVEN letters:

Passionate for God

Repentant in spirit

Open and honest

Victorious in living

Eternal in perspective

Networked with other PROVEN Men.

Plan to link together with other Proven Men as you learn how to live out a Proven life. It's a journey you never have to take alone because you're part of the family of God and Proven Men.

Appendix F: How Do I Feel?

To be open and honest in relationships you must learn to recognize your feelings. Use this short list as an aid in identifying your feelings. Keep returning here frequently.

<table>
<tr>
<td>
Happy?
ecstatic?
joyful?
thankful?
loved?
loving?
grateful?
included?
glad?</td>
<td>
Sad?
disliked?
unloved?
grieving?
sorry?
regretful?
miserable?
remorseful?
distrusted?</td>
<td>
Confident?
respected?
secure?
safe?
sure?
capable?
optimistic?
appreciated?
pleased?</td>
<td>
Angry?
mad?
hateful?
bitter?
upset?
furious?
outraged?</td>
<td>
Depressed?
insulted?
lonely?
bored?
withdrawn?
excluded?
incompetent?
neglected?
abandoned?</td>
</tr>
<tr>
<td>
Stressed?
nervous?
tense?
negative?
exhausted?
debilitated?
weary?</td>
<td>
Indifferent?
unconcerned?
weird?
strange?
foolish?</td>
<td>
Afraid?
threatened?
insecure?
unsafe?
paranoid?</td>
<td>
Discouraged?
frustrated?
exasperated?
overwhelmed?
defeated?
disappointed?</td>
<td>
Hurt?
betrayed?
misled?
resentful?
cold?</td>
</tr>
<tr>
<td>
Content?
peaceful?
gratified?</td>
<td>
Anxious?
worried?
embarrassed?</td>
<td>
Confused?
dismayed?
unsure?
perplexed?
shocked?</td>
<td>
Jealous?
envious?</td>
<td>
Greedy?
selfish?
arrogant?
smug?</td>
</tr>
</table>

Appendix G: Developing a Heart of Worship

The letter ***P*** in PROVEN stands for Passionate for God. Part of being passionate is having a heart of worship. What does this mean? It's when your desire to live for Christ becomes a consuming fire (see Hebrews 12:28–29).[1] Do you want to praise Jesus from deep within your heart and soul? Do you long to know God, to learn His names, and to see Him in His glory?

There are many ways to strengthen or deepen your passion for God, including improvements in your prayer life, singing and listening to Christ-centered songs, and writing your own psalms and letters to God. The key is to engage in purposeful worship of God and pursue intimacy with Him. This article suggests some ways to crank up the heat and allow God to fuel the flames. Use your freedom in Christ to develop other forms of thoughtful worship and praise. Be creative and make it exciting. Make a plan or you won't do it.

Some suggestions for developing a greater heart of worship include:

Pray with passion. God is not a vending machine that gives you anything you want if you just ask. The Lord is a real being, and He wants a real relationship with you. Prayer is not about receiving things from God. It's all about communication with the living Lord. It's about striving toward becoming best friends. Honestly evaluate your prayer life. Is it your goal to become so close to God that you know His will and long to see it accomplished, or do you rush to ask Him to give you something? If the only time you ever spoke to your neighbor was to borrow a tool, what kind of friendship would that be? God deserves better and wants more than a hurried "bless me" request. Besides, He is more interested in living the story with you. The more time you spend with God, the more you'll know His will—His good, pleasing, and perfect will (Romans 12:2). Then, when you do ask God to do something, it will be asking Him to do that which He already desires to accomplish. Prayer also includes listening and waiting. Don't be in such a rush to end prayer. Talk to the Lord as a personal being, sharing your struggles, fears, hopes, and dreams. Become friends.

A good way of keeping the focus off yourself (and, hence, not making selfish requests) is to replace asking for your own blessings with petitioning God on behalf of others, such as a co-worker, your pastor, or those you know are hurting or sick. *It's okay to ask God what He wants to accomplish through you and your prayers.* God doesn't hide Himself from those who earnestly seek Him and long to do His will. Again, guard against viewing God as a tool for bestowing blessings. Make your top priority getting to know God.

Tip: Read a book on prayer such as *The Circle Maker: Praying Circles Around Your Biggest Dreams and Greatest Fears* by Mark Batterson. Read it slowly; even just a few pages at a time. Ask your pastor for other books.

---

1. "Therefore, since we are receiving a kingdom that cannot be shaken, let us be thankful, and so worship God acceptably with reverence and awe, for our 'God is a consuming fire.'"

Pray with others. Consider prayer walks in the woods with your wife, if you're married, or other Proven Men. Passionate praying builds strong bonds. Don't miss out.

Read the Bible daily. The Bible is God's very Word to you. It actually nourishes your soul just like food nourishes your body (Matthew 4:4).[2] The Word of God is living and active and penetrates a person's soul and spirit (Hebrews 4:12).[3] Therefore, do not neglect it (Psalm 119:6).[4]

Reading the Bible to find out about God is far different from reading it as part of your plan of pursuing the Lord to get to know Him. If your reading of the Bible has been dull or infrequent, change your heart and mindset. Set your sights on reading to become intimate with God. Guaranteed—if you seek the Lord with all your heart, you'll fall in love with Him. He has no blemish or spot to turn your eyes away.

Consider beginning afresh by reading Psalm 119:1–40. Adopt this psalm as your own plea. Ask God to reveal Himself to you. Determine in your heart that you'll set out to enjoy God instead of reading the Bible to check off a list of things Christians are supposed to do. If you still struggle with desiring the things of God, spend time reading Psalm 51 and wrestling before the Lord until He grants you repentance and creates in you a clean and new heart that lives for Him. Don't take no for an answer.

When you read the Bible, read slowly, asking the Lord to open your eyes and heart to what He has to say to you. Don't race. Read until God shows you something new or exciting, then dwell on that point. Talk to God about it. Meditate on that new insight, and plan how it can be put into practice in your life. Get into a habit of making notes or circling words. Contemplate how to do what it says. You'll find that God has a lot to say if you'll listen and seek.

Study the Bible. This is slightly different from reading the Bible. By regularly studying passages, you should grow even deeper in your relationship with God. Consider a word study. For instance, use a Bible concordance and look up every verse containing a particular word, such as "perseverance," "suffering," "hope," or "grace." Choose a new word each time. Be sure to ask God to give you deeper understanding of these passages and to teach you what He wants you to learn about Him and about living a Proven life. Then do what the Lord reveals. Apply it in your daily life.

Write psalms to God. A special way of focusing on God and drawing closer to Him is by writing letters to God, which can be your own version of a psalm. It's easier to do this than you think (see Appendix H). The Bible repeatedly tells you to sing psalms, and writing them is a form of singing them from your heart and soul (Colossians 3:16).[5] God will be pleased to read your heartfelt letters to Him. You'll also get to better know and appreciate the Lord!

---

2. "Man does not live on bread alone, but on every word that comes from the mouth of God."

3. "For the word of God is living and active. Sharper than any double-edged sword, it penetrates even to dividing soul and spirit, joints and marrow; it judges the thoughts and attitudes of the heart."

4. "Then I would not be put to shame when I consider all your commands."

5. "Let the word of Christ dwell in you richly as you teach and admonish one another with all wisdom, and as you sing psalms, hymns and spiritual songs with gratitude in your hearts to God."

Sing songs or hymns. Singing songs to the Lord isn't just for Sunday church services. Pouring out your heart in singing to God adds a different element of worship that can be deeply moving. Play worshipful songs in your car and at home and sing along. Don't be inhibited in praising the Lord. Ask God to tear down walls so that your heart is free to meet with and worship Him. It's okay to lift your hands in worship. Bust out of your constricted heart.

Tip: Consider strictly limiting or eliminating altogether secular music and television, because such songs and programs often contain values inconsistent with pursuing God with all of your heart and otherwise compete in terms of time and energy with your worship of God.

Meditate upon the names and attributes of God. You were created to worship God and to experience more and more of His nature. Meditating upon the beautiful names of God helps you get to know your dear Creator on a deeper level. Who doesn't like their name sweetly whispered by a loved one? Read God's names softly or aloud, but make it your goal to show reverence and invite Him into your heart as you communicate with Him in this intimate way. (See Appendix C for a list of God's names.) Similarly, meditating upon the attributes of God opens you up to His perfect nature and helps tear down walls that keep you trying to control life. The more you see God as good, the more you will allow Him into your life! (See Appendix D for a list of God's attributes.)

Condition your mind. Every man daydreams and has a private thought life, but God tells you to take captive every idle thought and make it conform to Christ (2 Corinthians 10:5).[6] You're not to be conformed to this world (Romans 12:2)[7] or to love anything of this world (1 John 2:15).[8] Even fantasies about being a hero or winning the lottery can distract you from focusing your thoughts upon and trusting in God. Replace your former way of thinking with things that are true, noble, right, pure, lovely, admirable, excellent, or praiseworthy (Philippians 4:8).[9] Put a bouncer at the door to your mind. If you don't, then worldly lust will always be an occupant.

Include others. Each man needs relationships. God created you to love Him, which is the greatest commandment, and to love others, the second greatest commandment (Matthew 22:37–39).[10] By developing and cultivating relationships with others who are actively seeking the Lord, you'll have friends you can talk to openly, sharing your struggles as well as engaging in praise and worship. Two Proven Men are as iron sharpening iron (Proverbs 27:17).[11] Therefore, link up with other Proven Men. Also, attend church to join with others in worship.

6. "We demolish arguments and every pretension that sets itself up against the knowledge of God, and we take captive every thought to make it obedient to Christ."

7. "Do not conform any longer to the pattern of this world, but be transformed by the renewing of your mind."

8. "Do not love the world or anything in the world. If anyone loves the world, the love of the Father is not in him."

9. "Finally, brothers, whatever is true, whatever is noble, whatever is right, whatever is pure, whatever is lovely, whatever is admirable—if anything is excellent or praiseworthy—think about such things."

10. "'Love the Lord your God with all your heart and with all your soul and with all your mind.' This is the first and greatest commandment. And the second is like it: 'Love your neighbor as yourself.'"

11. "As iron sharpens iron, so one man sharpens another."

Corporate worship that joins hearts and voices in hymns and praise to Jesus is uniquely different from how one person praises God alone at home. Don't miss out on it!

There are many ways to live for the Lord and worship and praise Him. God desires that they become your way of life, but you must plan for them. Go ahead and schedule each of these things into your daily life right now. Write out a daily timetable. Rise early each day to meet with God, and fix your gaze upon Him throughout the day. Eliminate things that compete or hinder your new lineup, or else you'll soon forget your promises and commitments and return to the former habits you had in living on the fringes of the Lord's courts instead of joining Him at His table.

Appendix H: How to Write a Psalm

One of the best-loved books of the Bible is Psalms. It's a marvelous compilation of praise and prayers to God. Many Christians have discovered the tremendous benefit of writing their own psalms or prayer letters to God. What about you? This article will help you begin to experience the intimacy you can have with the Lord through pouring out your heart to Him in your own psalms.

WHY WRITE PSALMS?

The Lord is pleased not only when you praise Him but also when you openly talk to Him. Sometimes, however, you're not sure how to have an *open and honest* relationship with God. Writing a psalm is a lot like writing a letter to a close friend and sharing of yourself with him. Your friend is interested in your sharing personal things about yourself just as you're interested in knowing him. When you write psalms to God (or, for that matter, when you pray), your goal is to build a two-way friendship. You're developing a relationship where you can be *open and honest* with your feelings.

WHOM ARE YOU WRITING TO?

In any letter, what you say and how you say it depends on to whom you are writing. A scribbled note to a friend would be different from a letter to the President of the United States. (Of course, if the President were a close friend, a scribbled note would be welcomed.)

The way you write a psalm will greatly depend on who you say God is. Is He a big father figure? The Sovereign King of the Universe? Your best friend? You need to be careful not to think narrowly about who God is because that will limit what you think you can or should say to Him. If you focus on only one or two of His characteristics, like love or mercy, you miss out on so much of God. In fact, God is also good, holy, just, beautiful, perfect, life, supreme, all-knowing, all-powerful, unchanging, wise, jealous, faithful, true, kind, and patient. The more you get to know God, the more you can richly communicate and have a fulfilling relationship with Him.

HOW TO WRITE YOUR PSALM TO GOD

Writing the first few words can be the hardest. Before you begin, take a quiet moment to reflect and pray. Ask God to still your heart and mind. Ask the Holy Spirit to lead you in what to write. Is your heart filled with praise, or are you struggling with something and in need of wisdom or grace? The topic you write about in your psalm should be in line with the present condition of your heart. Of the 150 psalms of the Bible, only about one-half are primarily praise or thanksgiving oriented. Many others are pleas for mercy, cries for help, offers of repentance, requests for strength, or requests for wisdom. It's clear that each of the psalms in the Bible is an expression of the person's heart at the time the psalm was written. Similarly, when you write a psalm, start with how you are feeling right now. Don't think you must write a praise psalm every time. If you're angry, it might be phony to try to write a love song to God. Instead, cry out to Him. Tell God that you're angry or hurt. Seek His mercy, grace, or love. Ask questions. Make statements. Be real! No matter how many psalms you write, wait upon God for guidance each time. Close your eyes and pray. Search your heart and ask God to speak to you. Then pick up your pen and write down a few words. Ask yourself: "How do I feel?", "What am I thinking?", "What are my attitudes?" "What circumstances am I facing?" For instance, if God has answered a prayer or blessed a loved one greatly, be ready to praise Him. Listen for God. Ask Him to guide your words. A psalm may begin like this: "God, You are so good" or "Your name is beautiful." Then stop and listen to God. Ask Him to fill your heart. Seek to share your innermost feelings. Don't become concerned about whether the next set of words rhyme or sound eloquent.

Don't try to force things or attempt to write like someone else. Be yourself and speak from your heart. The style of writing isn't important. God isn't holding a literary contest to see who can string together the fanciest sounding words. Rather, He wants your heart. He wants you to be eager to meet with Him in prayer and to open your life to Him as a friend. A psalm can be a great way to tell God you love Him as well as a way of crying out to Him for help.

After writing a few lines, read and reread what you wrote. You'll rarely need to rewrite or edit. Reviewing what you've written helps you stay focused and keeps your heart on track. A psalm of about thirty or forty lines can take fifteen or twenty minutes to write, but you don't have to spend that much time. You may need only a few minutes to write a psalm that glorifies God. Get started and stay with it!

Appendix I: The Nature of Sexual Immorality

There are many reasons that men remain trapped in bondage to sexual sin. Freedom, however, begins by recognizing the nature of your sinful condition. Unless you accept your need for change, it won't last. Keep an open heart and be ready to respond as you read this article.

Sexual immorality must be overcome (Ephesians 4:19–24; 5:3; Colossians 3:5–7; 1 Thessalonians 4:3–7). Consider a few common sexual sins and how they interfere with your relationships:

Lustful thoughts are real sins. Perhaps the most overlooked and yet dangerous sexual sin is lustful thoughts. Fantasies are fabricated scenarios intended to serve you, please you, and give you what you claim you deserve. Because they're hidden, lustful thoughts don't receive much attention. In fact, some men don't consider thoughts to be wrong if they're not acted upon physically.

Jesus says, however, that anyone who even looks at a woman lustfully commits adultery in his heart (Matthew 5:27–28). Why are lustful thoughts so serious that God calls them adultery? The Lord desires your heart, plain and simple. Jesus doesn't want mere outward appearances or actions from you (1 Samuel 16:7; Galatians 2:6). Your thoughts reveal the true focus of your heart. You cannot serve two masters (Matthew 6:24). This means you cannot pursue selfish sexual desires while seeking to love and serve the Lord. You may try, but you'll always be frustrated in the end.

Fantasies are forms of false intimacy that keep you from being fully devoted to real relationships that are open and honest. Fantasies tend to make you view people as objects. Lustful thoughts can demonstrate that you're not content and actually may keep you from going to the place where contentment is found (Hebrews 13:4–5). When you're not content, it's because some area of your life is not in line with God.

When you lust, you're seeking more and more self-pleasures in a vain attempt to fill a void in your life. You incorrectly think that if you only had more sexual pleasures, you'd be fulfilled, but lust can never satisfy, and it doesn't fill the place in your heart meant for Jesus. The result is emptiness because you don't have an intimate relationship with the Lord, who is the only true source of peace and contentment.

Lustful thoughts violate the unity and intimacy God designed and reserved for marriage. Although God made you a sexual being, He intended that sex would occur only with a spouse (Proverbs 5:1–23). Please understand, God instructs you to be faithful for your own good. It leads to security and unity that God intended for marriage. By remaining pure in your thought life, you also avoid feelings of guilt and shame that drive you further in the destructive cycle of seeking temporary pleasure in a momentary fantasy that leaves you feeling empty or deficient.

Masturbation and pornography are advanced forms of lust. Just like fantasies, masturbation cannot fill the emotional and spiritual need inside your soul. With pornography, the difference is that you use your mind as the vehicle of self-pleasure. Both pornography and masturbation stimulate fantasies and lustful thoughts, and both involve a heightened and direct inward focus on the satisfying of your personal desires. Although you often try to justify these things with notions that you deserve a little pleasure or that nobody gets hurt, you and others are damaged (Ephesians 4:19–24; 5:3–5).

Pornography grieves God. He knows that it breeds discontentment, fills your mind with thoughts that consume your attention, and distracts you from pursuing what is good. Whether you admit it or not, when you masturbate or look at pornography, you experience guilt or shame that feeds a continual downward cycle. You then isolate portions of your life from others and hide from Jesus. These things desensitize you and blind you to the truth about who Jesus is and how much He wants to meet your true needs.

Satisfying sexual urges daily may reveal that sex controls you. A misunderstood area of sexuality is the notion that a person must have sex almost every day to be satisfied. Although God did design and create you to be a sexual being, and while you certainly are capable of wanting sex daily, God never intended you to satisfy every desire that enters your mind (Ephesians 2:3; 1 John 2:16).

Pursuing daily sex may reveal that sex is your master, not the Lord. Over the years, you train yourself to sexualize things and lose sensitivity to sin (Ephesians 4:19). You might try justifying your actions or impulses with notions such as, "I am only lusting after my wife" or "God made me more sensual than other men." However, the man who seeks to satisfy all of his desires, often without true regard for his wife, is one who will never find contentment. The endless hunt for satisfaction, with sex often the target, is a constant cycle of frustration. When you have expectations of how often you should have sex, chances are, you're living for self-gratification, which only sets your heart on a continuous pursuit to satisfy a desire that will always want more. The only real answer is to discipline your sexual urges by fixing your gaze upon the Lord, the true source of satisfaction.

Do you see your thoughts and conduct as God does? Are you broken over how you have used God's gift of sexual intimacy for selfish purposes and practices? A hard or selfish heart won't hear God or seek lasting change. Ask yourself, "Am I humble enough and seeking intimacy with the Lord enough to be able to hear His voice in this regard?" Consider Romans 12:1–2: "Therefore, I urge you, brothers, in view of God's mercy, to offer your bodies as living sacrifices, holy and pleasing to God—this is your spiritual act of worship. Do not conform any longer to the pattern of this world, but be transformed by the renewing of your mind. Then you will be able to test and approve what God's will is—His good, pleasing and perfect will."

While meditating on this, turn to the Lord with a willing heart and teachable spirit. Ask God to speak to you and to reveal in which areas of life you're holding onto control instead of yielding to Him. As you constantly evaluate your actions and motives, keep asking yourself questions such as:

- Is it my desire to be a living offering to a holy God?
- Am I able to discern God's will for my life?
- Under God's scrutiny, are my thoughts, motives, or actions absolutely pure?
- Am I relying upon the views of others or on societal norms to justify my sexual practices?

The Lord doesn't want you to remain ignorant about sin. He wants you to overcome it. God knows that you cannot stop sinning, so He provides the way out. Turn to Him now and ask Him to speak to your heart and open your eyes to all forms of sinful practices that you justify or allow to remain in your life. Until you see these things as keeping you separated from all that God wants for you, you won't seek repentance. Instead, you'll only play a game at trying to stop, or you'll deceive yourself into thinking all is well. The roots of selfish practices, however, will never be far from the surface, taking various forms of anger, greed, lust, worry, and other stealers of peace and contentment. Spend time right now meeting with God, seeking truth, repentance, and brokenness.

Appendix J: Freedom from Sexual Bondage

BREAKING THE GRIP OF LUST—THERE IS ONE WAY OUT!

For twenty years, sex controlled Joel's life. Lustful thoughts constantly filled his mind, and pornography and masturbation were no strangers to him. Even after Joel accepted the Lord into his heart, this secret sin remained. Joel needed help, but he was too ashamed and proud to admit it. Twenty years ago, he finally let go, and God broke the grip of sexual bondage. Today, his marriage is wonderful, and his relationship with Jesus is real and fulfilling.

Men everywhere are asking for a proven path for overcoming habits of sexual immorality. Some are perplexed because they have beautiful, loving wives and cannot understand the allure of pornography. Others try justifying urges because their wives withhold sex or intimacy. In each situation, they share in a search for freedom from sexual bondage.

It's important to state up front that there are no magical formulas or quick fixes. However, there is a way out. The only road to freedom from sexual obsession is an intimate and daily relationship with Jesus Christ. Without that relationship, some form of sin will always tear you down. The good news is that Jesus loves you and wants to stand alongside and free you. He wants to be an active part of your life. He made you in such a way that you would share your life with Him daily. This article briefly explains the path for overcoming habits of sexual sins while striving toward a growing personal relationship with Christ.

SEXUAL IMMORALITY HINDERS YOUR RELATIONSHIP WITH GOD

God doesn't sit in heaven making up rules and waiting to punish you for breaking them. Instead, He purposefully created you in His image (Genesis 1:27) with the intention that you would not only love and worship Him (Matthew 4:10), but also be His child (John 1:12; 1 John 3:1) and His friend (James 2:23). The Lord is a personal God and is truly interested in a close and meaningful relationship with you.

Consider this: What if you had an adult son whom you loved deeply? What if he was working on an important project and might be awarded the Nobel Peace Prize, but he never visited, called, or wrote to you? Instead, you learned of his great accomplishments by reading the newspaper. While I am sure you would be proud of his good works, would you not rather have a hug, talk to him, and hear him say, "I love you"? Well, that's how you treat Jesus each day when you try to lead a good life but don't talk to Him or tell Him, "I love You." God wants far more from you than your good deeds. He wants your friendship; He desires a daily, intimate relationship with you.

God's commandments aren't designed to be a burden but to foster your relationship with Him so you may prosper. Jesus tells you not to commit adultery in your heart (Matthew 5:27–28) or engage in other forms of sexual immorality such as lust, pornography, or masturbation, so you won't damage your relationship with Him or others. He knows that in the end, these things lead you down the wrong path and produce shame, guilt, bitterness, hurtful feelings, emptiness, and loneliness. God wants you to avoid this pain. He calls you to be pure and holy because He is pure and holy (1 Peter 1:16). Best friends share things in common, and Jesus wants you to be like Him.

When your thoughts or actions become self-centered, you move further away from your loving God. Sexual sins magnify this effect. Your body is a temple of the Holy Spirit, who lives inside you if you trust in Jesus. Therefore, sexual sins are sins against God's temple (1 Corinthians 6:18–20).

Listen carefully to what God is telling you: "In view of God's mercy... offer your bodies as living sacrifices, holy and pleasing to God—this is your spiritual act of worship" (Romans 12:1). When you selfishly give yourself over to sexual desires, sex becomes your master—the focal point of your life. Jesus wants to be the center of your life, thinking, and actions. He wants to meet your needs. Each time you lust, masturbate, or look at pornography, you place God on a shelf and forget about the One who loves you and gave Himself for you. You turn away from Jesus and disregard the good things He alone can give.

THE ROOT PROBLEM

You need to realize that there are deeper problems in your life that must be addressed before bondage to sexual immorality will end. Masturbation, pornography, and lust aren't the sole source of the problems in your life. They are symptoms being fed by something else. There is a root that feeds sexual immorality and keeps it alive. This holds true for all who face sexual struggles. The root cause is selfishness and the pride that accompanies it. Selfishness is being overly concerned with your own welfare or interest, and pride is the attitude and behavior resulting from an exaggerated self-worth or an entitlement attitude. Together, these lead you to think that you deserve to be served and to have every desire fulfilled. Until you come to grips with the seriousness of selfishness and pride in your life and battle these root sins, you'll never really have lasting freedom from bondage to sexual immorality.

The best way to explain this is to picture your hand. Look at your palm right now. In the center of your palm are selfishness and pride. Each of your fingers, stemming from your palm, represents a sin, such as masturbation, lust, greed, envy, and jealousy, flowing from selfishness and pride.

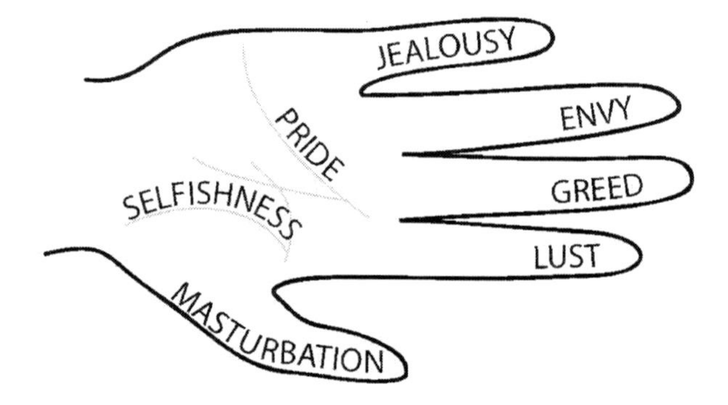

It's not enough for you to merely remove a particular sin. It may be possible out of sheer determination to bend a finger and stop masturbating for months or years. Maybe you can even bend a few fingers at the same time. However, if you allow selfishness and pride to remain in your life, you'll still have barriers that block an intimate relationship with God, and the roots of sexual sins will still be present. Also, another selfish action, such as anger, will take its place.

When you make it your goal to overcome a particular sexual sin, such as masturbation, you set your sights too low and aim at the wrong target.

Failure is assured. You'll never be free from sexual bondage until you address selfishness and pride.

How do you stop being selfish and prideful? By yourself, you cannot. That's why you must trust Jesus and turn over complete control of your entire life to Him. This is not merely a slogan or something for your ears to hear, and it's not about being more "religious." It's becoming a new person in Christ. The more you draw near to Jesus Christ and take on His character as your own, the less you'll be consumed with self-interests. When you live by following the Spirit of God, you won't gratify the desires of the sinful nature because the sinful nature is contrary to God's character (Galatians 5:16). It goes like this: The more you seek to love and follow Jesus, the less selfish and prideful you become, but the more you withdraw from Jesus, the more self-centered you become—which leads to pursuing selfish pleasures such as lust. That's why there is no freedom from sexual immorality apart from having a real, personal, daily relationship with Jesus Christ, one in which you seek Him with all of your heart.

When you commit sin, such as masturbation, it leads to feelings of guilt or shame. This, in turn, causes you to hide areas of your life. You walk away from God. Once separated, you continue to sin, heaping on more guilt and shame, leading to more hiding. Pretty soon, you're caught in a spiral leading ever further downward. The only road that leads to a restored relationship with God and freedom from the downward slope of sexual bondage is to walk the path that leads to experiencing Jesus Christ on a personal level, and becoming totally dependent upon Him each and every day.

GOD HEALS SLOWLY FOR A PURPOSE

An everlasting commitment to walking with and yielding to the Lord marks the beginning of a new Proven life. However, you shouldn't expect to be freed instantly from all aspects of sexual sin. God often heals slowly for a good reason. Because you may have spent years developing ungodly practices, it will take time to work them out of your life. Another thing to remember is that if you were instantly freed of bondage, you likely would boast, "I overcame," but still go on living a selfish or prideful life.

Because Jesus desires a personal and intimate daily walk with you, He wants you to develop a practice of meeting with Him every day. When you're taking the steps necessary to overcome sexual sins, you're putting into practice a relationship with Jesus. Don't you get it? Jesus doesn't want you merely to lead a good life free from sexual impurity. He wants to be involved in your life and to be close to you. By requiring the healing process to be one in which you must rely upon Him over an extended period of time, you'll be talking to and sharing with Jesus daily if not moment by moment. In the end, you'll not only be free from sexual bondage but also develop a strong, fulfilling, and intimate relationship with Jesus Christ. In essence, you'll be stamped Proven. It makes perfect sense.

MAKE A COMMITMENT NOW

God is calling you right now to put aside selfishness and pride and to follow Jesus Christ. If you've been sexually impure, go to Jesus right now. No matter what your sexual sin, He is faithful and willing to forgive and purify you (1 John 1:9). God wants to forgive you, but you must ask to be forgiven, and you must trust completely in Jesus Christ for healing. This happens when you, (1) acknowledge and confess that your selfishness and pride are sins against God, and (2) give total control of all areas of your life to Jesus. True repentance must occur before God changes you. Right now, close your eyes and admit that you have made satisfying your desires the focus of your life and acknowledge how your pride has blinded you to God's truth. Confess your sins and spend time asking Jesus to take total, permanent control of all areas of your life.

DO BATTLE ON BOTH FRONTS

Trusting in Jesus Christ for spiritual rebirth won't remove all sexual desire; you were created as a sexual being. However, turning to Jesus does usher in a conflict of desires.

Let me explain. When you trust in Jesus to be your Savior from sin and to be the Lord of your life, He immediately gives you a new nature and the Holy Spirit. The old nature, however, still remains; it still desires selfish sexual pleasures. The new nature desires sexual purity and holiness; therefore, a battle rages inside you between the dueling natures of self-centered and God-centered desires (1 Peter 2:11). Both compete for you. Which will you serve?

Your new nature, when yielded to the power of the Holy Spirit, will give you mastery over the old nature. The key to victory over sexual bondage is developing and maintaining an intimate, daily walk with the Lord Jesus Christ. It starts by flooding the new nature with healthy influences while at the same time starving the selfish nature by eliminating those influences that reinforce the old way of thinking and acting. These two things—eliminating self-centeredness and increasing God-centeredness—cannot be compartmentalized but must be simultaneously incorporated into your very way of life.

Loving God with all your strength. Jesus said that the commands of God can be summed up in two commandments (Mark 12:30–31): "Love the Lord your God with all your heart and with all your soul and with all your mind and with all your strength. Love your neighbor as yourself."

These should be your guiding principles in life. If you follow them, you won't be permanently ensnared in sins flowing from selfishness and pride.

Loving God with all of your heart, soul, mind, and strength means that you must pursue Jesus Christ with at least the same level of passion that you had pursued lust. The love of Jesus should be on your mind all day. In practical terms, loving God includes setting aside time daily to meet privately with Jesus in open communication. Begin by simply talking to Jesus Christ as you would a friend. Tell Him about your struggles and fears. Ask Him to rescue you and to give you His strength. Pour out your heart to Him. The more you get to know and trust Jesus, the more you'll want to praise and worship Him from your heart and desire to follow His ways (see Psalm 119:1–40).

Another important way of experiencing Jesus in your life is by reading the Bible, which is God's written revelation of who He is and His truth about life. Begin now by reading a few pages every day. Ask God to reveal Himself to you while you read about Him.

Loving the Lord also involves participating in a Bible-believing church. Although some are reluctant to attend church, it's important for several reasons. Jesus Himself established the church, and He loves and cares for it today (Ephesians 5:25–32). Church is where you can find support and strength, join men's fellowship and Bible studies, establish an accountability partner, develop relationships in which you share your life with other men, and encourage other believers (Hebrews 10:25).

Attending church is not about being religious, doing a good deed, or performing penance. Instead, participate because you want to meet with God, to worship Him, and to join with other men who are seeking Him. Please, even if you've had bad church experiences in the past, find a church that really follows the Lord, where you can link your heart with others who love and serve God with pure hearts. It's time to stop walking alone.

Learning to love others. God tells you that if you truly love Him, you'll necessarily love others (John 13:34–35). Consider this: If you have a good friend but have no concern for his son or daughter, what kind of a friend are you? Every human is God's special creation, made in His image just as you are, and He wants you to love them. This means you look out for their interests.

What about pornography? Are you showing a sincere concern for the woman in the picture? Of course not. This helps explain why selfishness and pride cloud your relationship with God. You should never use people for your own selfish desires or treat them as objects. You need to replace selfish and prideful thoughts with a servant's attitude. This involves investing your life in others—the opposite of selfishness. When you choose to love and help others instead of pursuing selfish sexual pleasures, a wonderful by-product is that the grip of lust will be continually diminished. In addition, the best cure for self-pity or loneliness is found in serving others. It will bring joy, satisfaction, and healthy relationships into your life.

Eliminate selfish practices from your life. Living a Proven life involves dying to selfish desires. It's time to get rid of all sexual immorality, including fantasizing, looking at pornography, or masturbating. This means far more than following a list of things to avoid. Although it may seem like a sensible way of controlling your urges, the Bible says that simply avoiding certain practices won't relieve illicit sensual desires (Colossians 2:20–23).

How do you eliminate immoral practices in your life without merely following a list of things to avoid? First, understand that by indulging in selfish practices, you've weakened your sensitivity to sin (Ephesians 4:19). You need to correct your thinking to bring an end to the fantasy life. The key is to recognize the sin in it.

Second, do as God says, which is to hate sin (Psalm 97:10; Proverbs 8:13; Romans; 12:9). If you're justifying your fantasy life or are chasing after pornography, then you're only playing a game at trying to stop. It must be viewed as an unhealthy, undesirable, unwanted evil in your life that is no longer welcome. Talk to God about this; ask Him to cause you to see it as sin. Then make a stand. Choose to hate it, and hate it hard!

When you find yourself in the middle of a lustful thought, immediately destroy it. Don't allow it to finish. Right then, say to yourself, "I take no pleasure from this thought. Through the power of Jesus, I reject it." Confess your sinful thought to the Lord and repent. Then immediately replace the thought. The more you continue to do this, the less frequently tempting thoughts will occur. But be prepared to do battle! It will take much discipline and effort to choose holiness and turn to God. Trust that the Lord will give you His strength. Struggles and trials develop perseverance and hope, which the Lord uses to transform you into His likeness.

Having accepted the importance of loving God and hating sin, it's still wise to establish certain boundaries to help in the battle against temptation. The point to remember, however, is not to rely upon boundaries as a way to obtain freedom from sexual bondage. It's a changed heart toward God that leads to a changed life. Again, this only occurs by daily walking with and being dependent upon the Lord.

Some practical things to do as part of an overall strategy of reducing temptations include throwing away all videos and magazines that were used in lust, even swimsuit editions. Use an Internet block on all computers or phones and don't go to Internet chat rooms, which breed false intimacy. If television instills in you selfish or lustful desires, then stop watching it! Replace secular music with Christian music.

Don't put yourself in situations in which you'll be tempted. You must make every effort to reduce tempting circumstances, such as lingering at your favorite magazine rack or Internet site. While you cannot avoid all contact with women, use wisdom about your interactions. Don't flirt, and don't go alone with a woman to lunch. Don't talk to women about personal matters, such as their marriage or finances. Apart from your wife, men should be your confidants and friends. Change any rituals you followed when you lusted or acted upon your lusts. Avoid old stomping grounds, such as the gym or a place that sells pornography. Consider changing your route home from work if you feel any temptation driving near a particular place. Take inventory and then set boundaries that you won't cross, keeping in mind that they were things you did as a prelude to the type of sexual immorality in which you engaged.

If, like Joel, you spent years developing habits of fantasizing, masturbating, or viewing pornography, you'll likely experience withdrawal symptoms, which can be nearly overwhelming. You may also feel a great temptation to continue in your prior routines or even feel like giving up. Stay the course! Although setting boundaries helps to reduce the struggle, it's only a small part of the battle plan. That's why it's vitally important that you simultaneously engage in the activity of loving God and others, as explained above. Otherwise, the room in your heart that you have swept clean of lust will remain vacant, waiting to be filled, and you may find yourself facing troubles even greater than before because some worse selfish practice moves in and takes its place (Matthew 12:43–45; 2 Peter 2:21).

Another point to remember is that when you experience a setback, you can't give up. Confess it to Jesus and talk to Him about it. He will forgive you. Then find out what caused you to stumble, and work all the harder at loving Jesus, at loving others, and at hating sin. You may also want to reexamine your boundaries and tighten them. Make all necessary changes to help prevent a reoccurrence. An accountability partner—someone you can call day or night when you begin to struggle with temptation and before you give in—is so important. If you do stumble, he is someone you can confess to, and he will help you back to your feet.

INCLUDING OTHERS IN THE HEALING PROCESS

When Joel tried on his own to stop lusting and masturbating, he felt defeated. It was like there was no one he could talk to who would understand and not judge. Joel thought he would take the secrets of his immorality to the grave. Perhaps the devil wanted to keep him isolated so that he would not turn to God.

You cannot overcome sexual immorality on your own. Freedom from sexual bondage requires dependence upon Jesus. God wants you to confess your sins to others (James 5:16; Acts 19:18). Confessing sins and maintaining accountability to another is like having a weight lifted off your shoulders. There will no longer be any area of your life that you must try to keep secret or hidden. God uses others to bring encouragement if you permit yourself to be vulnerable. A trusted friend can also help hold you accountable. Replace pride with humility and admit that you need God's strength and His use of other men in your life. Don't go it alone.

TEARING DOWN THE WALLS

Once you begin to turn away from sexual immorality, you still need to learn how to be vulnerable, caring, and loving with others. Generally, men who are struggling with sexual sin have developed a false intimacy. You unconsciously substitute sex or fantasies for relationships. You bury most of your healthy real feelings and rely upon sensual feelings. Part of seeking after sex is a search for intimacy without the risks and pain associated with relationships.

Even though you're forgiven for your sins when you accept Jesus into your heart, the past is not completely erased. The effects of years of hiding in false relationships don't just evaporate. The walls must be torn down in order for changes to be made in your life. Therefore, it may be necessary to spend a short amount of time evaluating how your prior influences (such as neglect or abuse) and learned relational styles (including ways of coping with hurtful experiences) have affected your current style of relating with others. Defense mechanisms (or the walls built around your heart) may have been designed as protective measures, yet they now block you from experiencing life as Jesus intended. God wants you to move forward and to be more like Jesus daily.

You need to learn how to be vulnerable, open, and honest in your relationships. After acknowledging that in the past you blocked off your heart or shut off some of your emotions, you can break the cycle in your present relationships so that you may more fully express your love to Jesus, your family, and your friends. While it may be helpful for some to have a Christian counselor as a guide through some of these steps, when you do look backward, the goal always must be to move forward. Never allow yourself to become consumed with the past or focused upon the wrongs of others. Instead, tear down the walls quickly and race forward toward the prize of having stronger and more intimate relationships with God and others. Finally, don't rely upon the counselor to keep you on the right path or allow him to be a crutch. Jesus is the answer, period, and you're the only one responsible for seeking after and yielding to Christ in order to be healed, transformed, and renewed by Him.

CONCLUSION

If you want to overcome sexual immorality, you cannot simply make it your goal to stop watching pornography or stop masturbating. Freedom from sexual immorality is a by-product of a right relationship with Jesus. It's a passionate heart toward God that begins a Proven life. The result of truly living for God daily is the basis for victory over selfishness and pride, the roots of sexual sins. Don't delay. Begin a right relationship with God today and include others in the healing process. Selfishness and pride will begin to shrink, and you'll no longer feel alone, helpless, or trapped in sexual immorality because you're now pursuing Jesus Christ and allowing Him to bring healing, satisfaction, and meaning in life.

Make a decision today to trust God with total and permanent control over your life. A victorious life will follow!

Appendix K: The Armor of God (Ephesians 6:11-19)

1 Helmet of Salvation
Sin starts in your heart but is carried out in your mind. If you don't take captive every idle thought and make it obedient to Christ (2 Corinthians 10:5), you're giving up valuable ground to the enemy. In fact, don't finish or enjoy evil thoughts, or they'll master you. Uncontrolled thoughts become action, and actions become habits. Undisciplined thinking keeps you in bondage to things like worry, greed, lust, doubts, and twisted doctrines. Therefore, immediately destroy all thoughts which are contrary to God's Word or your position in Christ. Slow down and listen to the quiet voice of your Commander-in-Chief through the earphone in your helmet and follow His orders. Read Philippians 4:8 and Colossians 3:12 for reminders of the types of things you are to dwell upon.

2 Breastplate of Righteousness
You guard your heart, and do battle against the old sinful nature. You protect your heart from condemnation (which are lies) because you know and believe that God gave you His righteousness.
By confessing your sins, repenting and remaining in God's camp, you won't give Satan an opportunity to take you captive or attack your vital organs.

3 Shield of Faith
Satan's fiery darts of fear and doubt are quickly extinguished when you hold the shield of faith—soaked daily in the eternal water of life (God's Word). You believe and rest in God's specific truths. You never let your guard down but actively build up and rely upon your faith.

4 Sword of the Spirit (Word of God)
Take the offensive in the battle. You won't find a better weapon for a spiritual fight than the Word of God (Hebrews 4:12). Use appropriate Scripture to submit to God and to resist the devil and he will flee (James 4:7). Grab hold of Scripture verses and fight back in the strength of the Lord, such as the 12 memory verses.

5 Belt of Truth
Stand firm in the truth. Know it, believe it, embrace it, and use it! (Say to yourself: "I am saved from eternal condemnation, I do not doubt that God is good or that He is sovereign over my life, and I test all teachings against God's Word.")

6 Prayer (Knees)
God answers real prayers. The condition of your heart and motives are key. For instance, you are to pray in the spirit at all times and especially for others (Ephesians 6:18), but, requests to God mixed with selfish motives are not prayers at all (James 4:3). God promises that when your prayers are in accordance with His will, the flood gates of heaven are opened (1 John 5:14). Therefore, the place of power is on your knees in submission to God in reverence and awe, seeking His perfect will.

7 Gospel of Peace
You wear God's shoes and eagerly run toward peace. By being humble, and especially forgiving others (Hebrews 12:1–17),you live out peace with God and others and thereby outpace the adversary. You will remain in peak condition and do whatever it takes to live out peace. You will not keep accounts, withhold love, or harbor bitterness.

Appendix L: My Purpose in Life

Do you ever wonder about your purpose in life? Often, people search for purpose in terms of a particular job or task that the Lord may want them to do. However, the more immediate and broader question that should be asked is: Why did God create me?

If you don't know and appreciate this overriding purpose in life, all of your striving may be in vain. Here's an eternal perspective that can change your life forever, provided you embrace it. In the Bible, God revealed why He created you, and He wants you to know your purpose and live it out. Simply stated, you were created to love and worship God and to have a close and personal relationship with the Lord—both as a child of God and as His friend (Matthew 4:10; James 2:23; John 1:12; 1 John 3:1).

Humanly speaking, it can be hard to accept that you were designed to worship and serve another being. Slavery and oppression may pop into your mind, but that's not how God acted in creating you. Although God did make you for His own good pleasure, He also gave you a free will—you can choose not to worship or praise Him. You don't even have to thank Him. You can fight against His purpose, but it will leave you empty, often searching for entertainment, alcohol, power, wealth, sex, or other things to fill the void.

This brings us to the second purpose for your being created: Having a personal relationship with God through Jesus Christ. By creating you for such a divine relationship, the Lord put within you a longing to seek out and relate to Him. In other words, God not only created you to be drawn to Him, but He also supplies you with the means to attain it. Accordingly, all your spiritual longings can and must be satisfied through a spiritual union with God, which He freely grants to those who earnestly seek Him (Deuteronomy 4:29; Matthew 7:7; Hebrews 11:6).

God dearly loves you. He desires men to be His sons and women His daughters—a family, if you will (Romans 8:14; Galatians 3:26; Hebrews 12:7; 1 John 3:1; 5:1–5). The Lord wants you to share personally in His name, inheritance, treasures, and blessings. The only way you can become God's adoptive son, however, is to agree to accept Him as your heavenly Father and to receive Christ's righteousness. No one really is foolish enough to think that he's perfect or that he deserves to be a prince to God's throne. Any imperfection disqualifies you. Inside, you know that you've rebelled and are in dire need of mercy and grace (Romans 3:23; 6:23; 1 John 5:10). That's why Jesus had to leave heaven and take the form of a man to become your Savior. Out of great love, Christ was willing to take your sin upon Himself and to replace it with His perfect righteousness. How wonderful it is to bear the name of God, which is given at such a high cost to God Himself. Settle with God that you have accepted Him (see Appendix E).

Eternal salvation is just the starting point. You still live in this world, and God wants your family relationship to grow and prosper now, long before entering heaven. Yes, you do have a purpose in life. It's a calling to enjoy closeness and friendship with the Lord. This is your lifelong journey.

God is calling out to you to be His friend. Will you respond? Will you seek to be His best friend? The

Lord makes available to you His strength and power to lead a Proven life. This life begins by passionately worshiping and glorifying the One who dearly loves you and gave Himself for you. By repentantly returning to Christ in humility, you position yourself to experience more and more of God's very nature. Through openly and honestly communicating with God in a real and personal relationship, you not only find fulfillment but also increase your capacity to have vulnerable relationships with others. Victorious living is gained by totally submitting and fully yielding to God. When you filter your life through the eternal perspective of loving God with all of your heart, mind, soul, and strength, the specific tasks God has prepared you to do will come into focus at just the right time. The walls are further torn down by *networking* in close relationships with other believers joined by the bond and blood of Christ into His church. God will use others to strengthen you as you strengthen them.

Once you welcome a Proven purpose in life and seek to fulfill it by and through Christ, you'll experience freedom from bondage to whatever idol or desire you had set in the place of worshiping God, whether it was sex, money, alcohol, TV, or entertainment in general. The Bible becomes your road map for living a holy and pure life, and prayer becomes your conduit to the source of this true life. The Holy Spirit of God Himself lives within you and acts to lead you further in divine intimacy with Christ (Hebrews 4:12; John 1:1–14; 2 Timothy 3:16). The more you seek to know God intimately, the more you fall even deeper in love with the Lord and burn with a passion and desire to continually seek His face (Psalm 27:4, 8). In short, it's God's will for you to be holy because God is holy (1 Peter 1:15) and to have a life marked by contentment and gratitude as you live out this purpose together with the One who gave you life (2 Timothy 1:9; 1 Thessalonians 4:7).

What a wonderful gospel and plan of an awesome God. The Lord gives you all you need to know and fulfill your purpose in life as well as the means to fully experience God Himself. He could not have given you more!

Are you grateful and filled with peace, joy, and contentment? If not, perhaps you've not fully acknowledged and sought to live out your true purpose for being created. Fortunately, God wants to grant you a humble heart of repentance and for Jesus to become a real part of your life. Go to Him now and ask of Him. The Lord promises to draw near to those who draw near to Him (James 4:8). God is so merciful that He gives you "today" to turn to Him and begin anew (Hebrews 3:12–15). Will you join with other Godly men living out their purpose for being created and being stamped Proven by God? Will you completely yield to Christ and become a needy, dependent servant of the Lord of heaven and earth? Right now, permanently choose to set the sails of your life toward living out the purposes for which you were created.

As far as what specific tasks the Lord would have you do, consider Ephesians 2:10: "For we are God's workmanship, created in Christ Jesus to do good works, which God prepared in advance for us to do."

There's no need to put all of your energy into trying to figure out which profession or ministry is His will for you. Instead, live to join Christ at every juncture in life.

How do you know what good works He has prepared for you? First, you can be sure they include those things which you must rely upon God to complete. Remember, He is interested in a continuing relationship with you, not merely accomplishing tasks. The Bible helps you maintain this eternal perspective, keeping before you the things that are within His will:

"It is God's will that you should be sanctified: That you should avoid sexual immorality; that each of you should learn to control his own body in a way that is holy and honorable, not in passionate lust like the heathen, who do not know God; and that in this matter no one should wrong his brother or take advantage of him" (1 Thessalonians 4:3–6).

"Therefore, I urge you, brothers, in view of God's mercy, to offer your bodies as living sacrifices, holy and pleasing to God—this is your spiritual act of worship. Do not conform any longer to the pattern of this world, but be transformed by the renewing of your mind. Then you will be able to test and approve what God's will is—his good, pleasing and perfect will" (Romans 12:1–2).

"Be joyful always; pray continually; give thanks in all circumstances, for this is God's will for you in Christ Jesus" (1 Thessalonians 5:16–18).

As you begin to evaluate your true and overriding purpose in life, stop and consider whether you're hearing God's voice on a regular basis. When you're close to the Lord, living in real dependency upon Him, He will reveal His plans to you. In fact, the Lord *confides* in those who seek hard after Him (Psalm 25:14). Therefore, knowing what God specifically intends for you requires positioning yourself to hear His voice by humbly living out all of the elements of a Proven life each day. Be patient and develop a growing relationship with God before expecting to know God's particular will for you.

In sum, Proven Men fully commit to the Lord and ask God to prepare and equip him to carry out God's good works that have been set aside to be completed together with and through Christ (Ephesians 2:10). He waits patiently and longingly for you to walk in stride with Christ Jesus.

Learn and apply in your life each of the letters in the PROVEN acronym so you will remain part of the Proven Men team:

Passionate for God

Repentant in spirit

Open and honest

Victorious in living

Eternal in perspective

Networked with others.

Appendix M: Your Next Bible Studies

As you near the end of the Proven Men study, a word of warning: Don't stop now. Plan for your next study before you finish this one.

It's a mistake for men looking for freedom to think they can rest at the end of twelve weeks. Before they know it, life's worries creep back in, and they drift away from the Lord. It won't take long to stumble because self-efforts always fail.

Never forget that sexual healing is a lifelong process. This study just laid the foundation for living a Proven life. The real test lies ahead. Will you march forward in union with the Lord, or will you stop growing and go back to relying upon your own strength? The Lord has begun a good work in you, developing perseverance and discipline (Philippians 1:6; Hebrews 12:1–2; James 1:3–4). Now keep moving—you're on the right track.

Consider repeating the Proven Men study. Many men have found it to be fresh the second or third time through. Each time you repeat it, you'll see something new about the Lord and about yourself. You'll also be better equipped one day to minister to other men who struggle with purity.

During your next studies, be sure to keep *networking* with other men. Most men who fade away do so because they did not stay linked together with other men. It's essential that you establish and maintain an accountability *(network)* partner. Give him permission to ask you to describe the thoughts you dwell upon, the struggles you face, and the times you stumble. Tell him also of your victories and your desire to be holy and pure in all areas of your life. When you return to this Proven Men study, ask him to join you.

The following proposed schedule is merely a suggestion. If you already have another study ready to go, great. Just be sure to invite another man to join you, and plan to repeat the Proven Men study in a few months. Daily studies are so important because they help position you to meet with God and to incorporate the Proven elements into your life. The format of the suggested studies is basically the same as this study. Plan to spend fifty minutes each day praying, reading the Bible, and using a daily study. Now that you're developing discipline and perseverance, you're ready for additional readings from various books. You're also encouraged to add a few minutes of daily reading from suggested inspirational books as a short family time of devotion.

Be committed to growing deeper with God and seeking hard after Him. At the end of the year, you can be on firm footing, walking in victory and ready for new challenges.

LIST OF MATERIALS

A. Study

Two proposed studies to use as study aids are listed below. They each take about 12 weeks to complete. Purchase one or both now. Feel free to ask your pastor to suggest a different study.

- *Lord, Is It Warfare? Teach Me to Stand: A Devotional Study on Spiritual Victory* by Kay Arthur (WaterBrook Press)

- *Experiencing God: Knowing and Doing His Will* by Henry T. Blackaby and Claude V. King (B&H Publishing)

B. Selected Reading Books

Develop a regular practice of reading books that foster living out a Proven life. Make time to read the following five selected books in the evenings and on weekends. If you set a goal of reading one every two months, you'll be able to read them within a year. If it takes you a bit longer, that's okay as long as you press on. To accomplish your goal, it may mean that you must stop watching TV or give up other activities. In short, be fully devoted to reading these books and applying important truths in your life.

- *False Intimacy: Understanding the Struggle of Sexual Addiction* by Dr. Harry Schaumburg (NavPress)
- *The Circle Maker* by Mark Batterson
- *Inside Out* by Dr. Larry Crabb (NavPress)
- *Celebration of Discipline: The Path to Spiritual Growth* by Richard J. Foster (Harper)
- *If Only He Knew: What No Woman Can Resist* by Gary Smalley (Zondervan)

Two additional suggested books for applying Galatians 2:20 in your life:

- *The Overcoming Life* by Watchman Nee (Living Stream Ministry)
- *The Road to Reality: Coming Home to Jesus From an Unreal World* by K. P. Yohannan (Gospel for Asia)

An additional book for relating to your wife is:

- *Every Man's Marriage: An Every Man's Guide to Winning the Heart of a Woman* by Stephen Arterburn, Fred Stoeker, and Mike Yorkey (WaterBrook Press)

C. Daily Inspirational

The following daily inspirational readings are optional. It takes only two to three minutes each day but contains profound insights and helps maintain an eternal perspective.

- *Jesus Calling* by Sarah Young
- *My Utmost for His Highest: An Updated Edition in Today's Language* by Oswald Chambers (Discovery House)

This reading and study program may seem a bit much, but trust that God will give you His strength and desire. By having the right eternal focus in life—to seek the Lord with all of your heart—you'll begin to enjoy and even desire the things of God more than the worldly things you used to chase after. It's time to make a serious choice regarding who you are in Christ. Fully commit to running the race to completion!

Perhaps you should give up TV for the next nine months so that you will not be distracted. TV consumes far more than just your time. The messages in most shows compete for your heart and values. The more you eliminate the prideful and selfish world values highlighted in TV shows and movies and replace them with seeking the Lord, the more your nature changes.

If you don't alter your inner desires, you won't experience lasting freedom. The old behaviors will return. However, as your heart toward God becomes more passionate, repentant, and open toward Him, your will and desire conform to His. The battle, while never over completely, gets easier because you're now are engaging in real and fulfilling relationships with God and others, and your new appetite is for things true, noble, right, pure, lovely, and admirable.

SAMPLE FORMAT

Monday through Friday

Spend fifteen minutes in prayer, being mindful against just petitioning God for things. Keep the focus on meeting with the Lord to know Him and to do His will. At times, return to the names and attributes of God (Appendices C and D) as forms of praise and worship in prayer. In addition, periodically read and write psalms.

Spend ten to fifteen minutes reading from the New Testament, beginning at Matthew. Set a goal of reading through the entire New Testament. When you finish it, immediately begin reading the New Testament again, even if that means you read through it twice or more per year. Don't race, but allow God to speak to you. The Bible is one of the special ways God communicates to you.

Spend fifteen to twenty minutes using one of the daily studies. Use it as a way of meeting with God to know, turn to, and trust in Him. Do the study Monday through Friday until you complete the whole study.

Evenings

Read one of the suggested books during evenings and weekends. For instance, on most nights, set aside ten to twenty minutes for reading. If you stay committed, you should be able to read two books in about twelve weeks. Don't be discouraged, however, if you're a slow reader. The important point is to keep reading and applying what you read. Also, look for ways to eliminate things that compete for your time and attention, such as TV or the Internet.

As an option, consider setting aside a few minutes each day or night, perhaps just before mealtime, to read from one of the daily inspirations. Include family or friends and discuss the reading with them. The key is to select a certain daily time and then be consistent.

Keep putting into practice the relational exercises in Appendix A, including regular couch time. Continue with sharing with others (especially a spouse, if you're married) the exciting things God reveals to you. Refer periodically to the *"Feelings Chart"* in Appendix F. Refuse to stay numb or void of feelings. Engage others in open communication, and keep talking to your accountability partner once a week.

Weekends

Set aside time over the weekends to pray and to read from the Bible and selected books. Put into practice all that you're learning. Be sure to attend church each week.

Appendix N: Falling in Love with God by Following His Ways

Once you've fallen in love with God, it's easier to obey Him. Right now, turn to the Lord. Enter His service with the goal of falling in love with Him while living out holiness in and through His power alone.

Falling in love with the Lord happens as you spend lots of time with Him. Then you'll find Him perfect, holy, and good. Your heart will melt, and you'll gladly follow His ways. Begin putting your heart, mind, and hands to His work.

TRAINING YOUR HEART: PASSIONATELY PURSUE INTIMACY WITH GOD

(Psalm 27:4, 8; 37:4–6; 40:8; 42:2; 62:1; 63:1; 103:1; 104:33; 119:10–16; 145:2)

- Spend lots of time with God in praise and worship. Be creative and purposeful.
- Know the names of God. Read and dwell upon them.
- Meditate upon the attributes of God. Be in awe and wonder of His perfect nature.
- Communicate with God in prayer. Talk *to* God, not *at* Him.
- Ponder the suffering of Christ. See His sufferings as proof of His great love.
- Sing spiritual songs. Speak from your heart and soul.
- Read the Bible. Take it in with the purpose of knowing God deeply and intimately.
- Write love letters to God. Expose your heart in open and honest communication.
- Express your feelings. Be open, honest, and vulnerable, not faking how you feel.

TRAINING YOUR MIND: CONSCIOUSLY STRIVE TO LIVE FOR GOD

(Romans 12:2; Ephesians 4:19–24)

Because God is good (Psalm 119:68, 135:3, 145:13; Mark 10:18):

- Trust Him with your life (2 Samuel 7:28; 2 Chronicles7:3; Psalm 119:68).
- Be joyful always, pray continually, give thanks in all circumstances (1 Thessalonians 5:16–18).
- Be humble, grateful, and content (Ephesians 4:2; 1 Peter 5:6; Romans 7:18; 8:3; 13:5; Philippians 2:14).
- Desire God's will, not your own.

Because God hates evil (Psalm 97:10; Proverbs 8:13; Romans 12:9):

- Stop each sinful thought and action right away, not finishing or enjoying it.
- Take captive all thoughts and conform them to Christ (2 Corinthians 10:5).
- Dwell on things that are true, noble, right, pure, lovely, admirable, and praiseworthy (Philippians 4:8).
- Fix your thoughts on Jesus (Hebrews 3:1).

- Put off the old selfish nature and put on the new selfless character (Ephesians 4:22–29).

TRAINING YOUR HANDS: FERVENTLY LOVE AND SERVE OTHERS

- Love others deeply (1 Peter 4:8).
- Consider others better than yourself (Philippians 2:3).
- Lead a quiet life and work with your hands (1 Thessalonians 4:11).
- Extend hospitality without complaining (1 Peter 4:9).
- Forgive freely (Ephesians 4:32; Colossians 3:13).
- Give instead of receive (Acts 20:35).

MAKING A COVENANT

The pursuit of intimacy with God is now the highest priority in my life!

Appendix O: The Purpose, Practice, and Power of Prayer of Proven Men

IN THE NAME OF JESUS

- Jesus will do what you ask in His name to bring glory to God the Father (John 14:13).
- You may ask Christ for anything in His name, and He will do it (John 14:14).
- Asking in Jesus' name is not merely saying the words, "In Jesus' name." It's similar to asking as though Jesus Himself were making the request.

RIGHT MOTIVES

- You don't receive because you ask with wrong motives (James 4:3).
- If you ask according to the will of God with faith, you shall receive it (1 John 5:14–15).

HUMILITY

- Abraham submitted to God while praying, even recognizing he was made from ashes. He didn't make selfish requests but prayed for others (Genesis 18:22–33).

REAL FAITH

- If you have faith and don't doubt, you can do all things (Matthew 21:21).
- If you believe, you'll receive what you ask for in prayer (Matthew 21:22).
- If you have faith, you'll do even greater things than what you have seen (John 14:12).
- Believe by calling on the Lord, because He answers His children (Psalm 17:6).
- Don't be anxious, but in all things, pray (Philippians 4:6–7).

JOINED TO THE LORD

- If you remain in Christ, and His Word in you, ask, and it will be given (John 15:7).

SINGLE-MINDED

- Be clear-minded and self-controlled so that you can pray (1 Peter 4:7–8).
- When you seek with all of your heart, you will find the Lord (Jeremiah 29:13).

GUIDED BY THE HOLY SPIRIT

- The Holy Spirit helps us pray (Romans 8:26).
- Pray in the Spirit (Ephesians 6:18; Jude 20).

EARNEST

- Elijah's earnest prayer stopped the rain for three years and then brought the rain (James 5:17–18).
- As Jesus prayed, His sweat was like drops of blood (Luke 22:44).

PERSISTENT

- Keep praying like the widow who continually went before the judge until he gave her what she wanted (Luke 18:1–5).
- Keep asking like the man with guests, who kept knocking at his neighbor's door at midnight until he received bread (Luke 11:5–9).

AT ALL TIMES AND IN ALL THINGS

- Pray continually (1 Thessalonians 5:17).

- Pray on all occasions with all kinds of prayers (Ephesians 6:18).

LOVE OTHERS AND PUT THEM FIRST

- You receive because you obey by loving God and others (1 John 3:21–23).
- Above all, love others (1 Peter 4:7–8).

FORGIVE OTHERS

- When you pray, forgive others so that your Father in heaven will forgive you (Mark 11:25).
- Pray for those who persecute you (Matthew 5:44).

PRAY FOR OTHERS

- It's a sin not to pray for others (1 Samuel 12:23).
- Join others in their struggle by praying for them (Romans 15:30).
- Stay alert and keep praying for others (Ephesians 1:15–19).

PRAY SELFLESSLY

- The Lord was displeased by the Pharisee who prayed about himself (Luke 18:11).
- Don't pray like hypocrites to be seen by men (Matthew 6:5).

SPECIFIC PRAYERS FOR OTHERS

- Ask God to give others the spirit of wisdom so they can know Him better (Ephesians 1:17–18).
- Ask God to strengthen others (Ephesians 3:16).
- Ask God to allow others to grasp the depth of His love for them (Ephesians 3:17–18).
- Ask God to help others be active in sharing their faith in the Lord (Philemon 6).

THE POWER OF PRAYER OF PROVEN MEN

- God tells you to pray, and He is pleased to meet with you and is moved by prayer.
- His church is to be a house of prayer (Matthew 21:13).
- If you're in trouble or sick, pray (James 5:13–14).
- The prayers of a righteous man are powerful and effective (James 5:16).
- The Lord hears the prayers of the righteous and delivers them from trouble (Psalm 34:15–17).

PROVEN MEN YIELD TO AND RELY UPON GOD

- Righteousness comes from God (Romans 3:22).
- God hears you not because of good things you've done but because of His mercy (Titus 3:5; Daniel 9:17–18).
- The righteous live by faith in God (Romans 1:17; Galatians 3:11).
- The righteous obey God (Romans 2:13).
- You can't become righteous by observing the law (Romans 3:20).
- Righteousness is by faith (Romans 3:22).

Appendix P: Network Partnerships, A Key to Breaking Free from the Grip of Pornography

Fighting to overcome pornography or other sexually compulsive activities is one of the hardest struggles many men will face in life. At times, it can seem like you're the only one in the battle. There are many self-help books, but they never seem to bring lasting relief. You keep asking yourself, "Why doesn't it work for me? Why am I still in bondage to sin?"

The one thing missing from a self-directed healing path is a *Network Partner*. Just how important is this? Well, no serious athlete would compete without having a coach, no successful business lacks managers, and no lasting government exists without various forms of accountability. Why would a man plan to battle by himself the sin he has yet to overcome on his own after years of trying? Let's face it, we all need accountability. In fact, God designed you to be accountable to others, and lasting freedom requires walking the road to victory together with another man.

What holds you back from living this out? Perhaps pangs of shame, guilt, and self-condemnation strike fear in your heart at the thought of openly sharing your failures and struggles. Maybe your pride and stubbornness won't let you admit you need help. Whatever your particular reason for shying away from accountability, one of the largest barriers to experiencing lasting freedom is a refusal to link up with another man.

WHAT IS A "NETWORK PARTNER"?

The word accountability means "being obligated to account for your actions" or "being responsible to another." A *Network Partner* includes, but is more than confessing sins (James 5:16), submitting to others (Ephesians 5:21) and engaging in relationships. Although few Christian men quibble over whether they're accountable to God, often those trapped in bondage to pornography balk at God's proclamation that His children must also be accountable to and *networking* with others. The solution is not trying harder in your own power, but addressing the stubborn pride that keeps you from surrendering. In fact, this same pride feeds your indulgence in forbidden sensual pleasures.

BIBLICAL NETWORK PARTNERSHIPS

The Bible paints a vivid picture of the partnering relationship that develops through accountability among the brotherhood of believers. Consider the following ways the Lord says you are to be mutually accountable to others:

- Helping in time of need (Proverbs 17:17).
- Providing instruction (Romans 15:14).
- Comforting (2 Corinthians 1:3–5).
- Serving in love (Galatians 5:13).
- Gently restoring (Galatians 6:1).
- Carrying others' burdens (Galatians 6:2).
- Speaking the truth in love (Ephesians 4:15).
- Admonishing (Colossians 3:16).
- Building up (1 Thessalonians 5:11).

- Correcting (2 Timothy 4:2).
- Encouraging daily (Hebrews 3:13).
- Spurring on (Hebrews 10:24).
- Meeting together (Hebrews 10:25).

Clearly, Biblical *networking* is centered upon open and real relationships, and it requires you to concentrate on others instead of yourself, your rights, your expectations, and your circumstances. By removing yourself from the center, you not only become useful in the lives of others, but also gain an eternal perspective so necessary for living out a Proven life.

True Biblical *networking* positions you to engage in spiritually mature roles in aiding others, such as:

- Keeping confidences (Proverbs 16:28; 17:9).
- Warning to flee idolatry (1 Corinthians 10:14).
- Encouraging to purify self (2 Corinthians 12:21).
- Inspiring to stand firm (Philippians 4:1).
- Warning against being idle (1 Thessalonians 5:14).
- Urging to abstain from sin (1 Peter 2:11).
- Pointing toward heaven and staying pure (2 Peter 3:14).
- Reminding to love others (1 John 4:7).

A *Network Partner* is just that, a partner. Each are co-pilgrims, sharing similar goals and desiring the other to succeed. Both support, serve, and spur the other. As iron sharpens iron, so do two Proven Men sharpen each other (Proverbs 27:17).

PRACTICAL MATTERS FOR NETWORK PARTNERSHIPS

Are you ready to follow the Lord's teachings and ways by incorporating *networking* into your life? Below are some practical ways of beginning the process.

Choosing your *Network Partner.* Your Networking Partner should be someone with a similar goal of seeking after the Lord with all of his heart. He doesn't necessarily need to struggle with the same sin, but it's important that he has a soft heart and wants to grow closer to the Lord. Don't eliminate a man merely because he isn't a spiritual giant. A heart that desires to grow will make him a great accountability partner.

He must be willing to commit to being *open and honest.* One of the biggest problems many men face is a reluctance to be vulnerable with others. Therefore, your *networking partner* must be willing to push through discomfort. Each of you needs to share intimate details regarding struggles, failures, hopes, dreams, and victories. This includes recognizing and then talking about feelings. Each must have the freedom and expectation to ask the other hard personal questions. Of course, confidences must be kept, because nothing breaks down a relationship faster than gossip (Proverbs 11:13; 16:28; 20:19).

Finally, your primary *networking partner* should not be your spouse or any other person of the opposite sex. There are many reasons, including that you need to develop other intimate relationships in order to foster a better relationship with your wife. In addition, it's damaging to a marriage to turn it into an accountability relationship, especially in the area of sexual sins. It often leads to a spouse engaging in a heightened role of looking for and finding faults in order to point out every sin committed. Moreover, it's not necessarily in the best interest of a spouse to know every minute detail of sexual sins, which can cause needless damage. For example, you should not confess to your spouse each and every lustful thought, which likely includes her friends. This will make her feel insecure, inadequate, and jealous. In short, you need a safe place to confess your sins in Godly accountability with other Proven Men.

Finding a Network Partner. Your church is one of the best places to look. There you can meet and develop relationships with men at a variety of men's functions, such as prayer meetings, Bible studies, breakfasts, and church-sponsored sports activities. You may also link up with men at church events such as coffee after church, corporate meetings such as prayer services, or a small group. You can also ask a pastor or other church leader for potential *networking partners.* Many churches have men's ministry leaders who you can talk to for help finding accountability.

These principles apply equally for teens looking for *networking partners.* Of course, the teen would contact the Youth Pastor and also look to youth ministries at church. In addition, there are some good outside Christian organizations to consider as potential places to look, such as Fellowship of Christian Athletes, Navigators, Youth for Christ, or Young Life.

If you're not regularly attending church, it may be time to start afresh (see Hebrews 10:25). There also are online accountability groups such as www.BeFreeinChrist.com. You can ask someone from a group such as this to work through the study with you, hold you accountable, or be a source of encouragement.

Finding a *Networking Partner* requires that you move outside of your comfort zone. It will even require that you take the initiative. It will be worth it because it will help you engage in open relationships and to *network* with other believers, which are essential components to living a Proven life. There is simply no replacement for personal interactions with others.

Deciding to take the risk. Right now, you may be facing a huge dilemma: "If I don't gain a *Networking Partner,* I won't experience lasting freedom and live a Proven life, but if I do share my struggle with others in the church, I may be judged or rejected." This fear is real. It's what keeps most Christian men planted in the pews. However, God demands that our sins be exposed to light to be eradicated, and accountability is a primary method. That doesn't mean there won't be pain associated with the process. In fact, if one *networking* relationship doesn't work, find another. Freedom is not a one shot deal but a new and lasting Proven lifestyle. Accept that God is sovereign and will provide you with all the strength you need in every circumstance.

Using the Proven Men study. The twelve-week study was specifically designed for use with *networking partners* and can be a terrific way to initiate or strengthen accountability. First, each man personally opens his heart to change while meeting with the Lord during the daily study. Second, the study incorporates times of prayer for your *networking partner.* Third, the study is geared toward weekly discussions. There's also a Leader's Guide to help you form support groups.

CONCLUSION

Many, if not most, men in the church face significant struggles with sexual purity, including pornography and masturbation. Most remain in bondage because they don't want to be the first to risk seeking out *networking partners*. Won't you break the mold, for your sake and the other men in your church who need it as much as you do? The prescription for lasting healing is incorporating all six letters of a Proven life, including *networking* with other Godly men. *Networking* is God's way of putting the final stamp upon you and freeing you from the false intimacy of pornography and masturbation. Don't stop short of God's promises and power by remaining isolated and closed. Choose today to take all steps necessary to link up with another man in an *open and honest* networking partnership.

Appendix Q: Joel and Tim's Stories

Virtually every man is fighting to gain or retain sexual integrity. No walk of life or personality is immune from this battle. The testimonies of two common men are detailed to assist you in examining and understanding how the PROVEN Model can be applied in your own life.

Joel, who is the author of this study, was the typical overachiever who could accomplish anything he set his mind to, but his life was being poisoned by fantasy and masturbation. Tim, on the other hand, was berated by his father and felt he could please no one. It carried over into his married life. He escaped into pornography and masturbation as much as ten times a day, hoping to squeeze out some affirmation in his false, substitutionary fantasy world. Both men vowed to take their secret sins to the grave. Fortunately, both eventually surrendered to the Lord, using the PROVEN Model and 12-week study as aids in reclaiming their lives. This unlikely pair ended up becoming accountability partners, and both Joel and Tim are now walking in victory.

Each of us has some of the character of Joel or Tim in our lives. Take the time to look for commonality of issues and adopt similar solutions. Joel's testimony is a bit longer because it emphasizes the road to recovery, while Tim's testimony is more blunt. Both are written in the first person, so you can be brought into his story, using it as a basis for connecting your own life to his and adopting the same road to freedom.

JOEL'S STORY

Currently, I am living a victorious life by the power of the Lord and actively training others to break free from the grip of sexually addictive lifestyles. However, not too many years ago, my marriage was in deep trouble because of the impact of sexual immorality in my own life. At that time, outwardly I was a model Christian and very active in the church. But this only led to a great fear of rejection by the church if I admitted that internally, I struggled greatly with sexual sins. Because all that I cherished was slipping away from me, I finally risked telling a pastor that I needed help with my sexual struggles. Surprisingly, he didn't judge me. Instead, he loved me and guided me to other Christian men who had faced similar struggles, and I began experiencing freedom through Christ. I was no longer alone. I was finally ready to do business with sin at the deepest level of my heart and ready to be changed from the inside out.

Below is how I ended up in the serious state of bondage to sexual immorality, but it's also my testimony about how, by God's grace, I was called out of despair to begin living a Proven life, exactly the model established in the Scriptures (see 1 Corinthians 6:9–11).

Childhood Influences

There were many factors in my childhood that contributed to me suppressing my feelings, withdrawing from intimacy, and escaping into fantasy. I grew up believing that men don't cry and that it was weak to show emotions. It was also unthinkable to ask anyone outside the family for help. If I could not do it myself, I didn't need it. It was also important not to do anything that might be embarrassing. Therefore, it seemed much safer not to be open or vulnerable, lest someone think I was not perfect.

I also grew up without much affection from my father. Although I figured my dad loved me, he never verbally or physically expressed it. I grew up believing that men just don't say "I love you" or hug each other. For a variety of reasons, I didn't spend much time during my childhood with my father, who was busy providing for a large family.

When I was about twelve, I found Playboy magazines hidden in a room. About that time, I also learned about masturbation from friends. As I looked at the pictures of the naked women, I began fantasizing about sexual matters. In fact, I soon became fixated upon sex. I began seeing women as objects of desire. I would masturbate almost every day while thinking about sexual images or fantasies. Although I usually felt guilty afterward, each night, as I closed my eyes, sexual thoughts flooded my mind, and I would begin the ritual all over again.

Adult Practices

It was during high school that I went to my first X-rated movie and even to a topless bar. I began buying my own *Playboy* magazines as well as more hard core pornography. Sex was always on my mind, and I could easily find sexual images or ideas almost everywhere. I would often purposefully keep these images in my mind so that I could use them later when I would masturbate at night. During college, I also began having sex. This only fueled the fire more. I still continued to fantasize, and I masturbated each day that I did not have sex. Each relationship ultimately ended without satisfaction. Although I knew deep down that lustful thoughts and masturbation were wrong, I held on to the belief that as soon as I got married, I would stop.

During law school, I accepted Jesus into my heart as Lord and soon after met the prettiest, most wonderful woman in the world. We were married within a year. Everything was falling into place. However, the lustful thoughts and temptations to masturbate didn't go away. I was a Christian and now married, but I still maintained my former fantasy thought life and other impure sexual practices.

I continued to keep opening my mind to sensuality daily. I was fixated on beautiful women in TV shows, commercials, or magazines. Even on the way to work I noticed and fantasized over sensually dressed women. Giving over to lust only heightened my desire more for sex, making me think I needed it every day.

By now, my wife and I were involved in many activities at church and were viewed as a model couple. She became a staff member, and I was active in many ministries for the church. I simply was too proud and ashamed to seek help. My world seemed to be closing in on me, and I needed to find a way of escape. I knew it was just a matter of time before I would drive my wife away, and she was too precious to lose.

I begged God with tears to take away the temptations. I wrote out every verse in the Bible about sexual immorality in the hope that my actions would conform to what I read. I even went to a Promise Keepers event and confessed to a counselor on the football field that I masturbated. However, no matter what I tried, after about three weeks I would begin masturbating again. In fact, my thoughts and actions continued to grow more and more impure.

Repentance and Commitment to Change

My mind was so constantly plagued with lustful thoughts that I was totally consumed with sex. I finally became so afraid of acting out some of the fantasies or actually committing adultery that I went to the pastor of the church. I admitted that I had a sex problem that I could not overcome. Although the pastor was shocked to know this about me, he didn't reject me. Rather, he cried and poured out his heart for me. He reassured me and told me that he loved me. That marked a new direction in my life.

I continued on the road toward God by having a repentant heart and confessing to my wife all my sins—sexual thoughts and actions, selfishness, and pride. For the first time in my life, I actually felt free. After linking up in accountability with a man who himself had overcome sexual addiction, I knew that I could live in freedom. I knew there was much work ahead, but I also knew there was hope, and I was 100 percent committed to being changed by God, willing to do whatever it took to live a pure life in dependency upon Him.

Early on in the process, my wife wasn't so sure that I would change. After all, I had been unfaithful to her from day one of our marriage. I still remember clearly one thing she told me that helped change the course of my life, which was: "You are sorry about the consequences, but you don't really see your conduct as wrong." I wanted to lash out at her, but she was absolutely right. I hated the consequences but didn't really want to stop. I hadn't seen lustful thoughts or masturbation as something that grieved God or as being evil. Besides, I secretly enjoyed certain aspects of the false intimacy of fantasy, lust, and masturbation. I knew I needed to die to lust and live for the Lord.

Praise the Lord that by God's mercy, my wife didn't abandon me. She stood by my side every step of the way. Of course, it took a long time to regain her trust, but for the first time I truly was willing to do whatever it took to stop sinning and to start living for purposes greater than my own selfishness. I received Biblical counseling weekly from another Christian man who had been addicted to sex. I also read several good books relating to freedom from sexual sins. I began to see that my thinking was backward and that my selfishness and pride fueled the lust. I finally realized that the only hope I had was in turning over all areas of my life to Jesus. I needed to adopt His plan for living instead of mine. I spent time daily in Bible study and prayer. I began to understand the root sin issues beneath the sexual behavior. I confessed my struggles to a trusted Christian friend who helped hold me accountable. This time I really wanted to be totally free from the bondage of lust and sexual impurity. More than that, I wanted to return home to God, to live out love, and to live for Jesus. It was only then that I finally began living a victorious life free from the grip of lust and masturbation.

The Root Causes of Sexual Bondage in My Life

All my life, I had lacked real and intimate relationships. These things were not modeled to me as a child, and I didn't seek after them as an adult. Instead, I allowed the pride in my life to lead to self-centered desires. The area of sex is a perfect place for selfish thinking and sexual behaviors to thrive. For instance, masturbation, pornography and sexual fantasies were fueled by my selfish way of thinking. Because I refused to permit emotions or feelings to exist in my life, I also substituted a false intimacy in place of real relationships. In fact, all of my relationships were shallow. This even included my relationship with God and my wife. The Lord was there simply to meet my needs, and my interactions with my wife were based upon sex and the fulfillment of my desires, not hers.

When I accepted the Lord into my heart at age 25, my selfish desires and patterns didn't just miraculously disappear as I had selfishly hoped. Because my prideful way of living, including lustful thoughts and masturbation, spanned many years, they had become ingrained habits that were done almost automatically and without reflection. The repeated conduct also desensitized me to sin. I had never learned how to be vulnerable, open, or honest with my feelings or with people. Therefore, it's no surprise that I wasn't immediately freed from sexual bondage or that I didn't step right away into a deep and intimate relationship with the Lord. I needed to learn how to shed my former ways and replace them with new Christ-like thinking and conduct. I set a course and began making changes in my life. Although it took time and hard work, I didn't give up. I was committed to being stamped Proven.

The PROVEN Model

I now see that the root issue underneath sexual bondage is a lack of intimate relationships with God and others, fueled by selfishness and pride. Freedom is not about stopping lustful thoughts or masturbation. They're merely symptoms of the wrong relationship and attitude toward God and others. Although there's no formula, I now see that God transforms and frees people from the grip of lust and other selfish ways using the acronym "PROVEN" which stands for being:

Passionate for God

Repentant in spirit

Open and honest

Victorious in living

Eternal in perspective

Networked with other Godly men.

Passionate for God

I had viewed God as a doorway to receiving answers to prayers or obtaining blessings. I didn't fully grasp how I could or should have an intimate love relationship with Jesus, but when the point in my life came that I could no longer stand the sexual sins and fake relationships, I finally turned completely to Jesus; this time for real, this time for good!

My mind was so warped with selfish and wrong thinking, it needed to be "transformed and renewed" (see Romans 12:2). For this to happen, I needed to flood my mind with Godly inputs while also eliminating selfish and sexual inputs. I began spending time praying each morning. My prayers changed from asking for blessings for myself to asking God to meet the needs of others.

I also poured out my heart to Jesus each morning, telling Him how much I loved Him and how hard the struggle was and asking Him for His strength. I asked Jesus to make me humble and to give me a soft heart toward Him and others. For the first time in my life, I actually started learning what it really means to love God and others. I began reading the Bible daily with enthusiasm and with new understanding as He opened my willing eyes to His truth. I finally began putting into practice what I was learning.

After working through the 12-week study twice and using other daily Bible studies for six months, I began craving more and more of an intimate relationship with Jesus. I also read two books that helped me see that I needed and could have a deeper, more dependent relationship with Jesus. (*False Intimacy* by Harry Schaumburg [NavPress 1997], and *Sexual Healing* by Mastering Life Ministries.) My eyes and heart were opened wide.

I kept finding myself wanting even more. I had tasted God, and it was good! But I still did not really know how to pray to Him like those that I was reading about in the Bible. My pastor recommended that I read some books on prayer. I learned how to pray like never before. My heart was convicted once again. I realized that I still had been praying to receive blessings from God instead of getting to know Him and changing my life to conform to His will. My prayer life dramatically changed, and with it my heart, once more.

Before seeking absolute purity, I prayed for only about one minute a day for things for myself. During the first twelve weeks of recovery, I disciplined myself (using a timer clock) to pray five to ten minutes a day and began focusing upon the needs of others. A year later, I began meeting weekly with other men to pray for things that were impossible without God. I consider these prayer meetings to be among the most precious activities in my life. The Lord gave me a new and passionate heart that's still growing!

Repentant in Spirit

Many times before, when I had tried to stop lusting after women, I failed because I was still secretly enjoying and holding onto some aspects of it. I didn't really hate it. The Holy Spirit began convicting my heart of the evil of sexually impure thoughts and behaviors in my life. It was only when I began hating sexual sins by repenting to the Lord over each one that they began to lose their grip over me. I realized that there was a connection between the selfishness and pride in my life and what my mind dwelt upon. Once I learned that selfishness and pride were where the war was being fought, I could begin to engage in the battle.

I began confessing to the Lord how selfish and wicked my ways were. I even wrote God a psalm modeled after Psalm 51—when King David repented over having an adulterous affair with a married woman. Each time I had a lustful thought, I would immediately call it sinful and ask God for forgiveness. My repentance was not merely words. I also began working very hard at removing all sensual inputs from my life and replacing them with Godly inputs.

I stopped watching all television for an entire year and refused to open magazines that I knew would have pictures of women in them. For a few months, I found it necessary to stare at the ground on my commute to work so I would not lust. I even strictly limited my interactions with all women.

One very important part of repentance was refusing to allow any sexual image or fantasy to stay in my mind. I would reject every such thought and image right away and actually refuse to take any pleasure from them. Whenever I looked at a woman and entertained the slightest impurity in my thinking, I immediately acknowledged and confessed it as sin, turned away from it, and asked Jesus for forgiveness. Although it seemed like I was confessing lustful thoughts every few minutes, I didn't give in. My attitude became: Because God hates sexual sin, so do I.

Open and Honest

Although I had lots of friends or acquaintances, I had never been in vulnerable, open, and honest relationships with anyone. I was afraid that people wouldn't like me if they really knew me. I closed off my emotions and feelings. I suppose I subconsciously thought that I was being protected by these walls around my heart, but I began seeing how hiding from feelings and true intimacy blocks us from loving others as God desires. Deep down, I knew that loving others and putting them first means more than just wishing them well or praying for them; it would require investing my life in their lives. Let me tell you, this was way outside my comfort zone. For instance, I usually stood stiff whenever the pastor or another man gave me a hug (which symbolized how I did not allow myself to have intimate relationships). I began to tear down these walls, too. I knew that if I could not be open and honest in my relationships with other men, even being vulnerable, I wouldn't be able to truly live out passion for God or be fully intimate with my wife.

I began learning that openness also means being open about bad or embarrassing things that happen. Because I was exposed to inappropriate sexual matters as a child, i.e. I was shown pornography and how to masturbate, I had to accept that I had been subject to a form of sexual abuse as a child. I read the book *The Wounded Heart* by Dr. Dan Allender (NavPress). This book helped me see how and why walls were built around my heart, beginning when I was a child exposed to inappropriate sexual matters. It also helped me realize that even after I stopped masturbating, some of my current ways of relating to people stemmed from the fact that I learned to keep clear of close relationships many years ago. Now that I could see this improper pattern for what is was and knew where it stemmed from, I could start replacing former ways of life with real *open and honest* relationships. Although it was difficult, I began making it a point now to recognize how I am feeling and to talk about things such as disappointment, fear, anger, and other topics that were once off limits. I now often referred to the *"Feelings Chart,"* attached as Appendix F to the 12-week study, as an aid to recognizing my own feelings. Today, I am able to go up to another man, give him a hug, and tell him I love him. I also maintain vulnerability with my accountability partner.

Victorious in Living

The Bible tells us that those who persist in sexually immoral ways will not inherit heaven (1 Corinthians 6:9–10). However, the good news is that the very next verse is: "And that is what some of you were. But you were washed, you were sanctified, you were justified in the name of the Lord Jesus Christ and by the Spirit of our God" (1 Corinthians 6:11, underline emphasis added). As I truly sought the Lord and committed to giving Him control, I felt Him not only telling me that even though I was currently struggling with sexual sin, I was called to lead a victorious life through God's grace, but also that He would lead me by the hand to holiness.

Each moment that I follow God's plan for living, I am leading a victorious life. It has been years since I last masturbated or looked at pornography. My relationship with my wife is better now than it ever was before because I have sought to put her needs and desires ahead of my own. The victory is that I have died to sexual immorality and chosen to appreciate and love the relationship with my wife. I see that my relationship with her is so much more than sexual. We are learning to work together in all things as a team. Although I still face the temptation to lust, I continue to be on guard. I have not grown complacent nor weary of the battle because my strength is in Jesus and not myself.

The effects of living victoriously through His power include a healthy and thriving relationship with Jesus that is continuing to grow. I love to read the Bible and to sing worship songs in church. I also write my own love songs to the Lord. I am developing real and intimate relationships with my wife and others. I actually talk about my feelings, admit I am wrong, and ask for forgiveness. I share my heart with others when I speak, and I am vulnerable.

Eternal in Perspective

When I was a slave to sexual immorality, all that I could see were my circumstances, my needs, and my desires. Without an eternal focus, I remained selfish—the fuel that ignites and feeds sexually immoral practices. After starting to see and appreciate God's perspective, plan, and ways, my vision was magnified and focused like a powerful telescope. I no longer was held captive by temporary pleasures that are destructive in the long run. God taught me and keeps teaching me that His eternal perspective is key to living a life of loving God and others. This eternal focus changed my life and keeps me on track today. I now desire and value healthy relationships with God, my wife, and other men so much more than the temporal pleasures I once sought from selfish sexual practices.

Networking with Others

Developing relationships with other men who faced struggles with sexual sins was very important in breaking free, and it continues to keep me on track. Other Proven Men are safe in being vulnerable, open, and honest without the fear of being judged. They also hold me accountable and encourage me when temptations seem great.

The importance of others cannot be overstated. I vividly remember the first time I heard a man say that he struggled with masturbation. I was shocked that he admitted it, but I was grateful. I had thought that I would take my secret life of lust and masturbation to the grave without ever telling another person. Having heard another Christian man admit his struggles gave me strength and encouragement to one day admit my own. Afterward, I linked up with other men that faced similar struggles. We encouraged each other in many ways, such as praying for each other, calling each other during the week, and sharing struggles and victories. *Networking* in this way is the model Jesus taught. He did not send out His disciples alone, but two by two (Mark 6:7; Luke 10:1).

Maintaining friendships and accountability with those who are *passionate for God* helps keep my eternal perspective and reliance upon the Lord. I need others, and I cannot go it alone.

I am convinced that the only road to freedom from sexual bondage begins with a close and dependent relationship with Jesus. It includes incorporating each of the elements of a Proven life. By having such right relationships with God and also with others, I no longer need or want the false intimacy and sexual impurity in my life that was fueled by selfishness and pride.

Will you to turn to the Lord Jesus Christ right now and trust Him to free you from sexual bondage? Begin a transition in your life this moment to live out a Christ-centered Proven life. Then stay the course and never give up. Jesus promises He will never leave you nor forsake you (Hebrews 13:5). He promises that if you completely trust in Him, you won't be tempted beyond what you can bear and that He will provide you with a way out so that you can stand up under it (1 Corinthians 10:13). Stop striving in your own strength and turn over complete control of your life to the Lord each and every day. I hope that my testimony is an encouragement to you and that you join me in living out purity as our spiritual act of worship by the power of the Lord Jesus Christ (Romans 12:1–2).

TIM'S STORY

"You're so stupid; I don't think you have the brains you were born with!" These were hard words but ones I grew up constantly hearing. It was especially devastating because they came from my father, a man I looked up to. Actually, the inability to please my dad shattered my very soul. It produced in me intense shame, guilt and self-condemnation. "I must be defective. I don't deserve his love. I don't deserve anyone's love."

Because my life was so hideous to my father, I was afraid to let anyone else get close. My heart, mind, and soul were paralyzed by fear—the fear of my dad or anyone else rejecting me. I shut down so severely and locked up so tight that I could not feel anything. I was completely numb.

What if others knew the real me? If my father hated what he saw, what would others do if learning of the darkness of my heart? I could never tell anyone what went on in my mind. I could not trust my feelings or thoughts to anyone.

When I was a child, a neighborhood girl wanted to play doctor. When she dropped her pants, I was flush with guilt. I knew it was wrong, and I was deathly afraid of being caught. At the same time, it was exciting. It was the most intense moment of intimacy I ever felt. It was a feeling I wanted to duplicate, but knew I could never seek out. That is, until I found my uncle's stash of *Playboy* magazines.

Every time my father would hit me or call me names, I could drift back to a safe place where I was loved, where I felt some pleasure. I would visit that garage daily. It was my hiding place. Each night I would masturbate myself to sleep. By the sixth grade, I was fat and wore braces. The ridicule was no longer limited to my home; I was the outcast of my school. The teasing burned like hot coals. It was so painful that I would do anything to keep from sight. I knew that I couldn't see the chalkboard in class, but I would rather die than give the kids another reason to laugh at me by wearing glasses. My resulting poor grades angered my father and induced fresh rounds of abuse. High school brought no relief. By now, I weighed 300 pounds. I had no expectations of ever dating a girl or pleasing my dad. Yet, an odd thing happened one day just before summer break before our senior year. As a pretty girl was trying to hold her boyfriend's hand in a church service, he threw her hand aside and murmured, "If you want to hold hands, hold Tim's hand." To spite him, she gripped my hand tightly. "Wow, that felt great." It didn't matter to me the reason why she held my hand; the point was that she was holding my hand. I now wanted her more than anything. In fact, I lost 100 pounds that summer and made a special trip to see her. We went roller skating, and she held my hand around the rink during a couples skate. "Perhaps I could have the beauty," I briefly thought. Moments later, I was shattered as she talked about her boyfriend. She said we wouldn't be able to skate like that again.

I couldn't stop obsessing over her. Of course, depression and reality set in. I was no good. Therefore, I would never risk again, a vow I planned to keep by refusing to date. With no future before me, my dad placed me in a Christian boarding school. I was out of sight and out of mind. I heard the words of the gospel of love and peace, but it was for others, not me. It never broke the barriers to my closed heart.

After finishing high school, it didn't take long before my dad had me working in his shop. I was no good for anyone or anything else. The constant strain of failing to meet his business expectations was met with a bottle of booze at night and frequent trips to the bathroom during the day to lose myself in masturbation. I would work twelve hours and then go straight to the bar. I finally had a friend. He would sit behind the bar and pour me drinks all night long. A few nights a week, I would go to a movie and pretend to have a different life, any life but mine. Soon I began going to strip clubs. For $120 per hour, a real woman would sit next to me and talk. We never had sex or even talked of sex, but it was the closest thing to intimacy I had since skating one lap around a rink many years ago.

Moving fast forward, I eventually did marry the first girl I dated. Of course, I was constantly pretending to be someone else and never let my guard down. The drinking and masturbation continued in full force. I knew that I didn't deserve a wife. Actually, she was beautiful and caring. I had no idea what she saw in me, but I couldn't afford to risk losing her. It was simple; I would refuse to let her see the real me.

We attended church each week, and she became quite active in women's ministries. I pretended to be spiritual and learned the Christian talk. Whenever she left for a meeting, I would shout out with glee, "I am free!" I felt free to be me. Of course, for the moment, that meant drinking and watching pornography. What happened next was the worst and best thing in my life. My wife came home early from the weekend retreat only to find the X-rated video on the coffee table.

She was horrified and felt betrayed. She threatened to leave if I refused to get help. She told me that she saw a mention in the church bulletin about a men's group called Proven Men and told me to go or else. The choice was hard, but I thought I could fake it through another phase of my life. I was a master at it.

What I didn't expect, though, was that the man leading the Proven Men group saw right through me. That, however, was not the thing that troubled me most. It was that he hugged me and told me that he loved me. He refused to judge me or push me away. It was not long before I told him my whole story, part hoping he would run and part hoping that God's healing was really attainable. This man would be my litmus test. I signed up for the 12-week study and made sure I kept each one. Actually, my wife had it marked on the calendar. I could not "forget." The study was more than I could handle. Of course, each night, I was still watching TV until 2 a.m., leaving no ability to rise to complete the study. But something was changing in me. I actually longed to be made well. Each week, I would cry during group meetings. It was the first safe place I could tell someone that I was a mess and not get beaten.

Twelve weeks was too short. I begged the leader to let me start again in the next session. Of course, he agreed. This time I worked through one half of the materials. As I did, it seemed like God was meeting with me. It was even like everything in the study was written for me. I felt that God did love me after all. I began going to bed earlier in order to rise to do the study. It actually became a companion.

My wife was noticing that I was being less selfish and actually wanting to help around the house. She commented that it was like we were having the honeymoon we never had. I actually stopped masturbating, something I had done daily for my entire life. More importantly, the walls around my heart were breaking up.

By now, I could not get enough of God. I asked the leader to allow me to go through the study a third time. My heart was so wide open that there were some days where I spent an hour praying. This time I completed nearly every day of the study. I had changed so dramatically that I was asked to co-lead the next group and then lead the following session. I was truly changed by God and stamped Proven. Sure, the Lord has more backward thinking to correct, but I now see Him as good and want to open my entire life up to Him. A wonderful by-product of this right relationship with God is that I now can be open with my wife and enjoy her and allow her to enjoy me!

If you're not where you want to be in your life, the answer is to stop running and hiding. God will meet you where you are and bring you along at the right pace for you. Don't give up, no matter how hard it is or how long it seems to be taking. Expect that it may take two or three times through the study before you give up control and allow God to work in your life. I cannot over-emphasize the need for you to also link up with another man in accountability. I am not talking about merely having another man ask you a few questions each week. I mean someone that you open your true self to on a weekly basis. It was the love of God through the love of other Proven Men that kept (and helps keep) me going. Hope and freedom are real and awaiting you too!

Appendix R: 12 Memory Verses

1. "'Teacher, which is the greatest commandment in the law?' Jesus replied, 'Love the Lord your God with all of your heart and with all of your soul and with all of your mind.' This is the first and greatest commandment. And the second is like it: 'Love your neighbor as yourself.'" (Matthew 22:36–39)
2. "Finally, brothers, whatever is true, whatever is noble, whatever is right, whatever is pure, whatever is lovely, whatever is admirable—if anything is excellent or praiseworthy—think about such things." (Philippians 4:8)
3. "I have been crucified with Christ and I no longer live, but Christ lives in me. The life I live in the body, I live by faith in the Son of God, who loved me and gave Himself for me." (Galatians 2:20)
4. "Therefore, get rid of all moral filth and the evil that is so prevalent and humbly accept the word planted in you, which can save you. Do not merely listen to the word, and so deceive yourselves. Do what it says." (James 1:21–22)
5. "Be joyful always; pray continually; give thanks in all circumstances, for this is God's will for you in Christ Jesus." (1 Thessalonians 5:16–18)
6. "Therefore, I urge you, brothers, in view of God's mercy, to offer your bodies as living sacrifices, holy and pleasing to God—this is your spiritual act of worship. Do not conform any longer to the pattern of this world, but be transformed by the renewing of your mind. Then you will be able to test and approve what God's will is—His good, pleasing and perfect will." (Romans 12:1–2)
7. "My dear brothers, take note of this: Everyone should be quick to listen, slow to speak and slow to become angry, for man's anger does not bring about the righteous life that God desires." (James 1:19–20)
8. "Godly sorrow brings repentance that leads to salvation and leaves no regret, but worldly sorrow brings death." (2 Corinthians 7:10)
9. "We demolish arguments and every pretension that sets itself up against the knowledge of God, and we take captive every thought to make it obedient to Christ." (2 Corinthians 10:5)
10. "Keep your lives free from the love of money and be content with what you have, because God has said, 'Never will I leave you; never will I forsake you.'" (Hebrews 13:5)
11. "Be completely humble and gentle; be patient, bearing with one another in love." (Ephesians 4:2)
12. "But among you there must not be even a hint of sexual immorality, or of any kind of impurity, or of greed, because these are improper for God's holy people." (Ephesians 5:3)